A Two Year Stretch

A Two Year Stretch

Captain William Goldthorp RAMC

SERENDIPITY

Copyright • William Goldthorp, 2003

First published in 2003 by
Serendipity
Suite 530
37 Store Street
Bloomsbury
London

British Library Cataloguing-in-Publication data
A catalogue record for this book is available from the British Library

ISBN 1-84394-072-8

Printed and bound by Alden Group, Oxford

To Margaret

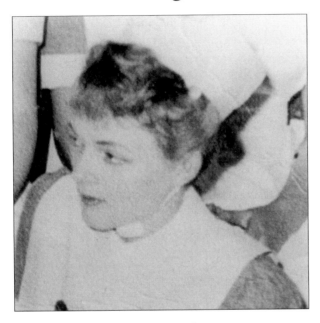

My Anchor

Will your anchor hold in the storms of life,
When the clouds unfold their wings of strife,
When the strong tides lift, and the cables strain.
Will your anchor drift, or firm remain?

We have an anchor that keeps the soul
Steadfast and sure while the billows roll;
Fastened to the rock which cannot move,
Grounded firm and deep in the Saviour's love!

Contents

Illustrations

Acknowledgements

Dr Brian Waring, whose memory in some cases is better than mine. Dr J.S. Blair, for his help, criticism and advice and the information I found in his book *Conscript Doctors*. My youngest son, who with great exasperation converted a computer idiot into a computer wizard, and to my wife for putting up with all the things I forgot to do, while writing the book.

Apologies

This book is basically based on reminiscences, aided by some aide memoires, colour slides, friends' memories and the odd document. I may have got people or occasions mixed up, my intention is to interest readers and not upset anybody. The ideas and opinions are mine and to some extent my friends' and comrades', that as far as I can remember, we had at that time. The book is not politically correct, but then that whole generation of us were not politically correct. If I tried to make this book politically correct there would be no point in writing it.

If I have upset anyone it has not been intentional. My most serious apologies however are for those who remember me, or were involved in situations I should remember and have forgotten. The language may be a bit ripe, but when, as all old members of all three services know, was it not?

Foreword

The book is a detailed account of the author's experience as a doctor in the British Armed Forces Medical Services.

Having wondered why when I was asked if I would write a foreword; I am pleased I agreed to do so. I have never worked either in the armed forces medical services or with the author - although I do know him as a professional colleague. I found the book fascinating and a 'very easy read'. It's a story well told. I was impresssed by the detailed account of events that the author encountered during his service as a Medical Officer in the British Army in many remote parts of the world. The book is well illustrated with photographs. The problems of an army doctor coping with emergencies in far flung places, with inadequate resources comes through clearly.

The author can't resist describing and commenting on the comparison between a doctor being able to provide holistic care to patients and the compartmentalized sub-speciality based care that is the norm in civilian life. The book clearly describes how the Forces Medical Services provide service to the wider community.

The book is readable, detailed, humorous and a good story. It should appeal to everyone. Nonetheless, it will be of particular interest to all those who have worked in the Armed Forces Medical Services; doctors and those connected with the forces medical services.

I enjoyed the book.

The Lord Patel

Introduction

Spring 1959, on the Dahla plain, close to the border between the Aden Protectorate and the Yemen. Sitting comfortably, looking eastward, on a beautiful starlit Arabian night. The sky not black, but an extremely deep purple; thousands of bright stars; it was easy to make out the 'plough'. The moon hung brightly a quarter way up from the horizon. My seat overlooked the wall encircling Dahla camp, close to the sanger at the South East corner, where the officer's tents, mess tent, and administration tents were located.

We were 3,500 feet above sea level; the moonlight lit up the plain in a beautiful panorama. Close at hand, field outlines, the odd dark patch indicating a crop. Small wadis crossed the plain, with dark lines alongside, where date palms, citrus, apricot and fig trees grew. Closer, the palm tree fronds moved in the slight breeze. Here and there, on a small hillock, the outline of small villages. Far away to the east, mountains rose; to the south, more mountains, the land sloping gradually before reaching the extremely rugged terrain, deep wadis through which easily ambushable tracks wound their way towards Aden. Aden was eighty miles south of Dahla, but it took 8-10 hours to drive there. We were fairly isolated.

Over my right shoulder the outline of Dahla could be seen, two miles away, on an outcrop of rock, the battlements of the small citadel showing against the starlit sky. Close to the north loomed the Jebel Jihaff, a steep three-hour climb to a company outpost 2,500 feet above us, where another occupied and farmed plateau could be found. The sides of the Jebel were various shades of brown, with dark shades as its rocks, gullies and trees tried to be visible through the moonlight.

I relaxed and grew comfortable, it would be 2 or 3 o'clock in the morning. The searing heat of the day was gone, but the freezing night of the desert had not occurred. The air was light, warm and balmy, and did not feel cold, although I was bare to the waist. The slight breeze wafted Arabian scents towards me - roses, tamarind, and fir, together with that ubiquitous hot smell of sand, sweat, camels and goats. Sometimes, one saw movement in the fields close to the wall. The commonest, scavenging pye-dogs, who's occasional gypping and howling, would rend the night air. Occasionally, a shy, delicate gazelle, and once, a troop of baboons, who usually sheltered and slept in high inaccessible cliffs at night. There were supposed to be leopards, but I never saw one, or heard one coughing.

I always took a bottle of a particular beverage, when I had one of these sleepless sojourns, from which I would take the occasional drink. Often I would be alone, but sometimes when I got there another officer was sitting nearby, or would join me later. We would sit near each other, chatting and laughing; whenever I took a swig from my bottle, I would offer him one, which was always gratefully accepted. These early morning sojourns occurred once or twice a month. After an hour and a half, I would feel relaxed, contented and happy; tiredness would creep over me. I would make my way back to my tent, wash and sleep the sleep of the just, waking about 08:30 a.m. My first action was to pour and drink a glass of ice-cold water, poured from a thermos flask. I would then look at the clock and swear 'Christ, I should have been in the MI tent at 6.30'. MI – Medical Inspection. Sick parade started at 6.30 a.m. A rapid shave, and into uniform; now, it was breakfast time. You hear nothing good of yourself when you overhear others talking about you, passing the mess tent:

'Doc's missed sick parade again.'

'Yes, he had the squitters again last night, I was there with him, drugged up to the eyebrows, as usual.'

'He took that bloody concoction with him again.'

'He went out like a light, when he hit his pit; he'll only be just coming round now.'

'Bastard won't let us have any.'

'He played merry hell with the adjutant when he found out he'd drunk a whole bottle of the usual strength.'

'It's nice to hear a Lieutenant give a Major a rollicking.'

'Doc's quite a card – gets away with it as well.'

'Bound to, the Arab soldiers think the sun shines out of his backside.'

'Morning Doc, how you feeling?'

'Fine, thanks.'

A little explanation is necessary:

Words: Verb, to squit, squitting or squitted. Noun, the squitters

It was more than that, the term also described how it sounded and felt. There was a marked difference between diarrhoea, dysentery and squitters. Squitters was sore, uncomfortable, painful, annoying, insulting and ego defacing, but you weren't ill.

The Squitters: an attack of

The day was normal; you went to bed as usual. At about 2.00 a.m., the most horrible painful stomach gripes or cramps would start. They probably lasted thirty to forty seconds, but it seemed like an hour. Then, you had a sudden and urgent desire to go to the toilet (latrine in our case). Like the Arabs, we wore longis at night - like a dress. You rushed to the latrine, hitching the longi up as you ran. I grabbed my 8-ounce bottle as I went. As your backside hit the seat, you let out the most resounding fart, that seemed to echo round the sides of the Jebel Jihaff. The force of the explosion was enough to take a rocket to the moon! It wasn't just wind, there was also fluid, and semi-solid (which I should call faecal matter, but we are in the army) shit, which sprayed in all directions. Then, for the next minute, your bowels emptied wind, water and the semi-solid stuff. The shrieks, whistles, tuba blasts and trumpet voluntaries would have done Black Dyke Mills Brass Band proud!

Then, it was over, but don't wipe your bum! In five minutes, it started all over again - abdominal gripes, wind, water and solid stuff, and so on for twenty or thirty minutes. The intensity gradually lessened. Finally, the squitters ceased, occasional cramps continued, but you dare not leave. From experience, you knew the squitters might return. So, you sat on, talking to your companion if you had one, admiring the moonlight plain, as described above.

After an hour, you felt safe enough to return to your tent. By this time, you had removed the longi, keeping it clean enough for the Dhobi man to wash it. Making your way back to the tent stark naked, passing a water butt on the way, and collecting a bucket of water. Back in the tent, you washed yourself and it wasn't your hands and face, followed by some delicate drying. A large quantity of highly alkaline fluid had been passed, and if you were not careful, the anal skin (the arsehole) could become very painful. We suffered from what we politely called the pre-historic monster (Dinah-sore-arse)!

I made my own soothing cream - Zinc oxide powder and Castor oil, with a few powdered cortisone tablets thrown in for luck. One would lie on the camp bed; sleep would not come immediately because of the cramps, but after about another hour, exhaustion crept in and you slept, waking about seven or so in the morning. A little weak, the regular officers made their way to the mess tent for breakfast; we had a routine each morning before breakfast, but on these occasions, the regulars varied it.

'A large gin and bitters' to the steward. Two swallows and it was gone, then a glass of cold water, flavoured by some vile army concoction said to be lemonade powder, two large gram tablets of sulpha-guanidine to prevent diarrhoea, but of the bacterial variety, Paludrine, anti-malarial and a 1 gram salt tablet. Breakfast could then begin. I usually ate breakfast after squitters; the regulars merely had another extra-large gin.

The Beverage

Lomotil and Imodium had not been thought of, never mind invented. Our standby was *Kaolin et Morph.* Kaolin and Morphine mixture, supplied in gallon bottles, quadruple strength. Two ounces in an eight-ounce bottle, filled with water, one tablespoon four-hourly; it is dangerous to exceed the stated dose.

I kept an eight-ounce bottle of quadruple strength alongside my bed for two years. 2–3 ounces would be down within five minutes. I would then slowly sip away until 5 or 6 ounces had gone. After 25 minutes, I would be feeling pleasantly relaxed and drowsy; the gripes would be much less painful. After an hour, I was cosy and comfortable, admiring the beautiful moonlit scenery. One and a half hours later, I was happily relaxed (morphinized) as I strolled back to my tent, washed my bum and applied my special ointment. I promptly fell asleep (or was it a coma), no hour of gripes lying on my campbed for me.

I have squitted in Aden, Dahla, on the Jebel Akhdar, in the middle of the Omani Desert, in Sharjah and Dubai, before they found oil, the Buraimi Oasis and Bahrain, but strangely enough, never in Somaliland or Kenya. That is, all over Southern Arabia; we began to suspect that somewhere was a Mad Mullah (Muslim Priest) trained in virology, working in a cave, like Arthur's Wizard, the Druid Merlin, inventing new viruses to annoy the infidel interlopers, the British!

From all this, the reader (I hope) will realize that my experience of National Service could be described as somewhat unusual. Now, read on.

Prologue

For many years now I have entertained my colleagues and nursing staff with tales from my National Service days. You ought to write a book they said. Not having kept a diary I declined. I do have over 550 colour slides, with names and dates that should help.

I have just read *The Best Years of Their Lives* by Trevor Royle and *Brasso, Blanco & Bull* by Tony Thorne. Tony Thorne describes his basic training for sixteen weeks, Officer Selection Board and officer cadet training, all very different from our training as Medical Officers. I will refer to his experiences often to contrast the difference between his experience as an ordinary National Serviceman and our privileged one as Medical Graduates. We were seven or eight years older than the average National Serviceman but it was only because of our medical degrees that we entered as commissioned officers. I doubt whether I or the majority of my colleagues would have passed the Officer Selection Board if we had been National Servicemen at eighteen. In other words I was very very privileged, although I would have preferred not to do it.

After almost completing my first draft, one of my colleagues from university and national service days, W. B. W.—, knowing what I was up to, bought me a book.

The Conscript Doctors
Memories of National Service
Compiled and edited by Dr John S. G. Blair.

An archive of the experiences and reminiscences of 202 National Service Medical Officers, newly qualified on call-up, from all three services has been made at the Wellcome Institute for the History of Medicine. The material is to be kept in perpetuity and protected until 20 years after the contributors' deaths. News of the project failed to reach me and many other colleagues, had it done so I may not have embarked on this book. On the other hand I probably would, one of the joys of a paper or memoir is being around to defend it if attacked.

I believe my experiences were equally interesting, entertaining, and even more unusual than Trevor Royle's or Tony Thorne's and matches the most bizarre of John Blair's stories. Although I am no writer I hope I can record them in interesting manner.

Chapter One

A Two Year Stretch

Well it seemed like it, at the time. We were guilty, of being alive, British, male and over 18. I was a rather Bolshie young bloke who wanted to get on with his training in his chosen speciality, which was going to be a long hard slog. If I were going to be a GP, it would just have been extra experience and not mattered so much. Looking back, however, makes me realize how idiotic and stupid I was.

As a recently married young man I should have taken a three year Short Service Commission. It didn't seem to cause harm to the careers of my colleagues who did.

Pay: 25 shillings a day, instead of 18

Marriage Allowance: 18 Shillings a day, instead of 15.

Transport provided to wherever you were posted, and Married Quarters. In Aden where I went, accommodation was prohibitively expensive.

My wife had got a Nursing Sister's post, at the Steamer Point Hospital with single accommodation. Conovid the first Pill didn't come out until three or four years later. Up to now we had managed quite well, with care, with what I now call Vatican Roulette (The Safe Period). The anxieties of one's husband leaving, after his embarkation leave must have upset the ovulatory rhythm. William decided it was time to join us.

Now I am retired it has been to my advantage I had been in the Health Service almost two years, and could claim the two years National Service, provided I continued paying my Pension contributions at House Surgeon's rates. If I took a Short Service Commission I had to leave the Health Service Pension Scheme, my subscriptions would be returned less Income Tax. The Government would pocket the share that they where supposed to put toward my pension. Contributions were not allowed during the Short

Service Commission. I would have had to start again five years qualified with no pension rights, and buy five extra years if I wanted a full pension. The government financed the £600 bonus after 3 years by paying us money that should have gone into a pension fund.

My Origins

I was born at Avondale, 46 Wharf Road, Crowle in the Isle of Axholme, Lincolnshire. That for a start will flummox everybody, because there aren't any islands in Lincolnshire.

An island is land surrounded by water. What about Wharf Road – we did have a wharf; it was on the Stainforth to Keadby canal. We were about 50 miles inland, the Isle is a little bit of Lincolnshire sticking out on the Yorkshire side of the Trent.

The Isle of Axholme was surrounded by water. The Trent to the east, the Idle to the south and the Don to the north and west. A detested Dutchman, Vermuyden, drained it with much animosity in Charles I's time. The Don was rerouted, now known as the Dutch river. The island is still surrounded by water, only now it is bigger with the new river to the west and river Ouse to the north. The Lincolnshire-Yorkshire border, the northwestern edge of the Isle can still be seen. A long depression in the fields. In Eastoft there are two streets, the high street in Lincolnshire and the other in Yorkshire. The Methodists, always a canny lot, have built their chapel on the old riverbed inbetween. The bed continues north for a mile, to Boltgate, the farm my grandfather owned, then turns northeast toward the Trent.

My parents: Doris a schoolteacher, Moses Oates's middle daughter, and Fred, at that time working at Lysaghts steelworks, Scunthorpe, and running an agency selling oil, grease and paint to the local farmers and businessmen.

Dad was born in Glossop, Derbyshire – how did he end up in Lincolnshire? Fred was one of those accidents middle-aged couples have when all the rest have grown up. Mother thinks the menopause has started, but suddenly realizes that she is not putting on weight because the weight is kicking. So William and Mary in their fifties, when life should have been quiet and easy, were landed with this tearaway, about 9 years old. William, General Manager of Glossop Cooperative Society, had to go out buying potatoes and other farm produce. He met Moses, 10 years his junior, Farmer and Potato Merchant, who was selling the stuff. Businessmen always discuss other matters as well as trade when they meet. William had a good moan about Fred, which Moses found highly entertaining. Moses went home and told his wife Eleanor all about it.

Eleanor ran the large farmhouse at Parkgrounds containing husband, six children, two living-in maids and six living-in farmhands. 'Oh! The poor lad. One more won't make any difference, let him come here for the holidays.' From then on Fred spent all his school holidays at the Oates' farm. There was an unanticipated result, Fred went farming mad. He went to Glossop Grammar School and his father wanted him to go to university and was prepared to pay for him. Fred insisted on leaving at 15 and becoming a farm pupil. This was a decision he always regretted, which was why he was so interested in my education, always gave me his full support and would have been prepared to pay for me had it been necessary.

The day before I was to sit the entrance exam for Goole Grammar School I received notice that I had passed the Scholarship examination for Scunthorpe Grammar School. The scholarship was means tested, my father who had been quite prepared to pay the full fees for Goole, spent hours with a friend reducing his income and increase his expenses to squeeze the last penny from the scholarship. He needn't have bothered, the following year the 1944 Education Act came in and secondary education was free.

Lindsey County Council Education Committee.

LINDSEY JUNIOR SCHOLARSHIPS, 1944.

This is to Certify that

WILLIAM GOLDTHORP

has been awarded a Junior Scholarship tenable at

SCUNTHORPE GRAMMAR School

County Offices, Lincoln,
August, 1944.

J.V. Birkbeck.
Director of Education.

I sat the next to the last round of the old school certificate, and did quite well with 5 distinctions, a credit, two passes and a fail. Matriculation was required for University entrance, 6 credits, of which one had to be Maths, one English Language and one a foreign language. My two passes were English language and French. I got a credit in English the following year. The fail was art. I had no wish to be a Plastic Surgeon. I could draw a straight line and always sewed the skin nice and neat. So long as everything works OK afterwards who is going to want to look inside to see if it looks artistic?

Fortunately I read the Northern Universities brochure, (Newcastle, Leeds, Sheffield, Manchester and Liverpool), and I found that I could apply for form R. If your other results were good enough you were granted exemption from one of the credits. If I had had to sit the French exam again I would still be trying to get into Medical School 50 years later. Edinburgh, Glasgow, the London Universities, Oxford and Cambridge all wanted a credit in Latin, so they were out.

I ended up with interviews at Birmingham, Sheffield, Leeds and Manchester. The first two were a shambles, Leeds went fine, but when I went into the Old Lavatory Brick Palace I felt as if I had come home. The uniformed porter at the entrance with gold-braided top hat greeted me. What a man, what a memory, within two months he knew the names of all the new students. All were addressed as Mr or Miss, becoming Dr as soon as you qualified. A graduate coming back to the medical school after 9 or 10 years would be greeted by name as soon as he knocked on the porters lodge.

The rather dark, slightly dingy, wide corridors seemed friendly. Benign portraits of cheerful Professors gazed down from the walls. The interview was in the Dean's office, a pleasant old chap Prof. H. S. Raper. Not the usual bevy of Doctors and Surgeons asking stupid questions, especially the one we all hated. 'Why do you want to be a Doctor?' The number of times I had discussed the possible answers to that, with other candidates, none of us had a decent answer. Why DID we want to be Doctors? We just did, and that should have been the end of it. Prof. Raper never asked it. He quickly put me at ease, and we chatted away for half-an-hour.

He told me that Manchester had adopted a new policy for admission, one which all the other medical schools eventually adopted. Manchester wanted academic ability. Selection was no longer by interview, then all you had to do was pass your subjects, admission was entirely up to you. If you got top grades in your subjects you would get in, if you did not you would not.

Lavatory Brick Palace, the medical school, was built of a yellow brick. A primrose colour, hence the name. It was at the back of the

UNIVERSITY OF CAMBRIDGE

LOCAL EXAMINATIONS SYNDICATE
SCHOOL CERTIFICATE

This is to certify that
WILLIAM O GOLDTHORP
of Scunthorpe Grammar School Doncaster Road
Scunthorpe Lincs
passed the **School Certificate** Examination in   July 1949
and reached the standards shown (Pass, Credit, or Very Good)
in the English Language test   Pass   and in
the following seven subjects:

English Literature	Very Good
British and European History	Very Good
Geography	Very Good
French	Pass
Elementary Mathematics	Very Good
Physics	Credit
Chemistry	Very Good

Index number   7055

Date of birth   7 July 1933   *CR Raven*
                                  Vice-Chancellor

THE MINISTRY OF EDUCATION accept the examination as
reaching the approved standard.
Signed on behalf of the Ministry of Education

R.N.Heaton
Under-Secretary

University behind Owens College alongside the old Architects' Department. There was also a tall square yellow chimney at one side.
It came from the boiler room and the crematorium where cadavers
that had been dissected were reverently disposed of.

During my first year there the chimney required repairing and scaffolding was erected around it. The work was completed on a Friday, the scaffolding dismantled to be collected the following morning. That night some bright sparks re-erected the scaffolding on one side. Then in large black letters wrote 'Frying Tonight' at the top of the chimney. The scaffolding was dismantled and returned to where it had been. What an uproar – severe retribution was threatened, but the culprits never found.

At the end of the sixth form, two years, I took what are now known as advanced levels. It was the first year they had been introduced to replace the old higher school certificate. I took and passed: Chemistry and Zoology at Scholarship level, Botany and Physics at Advanced level, plus General Studies. Sufficient to gain entry to Manchester, and be awarded a Lindsey Senior Scholarship. Student Grants had been started so that anyone who gained entry to University could afford to go. State Scholarships, and County Senior Scholarships, had predated them, and for a boy from a poor family, had been essential if he was to go to university.

With the existence of grants the awards were more of an honour, though the State Scholarship was worth about £15 and a County Scholarship about £10 more than a grant. All three were means tested. State Scholarship standards were extremely high, the school never managed to win more than one or two of those a year. They were way above my league. County Scholarship standards were high but not impossibly so. The school usually got between eight and ten of those a year.

Naturally all university fees were paid, in addition a subsistence allowance. Mine came to £180 per annum for a 30-week university year, with an inadequate supplement when I became a full time clinical student. This was made worse by the fact I could not get up to the money-making schemes I had indulged in previously. Of course in those days I was a minor, so the money was not paid to me but to my father.

Poor Dad when he received the first £60, he gave me a cheque for £20 told me to go to the Post Office and open an account. He would send me £20 every month, but there was no way he was going to let an 18-year-old lad loose in a city like Manchester with £60 in his pocket. I thought it best not to tell him that I already had one with nearly £250 in it. £250 is what a labourer would earn in a year. The PO also paid 2.5% interest. I had been breeding bantams since I was 8 years old. Eggs, cockerels and old hens were easy to sell, as rationing was still on. Farmers were always wanting odd jobs to be done. I had an official contract and salary for pumping the organ at the Metho-

UNIVERSITY OF CAMBRIDGE

LOCAL EXAMINATIONS SYNDICATE

GENERAL

CERTIFICATE OF EDUCATION

This is to certify that in the Examination for the General
Certificate of Education held in 1951 (Summer)

William O Goldthorp

of The Grammar School Scunthorpe

passed at the levels indicated (Advanced or Ordinary) in
the *five* subjects shown below:

Physics	*Advanced*
Chemistry	*Advanced*
Botany	*Advanced*
Zoology	*Advanced*
General Paper	*Ordinary*

Index number *3199/6*

S.C. Roberts
Vice-Chancellor

THE MINISTRY OF EDUCATION accept the examination as
reaching the approved standard.

Signed on behalf of the Ministry of Education

R.N.Heaton
Under-Secretary

dist Church with extras for weddings, funerals, etc. Supernumerary
Christmas postman, I always got the hardest bit, cycling out to
deliver to outlying farms. The regulars thought they were pulling a
fast one; they were not, on Christmas day I got a lot of large tips from
those farmers, plus numerous mince pies and glasses of sherry. At the

TELEPHONE 2447

LINDSEY EDUCATION COMMITTEE

SCUNTHORPE GRAMMAR SCHOOL,
DONCASTER ROAD,
SCUNTHORPE, LINCS.

J. A. Mc.IVER, M.Sc.(ECON.)
HEADMASTER.

10th. October, 1951.

Mr. W. O. Goldthorp,
"Avondale,"
Wharf Road,
CROWLE,
Scunthorpe.

Dear William,

It was with real pleasure that the Governors
heard of your good results in the Advanced and
Scholarship level subjects in the recent General
Certificate of Education examinations. We offer
you our congratulations, and best wishes for your
future career.

Yours sincerely,

Chairman of the Governors.

age of 16, I was hauled of to work on the farm. I had full-time summer work from 16 to 21. I became a cashman, cycling from farm to farm with anything from £100 to £200 in half crowns on my back. A half-crown, 2 shillings and sixpence, an hour's pay. Who would let a 16 to 20 year old lad roam the countryside with the cash equivalent of 1,600 hours work these days? I would pay the pea pullers, organize the day labourers, if my costs were less than the expenses allowed then the difference was mine. I was carrying out time and motion studies long before the phrase was thought of.

The first year then consisted of Chemistry, Physics, Zoology and

BJC.

<u>THE UNIVERSITY OF MANCHESTER</u>

The University,
Manchester, 13.
22nd August, 1951.

No: 241

Dear Sir/Madam,

I have to inform you that your application for exemption from Part I
(Physics &)
of the 1st M.B.,Ch.B. examination (Chemistry) has been approved subject to
your registering as a medical student not later than October 1952. If
your entry is delayed by National Service the exemption will be operative if
you register in the session next following your release from Service.

The exemption is subject to the payment of the usual exemption fee of 8
guineas; this fee should be paid to the Bursar and this letter should be produced at the time of payment. If you have already paid an examination fee in
respect of this or other parts of the examination the exemption fee is not
payable.

This exemption does not constitute an offer of admission to the Medical
School of the University.

Yours faithfully,

REGISTRAR.

W.O. Goldthorpe Esq.,
46, Wharf Road,
Crowle,
Nr. Scunthorpe.

Botany, repeating what had been done in the sixth form. A lovely relaxing year full of social life, you had already learnt it, a bit of revision was all that was necessary. If that year could be eliminated the course could be reduced to five years.

120 students were admitted that year; forty of us were selected to go straight into second year. In actual fact Anatomy and Physiology started at the beginning of the summer term, so that we were about 6 months behind the main intake. The make or break examination was the 2nd MB. The second professional exam, anatomy, physiology and histology, this exam had to be passed and only

MANCHESTER ROYAL INFIRMARY

OXFORD ROAD   MANCHESTER 13

ARDWICK 3300

December 8th 1956.

It gives me great pleasure to give Dr. William O. Goldthorp a testimonial. He qualified M.B.,Ch.B. (Manchester) in December 1956.

He did part of his clinical work on my unit and I found him to be keen, a hard worker, with a good knowledge of medicine. When he left the ward my comment on his record card was "good." I feel, therefore, I can recommend him for a post suited to his experience.

I wish him the best of luck.

Charles Sixton

M.D., F.R.C.P.

Consultant Physician.

UNIVERSITY OF MANCHESTER

Tel. ARDwick 3300
DEAN OF CLINICAL STUDIES
Dr. Wm. BROCKBANK

THE ROYAL INFIRMARY
MANCHESTER 13

December 8th 1956.

Dr. W.O. Goldthorp has been a student at this Hospital since October 1953 and has a good record.

I have confidence in recommending him for a Junior Hospital appointment.

Wm Brockbank

M.D., F.R.C.P.

Dean of Clinical Studies.

three attempts were allowed, if you got the 2nd MB provided your funds held out, you would make it. There was no limit to the attempts at the clinical exams.

Unfortunately when our group passed the 2nd MB, we took it with those who had already failed it once. We were taught alongside a group who had been shown not to be quite up to scratch. Although selected as a high flying group we were tarred with the same brush and were treated as such. It was very noticeable when we finally qualified sixth months early with the others who qualified sixth months late, when we started applying for house positions. Not that it mattered in the long run, some of the brightest students settled for General Practice, whilst some of the plodders who failed the odd exam became internationally known professors.

Chapter Two

House Jobs

December 1956. The future did not look very rosy for a new graduate. Firstly, and this did not bother a 23-year-old lad very much, the government was making a nice profit from our superannuation scheme. General practitioners in their late fifties and sixties were dropping dead left, right and centre. Usually from coronary thrombosis or bronchitis-related illnesses. It remained like this for the next 10 to 12 years until the early papers on smoking related illnesses came out. At that time the average GP smoked like a chimney. Now most doctors have stopped smoking and with luck will last long enough to ensure the government loses money on the superannuation scheme, although I would not put it past those bastards (Labour or Conservative) to alter the rules.

Employment prospects: it looked like we would all spend our lives in over-worked under-paid junior posts. Seven years on and there had been no expansion in NHS consultant posts, it was waiting for dead men's shoes. Every consultant post advertised attracted 70 to 90 applicants, probably all the senior registrars in that specialty. Senior registrars were selected from experienced registrars for consultant training and were supposed to be in training for 4 years after which they became consultants. There were numerous time-expired senior registrars in post for 7 or 8 years. They blocked all promotion for numerous highly skilled registrars who had higher qualifications and years of experience. They had nowhere to go except general practice where their skills were wasted, or dead end dogsbody jobs where they were at everyone's beck and call; Senior and Junior Hospital Medical Officers, posts that were eventually eliminated, although similar posts have been recently introduced under different names.

General practice was not any better, as well as a dustbin for disgruntled specialists and experts in tropical diseases thrown out of the Colonial Medical Service to make way for indigenous graduates, there were very few General Practice Principal Posts advertised. Again each advert would attract over 100 applicants. GP principals were responsible for this not the government. The government had planned a salary of about £2000 for GPs, about £60,000 today. GPs were paid a capitation fee for each patient registered, with was no limit to the number of patients who could register under one GP. In 1948 some GPs registered as many as possible, then employed assistants to help them. Pay £1000 per annum plus £150 car allowance, the principal pocketing the rest. Occasionally an advert for an Assistant with View appeared, this meant that if you worked satisfactorily for 2 or 3 years you would be allowed to join the practice. This was just a ruse to make the young doctor work harder. For recent graduates like myself the immediate future for the next few years was mapped out.

I spent four years doing house officer posts and National Service. What a difference, when I returned to England. The lads had discovered that Australia, New Zealand, Canada and the USA were crying out for experienced specialists and GPs and offering incomes far higher than the NHS. They disappeared in droves, even some senior registrars and newly appointed consultants. Forty per cent of my year disappeared, in some areas seventy-five per cent went. There was a chance now that you could become a consultant, if not you could always emigrate. In cynical moments I have often said, 'I was one of the unlucky ones, I actually became a consultant.'

You are now a doctor, but you cannot become fully registered until you have a year's experience in hospital, house officer posts. You cannot be provisionally registered until you have been appointed to an officially recognized post. So the interviews start. Nearly every graduate hopes his first post will be in his own teaching hospital. Training with the group known to be partial failures our chances were not high, particularly as the vast majority of posts were awarded in June, the normal qualifying time.

What a humiliation that first interview was, when all the latest graduates lined up before the self- appointed Gods of Manchester medicine, that is the teaching hospital consultants. Things have not altered in nearly 50 years; they are still self-appointed gods. They have also dreamed up a new term, 'Centre of Excellence'.

A Centre of Excellence is a greedy place, which grabs the major slice of any new funds available for the area. The same applies to any increase in junior hospital posts. If the government has not anchored it down with concrete that lot grab it. Fortunately it is full of highly skilled and experienced registrars and senior registrars who do all the work while the consultants tour the world giving lectures telling each other how good they are.

That interview, we all lined up in reverse alphabetical order, outside the consultants' committee room. Then marched in and lined up in front of the great gods, who looked at us as if we were something the cat had just vomited up. The secretary asked us to state our surnames in alphabetical order. We were stared at for a couple of minutes and told to march out again. We waited outside for 10 minutes, and the lucky(?) ones' names were called out. We were reminded that no-one had applied for the two house surgeon posts in ENT (Ear, nose and throat), but none of us thought that 6 months in that specialty would give us good widespread experience. It turned out that those of us that had not been appointed were the lucky ones. Six months doing nothing but cold orthopaedics, haematology or neurosurgery did not give good widespread grounding.

The next interviews showed medical nepotism at work. North Manchester (Crumpsall), South Manchester (Withington & Wythenshawe), and Hope, Salford, at least proper interviews this time, but it was change-over time, not many jobs available, all that were went to the sons of local GPs. We should have expected it, our fathers did not send the local consultants private patients. It never occurred to me, but I should have rung my father, asked him to contact our GP and get him to ring the consultant surgeon at Scunthorpe War Memorial Hospital. There would have been no problem; it was miles away from the Sheffield teaching hospital.

A week after qualifying and still no job, feeling disheartened we headed for the Dean's office. The secretary gave us a list of all the hospitals in the North Western Region that wanted House Officers. Close to the top was Bury General Hospital, I rang the hospital and asked for an application form. Next day I was called to the Dean's office. I was to attend for interview the following Friday at 4 p.m. I picked Bury because it was the nearest, it was easy to get to by train from Victoria station. I have never forgotten that passenger train, the carriages must have been at least 50 years old, all marked Lancashire & Yorkshire Railway. I wonder if British Rail ever got round to replacing them.

I went to the Hospital Secretary's office (the big boss.) A nice young lady showed me to a pleasant sitting room, where the candidates were waiting. The room was empty but tea, biscuits and ham sandwiches had been supplied. After 10 minutes a dapper, elderly Scotsman accompanied by a young Indian doctor (Dr Chadda) entered. They chatted away, discussed cases and helped themselves to tea etc. Eventually the Indian asked me what I was doing there. 'Waiting for an interview,' I answered. The Scotsman gasped and said 'I knew there was something I had to do but could not remember'. My interview started, I was talking to my future boss, Billy Morrison.

I was told that there were two house surgeons posts but one had already been filled. A local married couple who had lived in Bury all their lives had had a daughter when they were getting on a bit. She was their only child, of whom they were extremely proud. They had contacted him as senior surgeon and asked him if it could be arranged for their daughter to work there when she qualified. I had begun to realize at this stage that Bury was not exactly over-burdened with applicants for its posts. Old Billy had struck while the iron was hot. He had explained how important it was to follow the proper procedure in the new health service but he would try and see if it would be at all possible to employ their daughter. He promptly arranged for her to become his colleague's house surgeon, then rang her parents telling them that as a great favour he had been able to arrange a post for their daughter, thereby ensuring there was at least one house surgeon and boosting his reputation as a kind man. He did not tell me this, I found it out later, when I realized what a crafty old blighter he was. I loved being Old Billy's house surgeon; he almost converted me to general surgery.

We chatted about various things, and then he asked why I had applied to Bury. I mentioned my disappointment at not getting a teaching hospital post, and the way all the other posts had gone to doctors' sons. He said that he often had to manage for a few months without a houseman. He said, 'It looks as though we both are in luck. That is if you still want the job.' I accepted, he rang the Hospital Secretary, I was employed.

I had to see the Secretary to get a letter to say I had the job. This was needed before I could apply to the GMC for Provisional Registration. I also had to join a medical defence organization. I joined the Medical Defence Union, subscription £2 per annum, £40 for life membership, this covered for all legal eventualities, both private practice and the Health Service. My salary was £250 per annum. How I have wished I had taken life membership. When I was 60 I stopped accepting the odd 3 or 4 private midwifery cases I had done each year, my subscription that year for midwifery alone was £5000 plus £3,500 for gynaecology, and that was about 10 years after the NHS had accepted legal responsibility for its own cases.

House Surgeon, 15 January 1957

The Hospital Secretary himself, showed me round, the big boss and the insignificant house surgeon. It would not happen nowadays, it would be beneath the dignity of the senior manager to show a newly appointed consultant round a hospital, never mind the latest house surgeon. That Hospital Secretary and his 4 or 5 assistants has been replaced, by 3 or 4 departments, all with Senior, Deputy and Under Deputy Managers, plus secretaries better paid than consultant's secretaries, each employing 30 or 40 people, and we wonder where our taxes go.

That secretary was immensely proud of his hospital, he had spent years pre-NHS fighting for funds just to keep the place going, each new department represented battles lasting years to acquire the funds needed.

We ended our tour in the Casualty Dept, where we found Dr Chadda. He said, 'I'm glad you've come, this chap's broken his arm and I want to set it. The anaesthetic machine is over there. You put him out and I'll set it.' I hadn't given an anaesthetic in my life; my two weeks anaesthetic training has consisted of helping the consultant with his Times Crossword Puzzle. We had to give all our anaesthetics in casualty. It was all gas, oxygen, trilene and ether, I learned very quickly.

Off duty one night a week, one half-day a week and one weekend a month, starting lunchtime Saturday finishing 12 midnight Sunday. We did not mind, it was regarded as the last year of your training. No problem for a young single man, the hospital became your home, the living conditions were marvellous.

Furnished with desk, bookcase and two easy chairs as well as the usual bedroom furniture, more of a bed sitting room. Maid service, tidied and cleaned every day, cup of tea prompt at 7.30 a.m. Laundry, the maid checking it beforehand, anything that needed repairing or a button sewn on was sent to the linen room. A big lounge with a new fangled TV set, chess, darts, cards, table tennis etc. Large English breakfast, three course lunch, afternoon tea, three course dinner, a table looking as if it had been set for breakfast at supper time in case you had been too busy to eat at dinner time. There was a night chef who would produce a meal at midnight if you had been busy during the day. This was a leftover from the pre NHS days. Voluntary hospitals only could afford to pay residents £50 a year, but made up for it in other ways. Residence was compulsory,

£125 deducted from your salary. There was a sign of things to come. The local Brewery for decades had provided a crate of pale ale each week, to the doctors' mess and the male wards. A new manager noticed this and decided that the hospital could make a bit of money (minute in reality) by charging the doctors for the beer. The brewery found out and promptly stopped sending the beer, not only had the doctors lost out but all the male patients as well.

The social life was good, all members of staff took part. The hospital was legally responsible for its student nurses, who did not become adults until the age of 21. Tennis courts, hockey pitches etc have all been built over or turned into car parks. The nurses' homes into office blocks, the recreational halls with stages used for annual prize giving, dances, whist drives and amateur stage productions, converted to stores or divided into offices.

All this may seem trivial to modern managers sitting in offices with eight hour days, and no first hand knowledge of clinical work, but it was important for staff morale. There were only 12 of us in the doctors' mess, now there will be that number in one department alone. We jelled together in close knit group, like a platoon jelled together as described by Tony Thorne in *Brasso, Blanco and Bull.* Helping each other out at difficult times, which does not happen now. The difference being that Tony Thorne's platoon members became lifelong friends, we on the other hand went after 6 months to 2 years to a another hospital and doctors' mess forming another group of intense relationships, not having the time or opportunity to keep up old contacts.

This was not a good situation for a married man with a baby as I found out 4 years later. Salary £750 a year with £150 deducted for compulsory residence, alternate nights and alternate weekends off duty. I could not help noticing the adverts on the bus when I went to work. Bus Conductors wanted, £15 per week, £30 more per annum than me, for a 40-hour week PLUS overtime. My only thought was that I would not be a bus conductor forever.

What was my surgical experience that was going to be so valuable to me during my National Service? It was a time which we have been highly criticized for. It was the see one, do one, teach one era. In fact it was often more than that, it was read it up and then do it. Billy Morrison was a General Surgeon and I mean General. Surgical specialties, ENT, Gynaecology and Orthopaedics, there were no breast, genitourinary, pure paediatric, or gastro-enterological surgeons. Heart surgery in its infancy, neurosurgery, and chests were at the teaching hospital. I saw all there was to see, adults and children, emergency cases and the cold waiting list cases. There were no A & E departments, just casualty. The Casualty Officer went home at 6 p.m. and 1 p.m. on Saturdays. When we took over and did everything. We treated wounds from little cuts to massive big gashes, some facial ones, which today would be sent to the Plastic men.

Fractures: examine the patient, take, develop and print the X-ray, make the diagnosis, ring the SHO to come and give the anaesthetic. Rush up the back stairs to your room, where you kept Hamilton-Bailey's *Short Practice of Surgery*, all 1000 pages of it. Orthopaedics the 100 pages at the back, a quick read how to set that type of fracture, back downstairs to get to casualty before the SHO arrived to shout at you for not being there when you had interrupted his TV programme. The SHO anaesthetized the patient, you set the fracture and plastered it. If the SHO was covering casualty then he set the fracture and I gave the anaesthetic. All patients attended the fracture clinic the next morning. The limb was X-rayed again and if necessary it was reset. We never received any complaints from the orthopaedic department so we assumed our results were OK.

Both house surgeons had a Minor-ops list each week. We dealt with lumps, bumps and abscesses that GPs in pre-NHS times would have done in their own surgeries. They were paid on a capitation fee basis so they sent them to the hospital. One got the impression that the only way a GP could make a decent living was to palm everything off onto the hospital. Again we worked from the textbook, or asked the theatre sister for advice. I never stood on my high-horse as the newly qualified doctor. If the nurses thought you were too toffee-nosed, you were rapidly cut down to size. If you don't know ask the ward-sister, she probably had a younger brother your age or a son a few years younger. You would be mothered, looked after and advised. 'Don't go out with that girl again Doctor, she is not very nice. Now my Staff Nurse is a respectable girl and quite pretty.'

I got one of my biggest bollockings ever from Old Billy, and that was for filling a death certificate in correctly. The patient had a minor surgical problem and heart failure due to syphilitic aortic stenosis. His syphilis, a major venereal disease, had been treated years ago and was no longer active or infectious. He died, and I wrote the death certificate, as I was supposed to, Cardiac failure secondary to syphilitic aortic stenosis.

Prior to the Health Service, Billy had been a Honorary Surgeon, that is he carried out clinics and operations at the hospital, received no payment, but was allowed to admit his private patients and operate on them. In a wealthy area an Honorary could be a full-time surgeon, but many like Billy had to work as GPs as well. Billy had looked after this man's family for 25 years. He had not said a word to anyone about the syphilis. The family was up in arms, had played hell with Billy for not telling them and wanted the death certificate changing. I like a bloody idiot had let the cat out of the bag.

One procedure was taught to me by the actual patient. Saturday mornings alternated between urethral dilatations in the casualty department and circumcisions on baby boys at Ramsbottom Cottage Hospital. It was decided that my lady opposite number would do all the circumcisions and I would do all the urethral dilatations, much to the relief of the gentlemen concerned.

These were men who had acquired gonorrhoea before penicillin became available; women had an advantage, a urethra 1 inch long, men 7 to 8 inches long. A urethral infection caused by clap (much easier to spell) could be serious for a bloke, fibrosis may occur a stricture form, and he could not pee. All because he had been kind and given pleasure to a lady (some lady). Clap had been treatable by sulphonamides since 1935 but the gonococcus easily became immune. In Italy the gonococcus was resistant to every type of sulphonamide, which accounted for the phrase 'See Naples and die'.

During the Second World War it was one way the Italian ladies sabotaged the German war effort, unfortunately they were very popular and sabotaged ours as well. Willie Brockbank one of our lecturers was in the army in Italy. Apparently 20 miles behind the front line on both the West and East side of Italy were two massive base hospitals dealing with the casualties of Venus; within one month of the arrival of the first supply of penicillin both were empty and disbanded.

Every Saturday morning I had 10 to 12 urethras to dilate, the men turned up every 8 to 12 weeks. As usual I had read up how to do it. The first chap took one look and said 'Oh! Christ not another bloody youngster, how long have you been qualified?'

'Before Christmas,' I answered.

'How long have you been here?'

'A week.'

'You've not done this before?'

'No.'

'Ah! Well.' He walked to the trolley, with the sterilized instruments. 'Sister's set it out right. You see that tube, that's the local anaesthetic. Take the top off, you'll find a nozzle that goes into my John Thomas, squirt half of it in, then massage it back to me balls. These are the dilators. You lubricate them with that local stuff. Lift me up by the foreskin, then put the dilator in. When it comes to a stop swing me prick downwards and you'll feel it slip into me bladder. Don't bother with the little ones, start with number 5, when you get to 11 it will be a bit tight, you'll have to push hard to get 12 and 13 in, but I doubt if 14 will go through.'

I proceeded as instructed. He jumped off the couch, said thanks, put his trousers on, went to the waiting room greeted his friends and said 'We've got a new kid again, I told him what to do, he did OK, he'll be a dab hand at it in a week or two.'

House Physician

Slight improvement, salary up by £50, alternate nights and weekends, apart from the disappearance of Saturday mornings, that was to be my off-duty until 1975, apart from when my opposite number took his summer holidays when I would be on duty non-stop for the month.

The physicians Dr Davies and Dr Savidge were General Physicians, like the surgeons they dealt with everything. There were no haematologists, endocrinologists, gastro-enterologist, etc., etc. they did it all. There were skin specialists, VD specialists, and chests. The specialists with the Victorian Decoration are now known as Consultants in Sexually Transmitted Disease. Chests worked separately and were really experts in tuberculosis, a disease that was beginning to disappear. Ward acute admissions, other medical cases were seen in the outpatients with the consultant, who advised, criticized and taught. This was when I dropped a clanger with Dr Davies.

An elderly gentleman had been referred with chronic anaemia. I examined him, and following my intense instruction by Old Billy, carried out a rectal examination, and found a rectal carcinoma.

Old Billy went round chanting the adage 'If you don't put your finger in it, you put your foot in it.' He would do a rectal examination on a patient complaining of eyestrain, or a boil at the back of the neck. His reprimand was polite compared to other surgeons, 'See I told you so. If you don't put your finger, you put your foot in.' Which was a little different from the more usual 'You bloody fool, why the hell didn't you stuff your finger up his arse, for Christ's sake.' Coming from a highly respected surgeon, in whose mouth butter wouldn't melt, as he discussed, in perfect diction, surgical matters with his patients and their relatives.

Lady 'Oh! I do like Mr So and so, he is such a gentleman!'

Me silently 'That's what you think.'

I often wondered how such men reprimanded our female colleagues, ten per cent of graduates at that time were girls, but there were not women doctors but LADY doctors.

Dr Davies examined the old chap but being a physician he did not do a rectal examination. I watched Dr Davies carry out his examination and start to arrange the investigations; it became obvious that he was thinking of stomach cancer. I just said, 'I did a rectal examination, Sir.' He carried one out and said, 'I think you need a surgeon. Dr Goldthorp knows where Mr Morrison is, he will take you to him.'

Old Billy was in his outpatient clinic. I explained what had happened, how I had done a rectal, and Dr Davies had not. Old Billy was delighted, he was over the moon, he ragged Dr Davies for weeks afterwards. It did not endear me to Dr Davies, but another lesson was learnt. Do not tell a consultant anything that will enable him to take the Mickey out of another consultant. That is until you become a consultant yourself, and then you can indulge in gossip, spread rumours and criticize to you heart's content. If you do not do it about them, they will be doing it about you.

Work on a medical ward was different to now. Coronary thrombosis for example, there were no intensive care beds or coronary care units. A coronary at night would keep me out of bed 30 minutes. History, examination, electrocardiogram (we did those, no technicians to do them for us) read the ECG, ¼ grain of morphia for pain (same dose now 15 mgms.) start heparin and warfarin to thin the blood. Then back to bed, 50% were dead next morning, it was expected, the rest usually survived. I would find out and sign the death certificate in the morning. What could I have done if I had been told, and I would have played hell with the person who had woken me. I had a full day's work ahead of me.

Sometimes there were slack times, in the afternoon, when I would go to bed. The telephonist and ward sister would be notified. They protected you, only death-preventing messages were allowed through, even your consultant would be told to ring later. Messages were kept until 4 p.m. If there were none you would be woken about 6 p.m. There wasn't that ubiquitous bleep that allows all and sundry to find you.

Compare this to the current junior doctor. Admittedly the results for treating coronary thrombosis are far superior. Coronary care units have been with us for decades, with all the various monitoring devices. It takes the resident doctor almost two hours to get the patient sorted out, investigations done and the appropriate treatment commenced. When he returns to his on-call room and it is not too dirty with sheets that have not been changed for over a week, he may attempt to get some sleep, but the nursing staff will be ringing him every 30 minutes or so, to report and discuss any changes on the monitoring equipment, so he will not get any sleep all night. You cannot really expect him to put in a full day's work afterwards, but until recently our beloved politicians have insisted upon it. Only now are junior doctors beginning to get reasonable working hours, not because the politicians want to give it them, but because they have got to, by Common Market rules designed to benefit pilots and long distance lorry drivers. Common Market rules are also making them pay junior doctors for being on call in the hospital, long overdue.

After two months the Asian flu epidemic hit us, and I ended upsetting Dr Davies again. Nurses, doctors were all hit. Most of the hospital closed down. Only the serious life-threatening surgical cases were operated on. We managed to keep the medical wards open, and convert one surgical ward. Old people and those with chronic illnesses were dying like flies. Young people were affected too, the complication serious pneumonia, women, but particularly otherwise healthy young men. We were so busy that the consultants only saw the cases that were not responding to treatment.

I noticed that the registrar and SHOs were using intravenous tetracycline and other new drugs, but it seemed to me that those I prescribed the older penicillin and streptomycin got better quicker, so I continued using them. Three months later, an article in *British Medical Journal* stated that of all the treatments tried penicillin with streptomycin was the best. A divisional meeting was held to discuss this with Dr Davies in the chair.

I piped up, 'Yes I had noticed that so I kept prescribing them for the patients I saw.'

Deathly hush.

'You did not use intravenous tetracycline at all then?'

'No.'

'You know that we had ordered all patients to be treated with intravenous tetracycline?'

'No.'

'Weren't you at the meeting where this was decided?'

'What meeting?'

'You read the memo that went round?'

'What memo?'

Dr Davies was about to explode, when at last the registrar spoke.

'He was not there Sir, he was only the houseman, and we didn't think it worth while inviting him.'

'What about the memo?'

'There wasn't one Sir, the secretaries were off sick.'

'So Goldthorp, You weren't told?'

'No Sir.'

'Hmmm.'

Sunday morning of the third week, the male ward contained a cheerful raucous bunch of 10 blokes of my own age. I did a ward round and discharged them. That afternoon when walking along the main corridor on their way out, to their great joy they met me wrapped up in blankets, in a wheelchair, being wheeled to the sick-bay. It made their day.

My second three months as house physician were at Rossendale General Hospital. There was less acute work there, the male ward was massive 50 beds, and the female not that far behind. We were in the middle of the cotton belt, heavy smoking male factory workers, who had also been inhaling cotton fibres for years. Chronic bronchitis leading to right-sided heart failure. In October the ward filled up with them. Some for a month or so while they were put right, others for the winter until spring, going home in April. When I arrived the male ward was 30% full and remained that way for all the time I was there. The female ward was not much better. I had a relatively easy time, plenty to do, so I did not get bored, but many afternoons were spent in Rossendale.

Another difference at this time was visits to the hospital pub. Quiet evenings occurred, when we went to the nearest pub, always the same one. Imagine now the headlines in the *Daily Mirror* or *Daily Mail*. 'Junior doctors on duty in the local pub'. We would be ostracized, thrown out by the General Medical Council and marooned on an uninhabited island near the South Pole. It was the accepted thing, you told the telephone receptionist where you were going and went. If one of the consultants came in to see a patient he was worried about, the telephonist would tell him where you were. He would pop in, buy a round; discuss his case and chat for half an hour. He probably found out a lot that was going in that informal way.

At other times the waitress would just appear with a round of pints. Looking round there would be a lady and her family or a chap with his mates, recent patients. The Health Service had been functioning for less than a decade, they remembered what it was like beforehand, they were proud of it, and since the 1944 Education Act, many of us were from a similar background, proud of us as well. They made you feel very privileged, that's why the vast majority of us spent our lives in medicine, much different from the present day when 20% of graduates have left medicine four years after graduating.

Obstetrics

Toward the end of my six months in medicine I heard the house officer in obstetrics post at Fairfield General, part of the Bury Group, would soon be available. I asked Dr Davies to be one of my referees and rang Billy Morrison with the same request. Five days later I received a letter informing me that I had been appointed the next house officer in obstetrics, with the offer of a month's locum with Old Billy until the job started. It was not a good move, I had not found out who ran the Obstetrics and Gynaecology department. He was only an SHMO Senior Hospital Medical Officer, not the consultant; my two had just gone over his head and appointed me, without even bothering to tell him. SHMO's a dogsbody of a job, the majority of them highly qualified and experienced, without the pull to guarantee a consultant's post when the NHS started. But the NHS did not want to lose them. Salary less than a consultant's, no right to private practice, nominally under a consultant. A consultant whom they often far outclassed. The post was abolished about 10 years later when they were all made consultants en-masse.

A consultant was in charge of the department; he was getting on a bit. Qualifications, a Diploma in Obstetrics, a Diploma in Public Health and a top notch one, MD Doctorate of Medicine, a research degree, in Punctate Basophilia, an aspect of lead poisoning, very useful for obstetrics. We got the impression that he had started off with the intention of becoming a Medical Officer of Health, but got sidetracked into becoming the Honorary in Obstetrics. A job nobody else had wanted, there was not much money in it. Young married couples could not afford the fees. Those that could, the GPs before the Health Service kept for themselves. The really wealthy went to the Central Manchester consultants. Although self-taught, for two decades he had looked after all the serious cases on his own. The stress was beginning to show, I only met him three times.

Fortunately the SHMO was a workaholic. George Herbert E—. known as G. H. behind his back. G. H. was quite happy doing a 10 to 11 hour day, his week-ends started about 5 p.m. on a Saturday afternoon. He did everything, ran the department, all the clinics, most of the operating, lectured the student midwives, and all the administration. He was highly experienced, but was not a member of the Royal College of Obstetricians and Gynaecologists. He had been appointed the equivalent status to a consultant by Lancashire County Council before the war and did not see why he should be one, many had been made consultants without membership. The Manchester Obstetric authorities were adamant about it, he cruised through the exam while I was there and shortly afterwards became a consultant. G. H. and I got on very well. If Old Billy nearly converted me to General Surgery, G. H. kept me on the straight and narrow as an Obstetrician and Gynaecologist. Twenty years later G. H. was to flatter me greatly by choosing me to see his wife when she developed a problem.

There were three residents in obstetrics, a registrar, an SHO and me. Two of us shared a house with two other residents. The registrar had a nice bungalow, it was supposed to be married quarters, if the registrar was married. There was an ulterior motive to make sure a married registrar did not find a flat or rent a house in the area, the intention being to make sure the registrar was sleeping in the hospital even though it was his night off. That was a problem for our registrar, he had alternate nights and weekends off-duty. When he returned from a night out and went to bed, being the senior man close at hand and G. H. at home several miles away, he was always called first. He solved the problem at weekends by staying at his girlfriend's parents' house.

I worked opposite the SHO, on the maternity wards all day, he on Gynaecology. Alternate nights I did all the obstetric and gynae. emergencies. I was thrown in at the deep end; I was not too proud, indeed very relieved, to ask the senior midwife what to do next. Theoretically I was OK, during my month with Billy Morrison I borrowed a new textbook from the library and read it a couple of times.

We did not have an anaesthetist, I did it. I gave the anaesthetic, handed over to the midwife, went down to the bottom end did whatever was necessary, came back to the top end and brought the patient round. We did not have a resident paediatrician, there was one 4 miles away at Bury, so I had to resuscitate the baby as well. An anaesthetist would come from Bury for Caesarean operations but if he was already occupied G. H. would come in and do a spinal anaesthetic. The Consultant was never called, he was always unavailable. In any case the midwives said he was old fashioned and did not want him.

After three months, at breakfast the registrar was opening his mail. There was a small package containing three very long narrow needles and another long steel instrument. 'Pudendal block needles and guides,' he said, 'next time you do a forceps let me know.' So I did. He said 'I am going to show you how to do a Pudendal Block. You'll be able to use it for everything except removing placentas (afterbirth). I will show you once. Then you are never to wake me up at night unless a Caesarean needs doing.' This may seem a bit excessive but I have already described his working conditions. It may seem that I was left very much on my own, it felt like it at times, but I had the over-confidence of ignorance, and rather liked it. It was a few months before I realized G. H. had his spies everywhere, midwives, who observed and reported back all my actions.

Four things remain in my memory from my time at Fairfield.

The fantastic party the consultant threw when G. H. became a member of the college.

Triplets.

Midnight Dilatation and Curettage operations.

Me personally causing an epidemic of Puerperal Fever.

Triplets

I was called to deliver twins in a lady who was 38 weeks pregnant. The first thing I did was examine a beautiful X-ray of two babies presenting by the head. I swear to God there were only two. Twins tend to bleed after delivery. As soon as the second head was born

Jayne, Stephen and Margaret aged one, their parents sent this photo with a Christmas card (following page top) in 1959

- 32 -

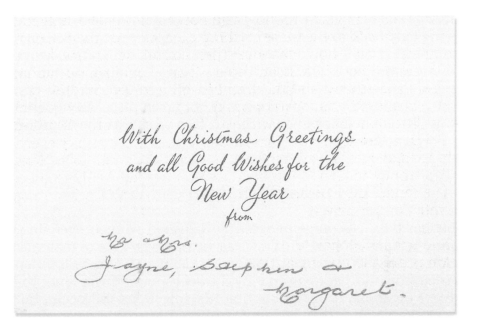

the midwife injected ergometrine, which makes the womb contract to a tight ball, anything inside is crushed. A pair of feet appeared. Numerous Anglo-Saxon expletives flashed through my mind, I used a four-letter word, I virtually screamed it – HELP! But Help was some distance away in bed. He had to be rung up. He would sit in a daze on his bed for a minute or two while his brain started to function. Help had to get dressed and negotiate a quarter of a mile of corridors to get here. No option – I did my first breech extraction, the first of about 200. An operation that is now a heinous crime, almost as bad as sitting there watching a lady having a spontaneous breech delivery. Caesarean Section is now mandatory. As I approached retirement I began to wonder why the Good Lord had not allowed women to evolve zip fasteners in their abdomens.

Midnight D & Cs

The theatre sister would arrive at 11 p. m., and start getting theatre ready. If I was in the vicinity, I would be told to clear off. At 11.45 two doctors would arrive. Five minutes later the Home Sister would escort an attractive young single lady to the operating theatre. The young lady would be a student nurse, pupil midwife or a young ward sister. She remained in the theatre for about an hour, whilst the Home Sister and Night Sister prowled the corridor like two of

Hitler's Gauleiters from the SS. Then the sisters would wheel the young lady back to the nurse's sickbay. Curiosity got the better of me. The next day I would sneak into the theatre sister's office, where the operating book was kept. Patients name, number, operation, surgeon, anaesthetist and theatre nurse all recorded. Surprise, surprise a blank space, an operation had not taken place. Any queries by me 'It's got nothing to do with you.' Ten years later the Abortion Act became law.

The Epidemic of Puerperal Fever

This has been a scourge of recently delivered women ever since Homo Sapiens evolved, until 1870 or so a serious cause of maternal death, 4 per 1000 births, at times of epidemics 10% to 15%. Often carried from mother to mother by the doctor or midwife. Since the advent of sulpha drugs and antibiotics, infections still occur, but are so easily cured, they are almost ignored. Puerperal fever, along with 10 others (smallpox, measles, typhoid etc.) was a communicable disease, which had to be reported.

Starting with an argument in a pub, our gang against two young recently appointed GPs: it started over fees for cremation certificates moving on to fees paid for reporting a case of infectious disease. The GP got 5 bob (shillings), we got one. This led me to the hospital library and to read the laws on infectious disease. All puerperal women (recently delivered) who had a temperature of over 100 degrees Fahrenheit and those with a temperature of 99 on three or more occasions had to be reported.

I now realized why on each ward was a dog-eared ancient book of certificates for reporting communicable diseases. I started to report the appropriate cases of puerperal fever, averaging 4 to 5 cases a week. Life carried on gaily for over three months. Then the local MOH (Medical Officer of Heath – Boss Public Health doctor) asked G. H. to pop into his office to see him when he had a few minutes to spare.

Eventually G. H. got round to visit him. The usual,

'Morning G. H.'

'Morning Jim' (for want of knowing his name)

'Sit down. Like a cup of coffee? Miss Smith, can we have a coffee for Dr E—.'

'How's your wife, family, kids etc. etc?'

'OK thanks.'

The usual start to discussion by both parties.

Then the MOH says 'G.H. Now what about this epidemic puerperal fever.'

G.H. sits up straight, eyes popping out of his head. 'What Epidemic?'

'Why, the one you've got at Fairfield,' says the MOH, leafing through a pile of certificates on his desk. 'Let's see, 16 in March, 20 in April, 17 in May and 4 so far this month. If it goes on like this I am going to have to close you down.'

G.H. shoots out of his office at a rate of knots. Races through central Bury at 60 miles per hour, crashes through two sets of lights on red, screeches to a halt in his car park, gallops to the Superintendent Midwife's office, slams the door open, nearly gives her a heart attack, and screams 'Why didn't you tell me about this epidemic of puerperal fever?'

The Superintendent Midwife, (Boss midwife) slowly recovers from a severe attack of palpitations, G.H. had never acted like this before, he was always the perfect gentleman, and he had always knocked before when he wanted to enter. Realizing that something was awry, she said 'Pardon?'

'Why didn't you tell me about this epidemic of puerperal fever?' Says G.H.

'What epidemic?' says the Super.

Deathly hush. Both leave the office at a rate of knots, heading for the Sister's office on each of the lying-in wards.

'Why didn't you tell us about this epidemic of puerperal fever?' They both screech at the ward sister, each one taken aback and somewhat upset by this unwarranted attack. Answer – 'What epidemic?'

Extreme frustration, steam coming out of both party's ear-holes. Then G.H. spots a brand new book of certificates, new bright grey, not the usual sun-bleached dog-eared one. He opened it, full of brand new certificates instead of the ones yellowed with age.

'Where's the old one?' says G.H.

'I don't know,' says the ward sister.

'You must do,' says G.H. 'You've got to keep the old ones by law.'

They searched through all the drawers and found it. G.H. looked to see who had signed the stubs, shouted, 'I'll crucify him', and left at a high rate of knots. I wonder who he was looking for?

The registrar, SHO and self were sitting chatting over a cup of coffee after lunch, in the lounge. The door crashes open, in rushes G.H. The conversation could now be described as being punctuated by adjectives of a rather sanguineous nature.

'There you are you idiot. Why have you been signing those certificates?'

'You've got to Sir, it's the law. I've read it up, and all communicable diseases have to be reported.' And proceeded to reel them all off.

He collapsed into an armchair, exhausted and relieved. 'Good God who've you been talking to?'

'Dr's A and B.' Mentioning the two young recent GP recruits.

'They've only just started, they don't know what goes on. Talk to one of the older ones, they don't have time to record such things as measles. Use your common sense; you don't do everything the government wants. Otherwise you get some medically qualified idiot who doesn't know one end of a stethoscope from another closing you down.'

G. H. a typical clinician was referring to his pal the MOH, Public Health doctors like their replacements the Community Physicians being desk bound wallas, not proper doctors. Clinicians completely ignore the fact that such people as Thomas Crapper, who invented an efficient water closet and Edwin Chadwick, who built sewers, saved more lives than the whole of the Victorian medical profession put together. *Thomas Crapper.* Yes that's where the word comes from; every time you use that four-letter word you are honouring the memory of a very good Victorian plumber.

'We don't report those cases, only the very serious ones, come to think of it we don't report those either.'

The epidemic came to an abrupt halt, simply by not reporting any cases. Which goes to show just how reliable government statistics are. All our fancy modern statistics put through ultra modern computers, gathered up and inserted by underpaid 20-year-old clerks with no medical training, and we wonder why they still get it wrong.

What help had been doing six months at Fairfield toward my army service? A lot. I would have had no problem in running a Casualty Clearing Station. Fifty per cent of the deliveries were done at home, many came in as emergencies, I had had a lot of experience in dealing with shock and blood loss. Add to that the emergency intake on the Gynae. Ward. The abortionists in Bury were very busy ladies. Not only more shock and blood loss but bacterial shock due to rapidly spreading blood infection.

In July, courtesy of the army, I had a day off, the medical examination for fitness day. Then there was an army centre on the outskirts of Chester. I had never visited Chester, walked the walls or admired the two-tier shopping streets. The army paid for the visit, a travel warrant. I was not an officer yet, so it was third class. I did not mind, even later as an officer, when I could travel first class, I still travelled third and pocketed the difference. What was very nice when I was a National Service officer was that my wife had a warrant, which allowed her to travel free, third class. My beloved wife being a natural aristocrat paid the difference and travelled first.

Thirty young doctors from the North West attended. I had never met any of them before. Serious discussions took place as to how we could avoid passing fit. For the first time in our lives there was an examination we all wanted to fail. No different to the group of 18 year olds Tony Thorne describes so vividly. I would estimate that no matter what walk of life you came from, 99% of recruits wanted to fail.

Our conclusion: the only hope, kidney disease, pass large amounts of highly dilute urine. After reporting in, we were informed that our examinations would begin at 2 p.m., 14:00 hours, as we would later call it. What better place to prepare than a nearby pub. Our RAMC sergeant was well aware of this ploy. Whereas Tony Thorne had to empty a full bladder into a tiny bottle, our sergeant supplied us with the tiny bottle and a bucket.

Our samples were lined up alongside the sink for testing. Nowadays it is easy to test urine, the doctor takes a little thin dipstick, different colours representing different substances, dips it into the urine and reads off a minute later. Then urine testing took about 20 minutes. For instance, the protein albumin, the top half of the test tube, had to be boiled in a Bunsen burner flame. If albumin was present it turned white. The test for sugar, various reagents were be added, then vigorous shaking of the test tube. Then there was acetone, blood and others to test for.

Being future Medical Officers we had the honour of being examined by a Major RAMC. He no doubt having had two or three pints with his lunch in the officers' mess arrived half an hour late. He walked into the room, up to the sink and with a sweep of his arm, pushed all our urinary samples into the sink.

'I'm buggered if I'm going to examine that lot. It looks like water; you've all been on the piss. Not one of you lot has kidney disease; every bloody group tries it on. It'll be a miracle if I find anyone who is A2'.

Medical Grades	A1	A2	A3		B1	B2	B3		C1	C2	C3

I passed A1, as did every one else.

I was fortunate to get out of the army in time, and only do two years. I watched with great pleasure as all three services screamed when National Service came to an end. No doctor would join up. In Germany they had to employ civilian doctors to look after the families.

It was not so good for the National Service doctors following a year behind us. Their two years up, they had to do another year, no option, a government decision, to refuse meant a court martial, prison sentence, in an army prison, an appearance before the General Medical Council, struck off, goodbye medical profession. There was a slight consolation, they got full regular pay, marriage allowance and married quarters. The army was scraping the bottom of the barrel; on my way home I met a RAMC doctor who was about 5ft. 8 ins. tall, 18 stone, who wheezed when he walked. He had been passed A1.

National Service officers then went on the Officer Reserve for ten years, if war was declared you would be immediately called up for duty. Late 1970 I receive an official army communication. Oh, it's my final official discharge, I thought. The message, 'Your period on the Officer Reserve has been extended another ten years!' Bl—y h-ll I thought, the b——ds will have me running up and down Wadi sides again at 45 while the younger b——rs stay at home.'

Getting Ready

Expecting to be called up any time, I took August off, the only time I never had a job from January 1957 to my retirement in 1998. I had been married for six months. It was the first time Margaret and I lived together for more than 5 days at a time. I read for, took and passed the examination for the Diploma in Obstetrics. With that I tried to have an army post in obstetrics, but ended up as GDMO (General Duties Medical Officer).

At the end of August I was told that I would be called up in the second half of November. I received my commission, 458736 Lieutenant William Oates Goldthorp. A very posh document on highly expensive parchment purported to be signed by her majesty herself. A valued personal document in some quarters, God knows where mine is, I have not seen it for over 35 years! All my degrees, diplomas and awards are expensively framed and hanging on various walls of our house. The precious commission, God knows.

Six weeks to wait, I found a locum SHO post in General Surgery at Louth County Hospital, where my wife's mother came from and had lots of relatives. It seemed a good idea, Margaret could take her off-duty days in chunks and we could stay together and get to know her relatives. What a lousy job, it was a house surgeon job they could get no applicants for, so the pay was upped to SHO rates. I was bored stiff, hardly anything to do. Most mornings I had finished by 10.30.

They had a hockey team, which competed in North Lincolnshire, we played Wednesday and Saturday afternoons, and practised two afternoons at 4 p. m. Male nurses, young administrators, lab. technicians, no one seemed to mind that we were playing hockey when we should have been working. The team's activities were followed with avid interest, a hospital morale booster. It won't be there now; the hockey pitch like most tennis courts will either have been built on or converted to a car park. Like all such small teams making up enough members to field a full team was difficult, I was roped in about two days after I arrived.

We looked after casualty. It was empty most the time. It was September, and the shooting season had started. Posh wealthy London businessmen came up to shoot pheasants, fortunately wearing thick tweeds because they were also quite good at shooting each other, usually the same part, the one that sticks out at the back. More normally in Harley Street it must have been a bit of a shock to be treated out in the sticks. In view of the position of the injury, the hilarity in the casualty whilst I prised lead pellets out of buttocks, with the farm labourer who had brought him having a cup of tea and looking on, was rather high. The victims themselves joining in, and occasionally cursing when the removal was more uncomfortable than expected.

And so at last the great day came.

Chapter Three

Basic Training

This lasted 6 weeks, divided into three parts.

1. Drill, square bashing.

2. Tropical Medicine and Army Administration

3. Health, Hygiene, clean water, latrines, campsite selection and legal matters

The first comment I have to make is a comparison to Tony Thorne's *Brasso, Blanco and Bull.* The constant repetitious use of one adjective which Tony Thorne writes as FOCKING, for the dimwitted it is wrongly spelt, o being usually replaced with a u. Maybe

National Service Medical Officer intake, November 1958. Author, back row, third from right. Mike Easty, middle row, fourth from left.

because we were 6 to 8 years older than his group, we were officers or doctors but that adjective was rarely used where ever I went. Swearing and cursing in abundance admittedly. Blaspheming and blood products galore. When it came to f—ing and blinding, it was blinding only. Tempers were lost; frustration reached extreme heights, Anglo Saxon virtuosity to be marvelled at but f—ing, no.

Another point, drill, this obviously must be rammed home day after day until it almost becomes a subconscious reaction, for both squaddies and officer cadets. That is why basic training lasted 16 weeks not two weeks as in our case. In fact our two weeks actually worked out as 7 days. After two weeks I had forgotten the lot. I was no more capable of going on parade than taking charge of a parade, as an officer should. All I remembered was to stand at attention, stand easy and salute after a fashion. Salute: a future Commanding Officer Lieutenant Colonel Maurice E. M. MacWilliam DSO, MC, TD, was to say, 'Bill, wave, smile and nod your head, say hello or good morning, but for Christ's sake do not salute. It makes me cringe. You have the unique ability to make the most god-awful salute look good.'

Square bashing

We left our various homes and travelled by rail warrant to Crookham somewhere on Salisbury Plain, arriving about 12.30. We were taken to the officers mess and shown where we would dine, where the baths, showers etc were, then trooped over a large lawn to two ancient Nissen huts, First World War vintage, where we would sleep. There were about 14 beds, narrow army issue, a chest of drawers cum wardrobe and chair, each hut heated, nominally, by two large cast iron pot-bellied coke burning stoves. We would fill them full of coke, open the air vents to full, the stoves would glow red-hot. Standing round or sitting round, your cheeks would roast while your backside turned to ice. Turn round, your backside roasted and icicles formed on the end of your nose. The windows were so firmly fitted that a gale came in one side and went out the other. There was a toilet, if it was occupied you could stand at the hut door and pee through that.

Morning ablutions meant negotiating the large lawn covered in freezing fog, or dashing through the rain with a towel over your head. The first night I slept in underclothes, socks, army issue woollen gloves, pyjamas, and battledress with the army officer's topcoat on top. There was almost a riot next morning, when instead of reporting to the Parade Ground for our first day of drill, we ransacked the quartermaster's stores. The quartermaster, a Major, refused to issue more blankets, so we took them. The adjutant was informed, quietened us down and said he would make sure the windows would be made airtight. I spent the rest of that fortnight sleeping in underclothes, socks, gloves and pyjamas, under six blankets, so there was a slight improvement.

The first afternoon was spent in collecting our kit. Two pairs boots, two battledresses, gym kit, housewife, webbing, belts, gaiters etc. etc. A representative from some posh London outfitter was there, we had to buy our own shirts, ties, brown shoes, officer's cap, overcoat, gloves and so on. We had received an allowance for this. The official mess kit for mess dinners we were told we did not need to buy and received no allowance, dinner suits were acceptable. Most of us managed all right, but it caused a lot of animosity with the officers in some of the top regiments, when their National Service medical officers refused to buy mess kits.

Unlike Thorne's squaddies we had to buy our own Brasso and Blanco, we bought one tin of each and shared them between us. We already had black boot polish. My webbing was blancoed once, my brass brassoed once, my boots were polished once. I did not have to spend hours at it like the ordinary intake did. After collecting our kit, our two drill-sergeants came round to our huts with a photograph of how our beds and kit should be prepared for inspection. On inquiring how often we would be inspected, the sergeants told us that officers inspected others and were not inspected themselves. That solved that problem; we stuck the photograph on the notice board and promptly forgot about it.

After the sergeant's visit we found an old football. There was a smashing flat tarmac area just outside, about five acres in extent, and we organized an impromptu game of football. We noticed a khaki clad figure gesticulating in the distance, looking like someone who was having a vertical epileptic fit. Not wishing to get involved we ignored him and proceeded with our football. Later a harassed little lance corporal came rushing up. He told us that the mad man waving on the horizon was the Sergeant-Major, and we had committed the heinous offence of not only walking on his beloved parade ground but had carried out the heinous insult of playing football on it. Such a serious crime had never been done before and we would all be rotting in hell for evermore, if we didn't get off it this instant, 'To quote the Sergeant-Major Sir'.

Square bashing started on Tuesday the first week, lasting until Thursday the second week. How does a Drill Sergeant address a commissioned medical officer, well no different from any other recruit, with a tiny difference? 'By Christ can't you get a bloody thing right. SIR!' You Bloody fool. SIR!'

Except for the second Wednesday when we had weapons training. Yes!!! Weapons training. But doctors are non-combatants, like hell they are. It's 1958 not the First World War. Even if our lads got seriously wounded, there was a 98% chance that they would survive and survive in good condition. Think what that does to a front line soldier's morale. Many more are wounded than killed. The first point in the evacuation scheme is the Regimental Aid Post. If the enemy can knock that out, kill the MO and his orderlies, he strikes a serious blow to the front line man's morale and reduces his fighting efficiency. Medical officers and orderlies had to be prepared to fight. Admittedly our day of weapons training was rudimentary in the extreme.

Wednesday morning we were lectured at, by an Armourer Sergeant and Corporal. In the morning we were told how a grenade worked. How to clean and load an officer's revolver. Clean and load a .303 rifle. A bren-gun demonstration, stripping down and reassembling. We volunteered to have a go.

'Not B—y likely, Sir, last time I let one of you lot have a go he wrecked it. I had to spend a week repairing it and making bits and pieces he'd wrecked.'

We gathered that training MOs about weapons was not considered a worthwhile job. Which the afternoon was to prove.

We started off throwing hand-grenades, which fortunately were all duds; otherwise the future physicians among would have blown us up. You could tell all the future surgeons like me, we pulled the pin, threw them properly and in the correct direction. Future physicians forgot to remove or dropped pins, hand grenades or threw them anywhere.

We then moved on to firing service revolvers, you couldn't hit a barn door with one of those things. We realized however that they would make useful weapons, in close quarter, hand to hand fighting, held by the barrel and used as a club.

On to the main Firing Range, with our sergeant and corporal, two battered old .303s, and half a clip, 5 rounds each. It was a chore for the armourers, they obviously thought it was a total waste of time, and took the Mickey in a dreadful fashion. Most of us had never fired a rifle before; we did not even hit the target at times. As a group we started to get annoyed. When my turn came I took careful aim and hit the target about 7 inches above and to the right of the bull.

'By God that's a miracle Sir. You've actually hit the target.'

'Would you mind winding the target back sergeant, I would like to see where the bullet went.'

'Why waste time, shoot the other four and get on with it.'

'I would like to see the target, sergeant.'

'Don't be stupid Sir, get on with it'.

'Forgive me if I am wrong sergeant, but I have been made to understand that a lieutenant outranks a sergeant.'

By now the sergeant had steam coming out of his ears, but we were pig sick of his attitude and my fellow MOs were gathering round and muttering.

'It might be necessary for a deputation to visit your CO tomorrow.'

'Right,' angry and annoyed. 'Wind it in for him corporal.'

Christmas 1942 my best friend Chippy Chapman's dad got him a Webley .177 air pistol, I was green, yellow purple and blue with envy. I drove my Dad barmy nagging him week after week about it. He just shrugged his shoulders, said. 'We'll see,' or 'Be patient,' making me ten times worse. Then July '43 he came up trumps, my birthday, a Webley .177 air rifle, far more accurate than a pistol, not just for target practice. You could actually KILL things with it. What a horrible kid, any townie, environmentalist or anti-hunter will say. Well from the Goldthorp side of me you are probably right. Don't forget the other half the Oateses, Tills and Everetts. They had been living for generations in and on the countryside of the Lincolnshire, Yorkshire border.

After a little target practice I set out to decimate, indeed hemi mate or even eliminate our local population of starlings and house sparrows. I hated them with good reason. Songbirds, thrushes, robins, blackbirds, chaffinches, tits etc I left strictly alone, but I had a financial reason for hating sparrows and starlings. For the previous 2 to 3 years I had been breeding and keeping Bantams. They laid very well in spring, steadily through winter, and not too badly in the summer, except the older hens who went broody. It was rationing time; I could get half-a-crown, two shillings and six pence for a dozen eggs. I set six broodies a year, 12 eggs each. My cockerels were healthy vigorous chaps. A 100% result 72 chicks, half would be cockerels, by November all well grown and annoying the neighbours. They and all hens over two years old would be culled, plucked and gutted by me and sold at five shillings a piece. No shortage of buyers, meat rationing.

I had given up my egg ration and got hen feed instead but it had to be paid for. It was not enough the rest had to be begged, borrowed or acquired, usually from my uncles' farms. My problem was that every time I fed my bantams, 10,000 starlings and 5,000 sparrows turned up for dinner as well. Indeed they would be waiting on the rooftops at breakfast and teatime. I strung lines of wire over the bantam pen and tied hundreds of dead starlings to it, where they slowly rotted away, in summer covered in maggots, which when big fell to the ground a welcome supplement to my bantams' diet.

After a couple of months I moved out into the bush, after rabbits and stock doves, (woodpigeons), both pests. The local farmers were delighted when we tried to eliminate them. The countryside was not the large 100 acre fields with no hedges, where a person can be seen for miles, but fields of 10 to 20 acres with large tall hedges, many still down to grass, it was possible to slip from field to field without being seen for 3 or 4 miles. At 10 I knew how to apply a rabbit chop to finish it off, and carried a sharp penknife to gut it immediately otherwise the meat went off. When I got home I had to skin it as well. I also had to dress the pigeons. (Dress means pluck and gut.)

Air rifles have another advantage; they can be used inside farm buildings without going through roof tiles. That's where the rats were. A rat's tail taken to the Clerk of the Drainage Boards office got you one old penny. One old penny would buy a large bag of chips; two would get you in the chicken run (front stalls) at the local cinema. That is when you actually had to pay to get in. Men older than 50 whether town or country will know how that dodge was worked.

When I was 13, a relative of my uncle wanted a safe home for his .22 rifle. My dad provided it on the understanding that I could use it. I was given strict instruction, keeping it clean oiled etc., target practice until I knew how it fired, and all its little idiosyncrasies. Taught to know where the bullet was going when it hit the target. A .22 bullet would go straight through a pheasant. There had to be ground or a tree behind your target. A .22 bullet fired into the air could kill a farmer ploughing a field a mile away The .22 rifle increased my rabbit quota, I did not need to get as close as with the air-rifle. Hares and a rare pheasant were now added to my tally. I was not a sportsman, I shot for the pot, if it was running or flying I left them alone. I wasn't going to waste a bullet on something that moved. .22 bullets were easy to get hold of but you did not waste them. All my friends had their sources and if one ran out, a bartering arrangement supplied them.

As you will appreciate I was well versed in rifle shooting. The corporal wound the target back, my shot was about 7 inches above and to the right of the bull. I aimed 7 inches below and to the left. I got a nice group, a bull and 3 in the inner ring close to the bull.

'Do you belong to a gun club, Sir?' asked the sergeant.

I exaggerated a bit, put on our local accent.

'Naw, sargint. Am a skolaship boy. Me dad's a farm lay bro. Ah bin po-achin, sin ah wer 10 yr owd.'

He answered in his own 'Arh that fits. Awl arr best shots is country lads.'

No more problems, the rest had more serious instruction. Then the sergeant found some more half clips for us, and got his own back.

'I think you had all better have another go, except you Sir. It would be a waste of good bullets for you.'

Final Score: Even   Armourers 1 : Medics 1

The last Thursday we drilled all day really putting our backs into it. On Friday there was an official passing out parade, taken by the Adjutant. Our two Drill Sergeants were chaps our own age, we had enjoyed their efforts and company and did not want to let them down. The parade went of without a hitch.

Then the army played its first typical army trick on us. We were given 48 hour passes and railway warrants. Then we went to the MI Room, I will use this abbreviation from now on; it means Medical Inspection the army equivalent of a GP's surgery. There we received our first injection of TABT (Typhoid, Paratyphoid A & B, plus Tetanus) Then went to the mess for lunch. The afternoon was to be spent with three lectures on army administration then we could go home, to be back at Millbank, London on Sunday night. Tea would be provided after the second of three lectures at 4 p. m.

The speaker for the third lecture never arrived. People started drifting out, more like staggering out during the second lecture. Two thirds were left to take tea all feeling a bit queasy. After tea we made our way past a medical orderly at the door handing out aspirin tablets, back to our beds where most of us remained for 24 hours with nasty flu symptoms. Saturday afternoon, normality began to return as we surfaced, washed, dressed, shaved and made our way to the officers mess where, surprise, surprise they were expecting us for dinner.

Sunday morning a raucous Staff Sergeant who wanted us out of the Nissen huts by 9 a.m. rudely awakened us. Mattresses, blankets etc would be collected at 9.30 a.m.; we could spend the morning in the officers' mess. Church Parade was at 10.45. Lunch at 12.30 in the officer's mess. Transport would be provided for the railway station at 2 p. m. 'And by the way, there's a nice little pub 400 yards away on the road to the village to the right of the officers mess.'

Transport arrived as expected, a three-ton truck. Well you can't expect anything posh for National Service Men even if they are officers, because they aren't proper officers they are doctors. We were dumped at the railway station, and forgotten about. Square bashing was over; two weeks later we barely remembered how to stand at attention.

Millbank Army Hospital, London

It is closed down now, but it was our home for two weeks. How should I describe Millbank, a first rate Post Graduate Medical Teaching Centre in uniform. The training, a certain amount of Venereology and very intensive instruction in Tropical Medicine.

For VD we were brought up to date on the latest treatments, the legal situation, how to organize training sessions for young squaddies etc. The army policy was grab 'em and treat 'em as soon as possible, nothing should put in the way of rapid treatment, total confidentially. If the local Field Marshal wanted to know what was going on, tell him to piss off. Encourage protective measures, all MI Rooms had large supplies of condoms which soldiers going on leave, particularly in tropical areas, should be encouraged to take with them. They don't usually bother we were told and they didn't, most MI Rooms had boxes of Durex deteriorating in various drawers. As part of our instruction programme we were shown a cartoon, a museum piece even then dating from about 1945. *Ten Little Nigger Boys*, getting up to all sorts of antics and acquiring lots of nasty diseases. It was considered a reasonable way of training young soldiers; the shit would not half hit the fan if it were shown now. Robinson's golliwog on their jams is not politically correct, god knows what our liberals would do if they watched that cartoon. Venereal Disease was no longer a chargeable offence; a long battle had been fought by the RAMC and the army hierarchy over that, the ordinary soldier solving the problem by not reporting his infection until he was extremely ill.

In Tropical Medicine, the instruction was deep and intense. Lectures on all the diseases, sessions in the laboratories, what samples to take and when. One, the name escapes me, and *can't* be bothered to look up, you have to get up at midnight to take the blood sample because that is the only time it is there. How to prepare and stain slides. Then several three-hour sessions studying microscope slides, till you felt your eyes would pop out. It was at Millbank that I acquired an old army textbook on tropical diseases, which I was to find very useful. I threw it away years ago and could not remember its title. There it is in *Conscript Doctors.* 'The Memoranda on Medical Diseases in Tropical and Sub-Tropical Areas. 1948.' They were lying around all over the place. It had not been updated and this was 1958.

Social life, not much, 18 shillings a day did not go very far. The local pub, a cinema, but we did allow ourselves to screwed (not the homosexual variety) by visiting Danny la Rue's recently opened, expensive, overcharging nightclub. All the regular officers were raving about it. They must have been a gang of puffs, bloody waste of time and money that was. Brian Rix was at the Whitehall Theatre, that was a great night that one.

The Saturday of the weekend we stayed at Millbank an official Mess Dinner was organized, to show us the correct way to behave. For instance no matter how many pints you have had before the meal you must not leave the dining table before the senior officer present has gone, even if your bladder is up to your eyebrows. My bladder has never been one of my strong points. On that occasion, and others subsequently, when reprimanded by the Mess President I was always purposely rude. 'Buggar off, I'm going for a piss, if the colonel doesn't like it he can lump it.'

Millbank was a very enjoyable, memorable and instructive fort-night; probably it was all medicine and subjects that had been skated over before. Toward the end of the second week we were allowed to pick where we would like to be posted. Another Army con trick, did anyone ever read our preferences, I have doubts.

1. United Kingdom

2. Germany

3. East Africa, might be sent to Aden

4. Singapore

5. Hong Kong and the Far East

I selected 1,3, and 4. Number 3 three was the biggest lie out. It should have been, 'Aden, and you have not a cat in hell's chance of going to Africa', although I managed it. We left Millbank on Friday afternoon, a proper 48-hour pass this time, to report some-where on Salisbury Plain on Sunday evening, I just could not remember where. I found the name in John Blair's book. Keogh Barracks a week each, in the Army School of Health and the Field Training School.

The Final Fortnight

Lectures and demonstrations, water sources, water sterilization, campsite selection, refuse and sewage disposal. Latrine siting and construction. Latrines, I can remember two, cat sanitation and long drops. Cat sanitation, take a spade, dig a hole and cover it up. Remember *Ice Cold in Alex*, the German spy masquerading as a South African, wants to radio his controllers, so he picks up spade and walks off into the desert, that's cat sanitation.

Long drops – I was to find those in Somaliland, alongside married quarters and the small officers' messes. The long drop, a long deep hole, like a well, is dug and a hut constructed over it, it is a permanent fixture. Only used by a small group of people, it never fills up. Urine and faeces stay at the bottom of the 40-foot hole, undergo decomposition and drain away. It is supposed to be so deep that flies can't get down there, if they do any maggots that turn into flies will be too young and weak to fly out.

Cat Sanitation

We had demonstrations of latrine construction. Touring muddy fields in the pouring rain going from one exhibit to the other. Each exhibit showed all stages of construction from digging the hole to building the whole structure.

A series of lectures on the legal aspects of the army and a bit about your duties as a prosecution or defending officer in a Court Martial followed.

The most memorable session was the visit to the Medical Orderly's battle training centre, with its simulation and make-up department. We entered a large lecture area where the first thing we noticed was a dummy of a hanging man. A Staff Sergeant gave us a short talk on what the department did, then gave a short lecture on the changes to be found when a man had hanged himself. He demonstrated the purple face, protruding tongue, bulging eyes, wet crotch and the patch of urine on the floor. He moved onto another topic and two minutes later the dummy jumped down from its noose, smiled at us and walked away. That was the eye opener. We moved into another room containing 20 battle casualties. The first had had his leg blown off, the femoral artery was slowly pulsating away, draining his life's blood, he was deathly pale, severely shocked with tiny beads of sweat on his forehead. We had seen shocked patients in casualty, it was remarkably lifelike. We strolled round shattered arms, hands blown off, gaping head wounds with the brains showing, bayonet wounds, intestines hanging out, one had had his guts blown out by a grenade, shattered guts, blood and shit all over the place and it smelt like it too. Four groups of orderlies came in, selected four of the examples, carried out the appropriate resuscitation procedures, and carried the wounded away to the Regimental Aid Post. Movement occurred amongst the remaining wounded and 16 intact young men got up and took us for tea and biscuits in another room. What a demonstration, we were very impressed and said so, to the delight of the participants and make up experts who had joined us. A brilliant way to show 18 and 19 year old lads with no medical experience, what to expect and what to do. It was certainly the best afternoon of that fortnight.

At the end of the first week we got our postings. Mine was Aden, a visit to the MI Room revaccination against smallpox, immunization against yellow fever and one or two others was required. At the end of the second week we received our second TABT injection, this time with no problems. Then we went on our separate ways, unlike Tony Thorne's comrades, never to meet again. Tony Thorne describes how he developed life long friendships as a result of his basic training and subsequent Officer Cadet Training. There are 21 members in my group photograph plus our two drill sergeants (see page 40); at the time I did not make a record of names. Only one face I recognize, Mike Easty, who was at Manchester as a fellow student. His wife had just given birth to twins, so he was kept in England. Mike spent the whole of his career in the Manchester area, but not in the drainage area of any of the hospitals I worked at. Mike and I have never seen or spoken to each other since we said goodbye at the end of our basic training, it is nothing to be proud about, but probably reflects one's intense involvement in one's profession.

Home for Christmas, six weeks embarkation leave. A tour visiting friends and relatives. The only time before I retired, when having that amount of time of, I did not arrange a locum somewhere. Return to Portsmouth on the required date, report in as required. 'Oh! Not another one. You can beggar off home for two weeks, ship's not ready yet.'

Chapter Four

The Voyage

Middle February 1959. left Portsmouth on a troopship of the Empire Line, I can't remember its name, it was not the *Windrush*. That had caught fire and sunk off the coast of Libya a few years earlier. My memories of the voyage, boring, boring, boring, put me off cruises for life. Fortunately I found in the ship's library all four volumes, 700 pages each, of Churchill's recently published *History of the English Speaking Peoples*. I read the lot before we reached Aden.

The ship was half empty, half the troop decks unoccupied. There were only two of us in our four-berth officer's cabin. As soon as we had travelled beyond the three-mile limit, a game of Housey – Housey was arranged, the army version of Bingo. At that time illegal in UK, everyone rushed to join in, including me, who was totally ignorant of it. What a mind blowing game it turned out to be, a mental defective with an IQ of 50 would be good at it. Why it was ever banned in England I will never know, and why anyone with a single mental grey cell bothers to play, I have no idea.

Passport photograph

The bar also opened, NAAFI prices, 20 untipped Senior Service 11 old pence, instead of 4 shillings and sixpence, Gin, 7 shillings and sixpence a bottle, Whisky, 8 and 6, Brandy, 9 and 6, instead of 38 shillings, marvellous but I didn't want to spend the next two years pissed out of my mind. Smoking, well we had not had any of the published surveys about the dangers of smoking. I rather liked Players Perfectas, 5 shillings for 50. Nice big oval shaped cigarettes, who could have foreseen me in the future playing hell with my patients who smoked.

The food was superb, frequent beautifully cooked many-coursed meals, I think it was a way of avoiding boredom, I really tucked in, until the third day when I realized I would probably put on two stones in weight by the time I reached Aden. Meal times were avoided. Exercise, 8 times round the upper deck equalled a mile. Does anybody realize how mentally devastating running 24 times round the upper deck can be? Here we were on a troop ship and no thought had been given to passing the time, the sermons I used to sleep through at Fieldside Methodist Chapel in Crowle as a boy would have been a welcome relief.

There was a band and dances after dinner at night, only there was no one to dance with. There were a few officers' wives with their husbands, naturally they preferred spending their time with their husbands, although there was the only full Colonel's Lady who took me under her wing like a broody hen takes an orphaned chick. 'Would you like to dance Lieutenant?' it was like guiding a battleship, indeed she was a battleship. Why she took me under her wing I do not know, perhaps I had mentioned the sudden surprise Margaret had had which had messed up all our arrangements for Margaret to come to Aden.

The ship had been fitted with stabilizers so I had no problem with seasickness. We sailed uneventfully to Gibraltar where we spent the day exploring the old galleries and massive cannons from the siege of 200 years ago. Visited the Barbary apes, the apes threw rocks, mud and ape turds at us, which we returned except for the turds. Across the Southern Mediterranean in winter, still battledress weather, non-stop to Suez, it was not long after the Suez crisis, we were not allowed off the ship. The Gullygully man with his day old chicks and conjuring tricks was allowed on board to entertain us.

A four-day excruciatingly hot cruise down the Red Sea. We decided to acquire a tan, started sun bathing, no warnings about skin cancer then. All our concerns were about severe sunburn. Five minutes a side the first day, we decided on 10, building up to 30 by the time we reached Aden, extremely disappointed as there was no evidence of a tan.

There was of course a ship's MO, but there was one boring job, which had to be done every 3 or 4 days, that he wanted to jettison. Crabbing, no not the Cornish variety, these crabs were about 5 millimetres across, with two massive claws in front. These allowed them to negotiate areas covered with short curly hairs, armpits and the male bits ladies acquire a liking for. Crab lice, (he's got the crabs) they could flash round and infect the whole ship if anyone brought them aboard. Down in the bowels of the ship, on the troop decks, where it was hot, airless sweaty, where the stabilizers were less effective and the ship's motion was more pronounced. The lads lined up bollock naked with their hands on their heads and slowly filed past while we checked the hairy bits, it might seem a bit demeaning, but in fact was a highly ribald occasion.

Unlike some, I actually knew what I was looking for, having seen them twice once in Casualty and once when I examined a friend. The friend, a fellow student, had become very friendly with a young lady, their passionate affair lasted about 12 months during which they went at each other hammer and tongs. A couple of years later he was to say that he did not know why a pregnancy never occurred. He thought he was sterile. This proved not to be the case, he had no difficulty starting babies off when he got married.

Intelligent young ladies did not get pregnant, they visited Anson Road Family Planning Clinic, borrowing their friend's or big sister's wedding ring, giving the name and occupation of a fictitious husband and got a Dutch Cap fitted. This combined with a knowledge of female anatomy and a spermicidal cream was a pretty safe contraceptive and the boyfriend would not know. It had to be fitted every time danger was imminent. My married lady patients often complained about it. They got dressed up for a party and did not go. Hubby having worked a twelve hour day, came home dog-tired, obviously nothing was going to happen, so they didn't bother, as soon as he gets to bed he suddenly wakes up, full of the joys of spring, they had to rush off to the bathroom, and if they were not sharp about it when they got back, he was fast asleep.

Anyway my friend's grand affair, we all thought would last a lifetime, ran out of steam and he was alone, worse he was damaged goods. The other girls wondered, 'Why had she ditched him?' He wasn't to be trusted, oversexed and unreliable. Besides his first owner might want him back. He spent a year all-alone and was getting a bit desperate. His grant cheque arrived and he went down Denmark Road and employed one of the ladies who patrolled the area. Sure enough he had crabs, he was lucky not to have something worse.

I kept my council, said nothing, but word still got out. His pals were horrified, fancy having to pay for what was freely on offer all round them. If you were really that desperate, you could visit the five-fingered widow. In spite of what the Victorian moralists said we knew from experience that it did not make you go blind, your teeth turn black or your hair fall out. Although when I now meet my old student friends, I am not so sure about the latter.

We were a gang of healthy, robust, not all that bad looking blokes, surrounded by equally healthy, attractive, charming intelligent young ladies with a weather eye open for a suitable lifetime partner. The Manchester Royal Infirmary Nursing school was not a training school for nurses, it trained the future wives of GPs consultants, solicitors, barristers, judges, architects, headmasters, Lord Mayors, County Councillors, MPs, all the future leaders of the major professions in Lancashire, Cheshire and Derbyshire. Admission to the school was difficult, all well qualified, the type of girls who these days would became members and leaders of those self same professions.

Finally we sailed into the massive bay and deep-water harbour of Aden. To the north the flat sandy shore and the small town of Sheikh Othman. The prostitute and brothel area, by all accounts a right set of dogs, even the Highland Light Infantry wouldn't go there. Nobody would, the chances of a European remaining alive there at night were nil. To the east a broad sand spit almost a mile across where the Khormaksar air base, aerodrome, officers' and other ranks' quarters were. There was also a massive area of European houses, then Aden, a large old volcanic crater divided into two parts. Steamer Point, the army area, Indian and Arab traders, shops, hospital, schools, hotels, Officers' and Sergeants' and other ranks' clubs, chandlers, ships supplies etc. The old Arab quarter, Crater, teeming with various locals' houses, scruffy, dirty, stinking, where a few 10-storey blocks contained married quarters for other ranks. This was where the original Aden had been. Close to the base of a high mountain, the Jebel Shamsham, could be found several extremely large water cisterns, Sheba's Wells, here water had been directed and stored from the occasional annual rainstorm, in the days before Britain took over.

If you don't climb Jebel Shamsham you will go back to Aden. Everybody climbed it, except me, I went all over Southern Arabia but I never got round to it. I pray to God that it's a prophecy that doesn't come true. Sheba's Wells, named after the Queen of Sheba, Solomon's bit of nookey. She is supposed to have reigned over one of the areas in the Eastern or Western Aden Protectorates. Several hundred years BC spices, silks, jewels and other high value products, crossed the Arabian Gulf and travelled by camel caravan along the southern coast and up the west coast of Arabia. Several small cities grew up along the route, Sheba's was one of them. The archaeologists had tried to investigate the area but the local Yemeni Arabs assumed that every site was jam-packed with gold and either chased them off, or spent all their time watching what the archaeologists did, and getting in the way, so the archaeologists called it a day and went home in disgust. Whether they have had any success since I don't know.

What did I think? It was bloody hot and I hadn't any tropical kit. That Scotchman, The Pipe Major who wrote 'The Barren Rocks of Aden' wasn't wrong, there was not a green leaf or blade of grass in sight. The stink found wherever there was an Adeni tiny town or village, even house, that is if you can call them houses, dominated everything. The stink of sweat, sun, sand, shit, unwashed bodies, water shortage, goat and sheep dung, a stink never to be forgotten.

We docked, collected our kit, trunks etc., sweating in officer's shirts and battle dress, we were soon down to shirtsleeves, and no ties. Eight docs got of the ship in Aden, I well remember the comment of an elderly private, who by his appearance and efforts was little use to anybody, no wonder after about 20 years in, he was still a private. 'By Christ there's eight docs getting of this ship, what the hell's going to happen now!'

We were met by a Lt Colonel RAMC, jumping up and down in delight 'We've captured the Jebel Akhdar!' he says, assuming we would all be highly impressed.

'What the hell is he talking about?' we say.

If I had realized I was going to be stuck on top of it at that stage for nearly three months, I would have recommended giving it back. Having introduced himself, he took us across the road to a café, ordered a large iced Stim lemon for himself, and sat under an umbrella, leaving us standing and sweating in the sun.

We had arrived in Aden, what a God awful dump, and the time would come when arriving back in Aden it would feel like I had returned to civilization. There were fantastic things in Aden, like electricity, street lighting, flush toilets and water that actually came out of taps. Aden had been a staging post and coaling station on the way to our Indian Empire, a very important place. It had a special name, named after part of the body no one can live without.

What a joy to be here at last,

**ADEN, THE ARSEHOLE OF THE EMPIRE,
EVERYTHING PASSES THROUGH IT.**

Chapter Five

First Impressions

Our CO gave us our instructions. Transport will arrive to take you to the transit camp at Khormaksar, it turned out to be the usual three-ton truck. Report to the Staff Sergeant, he will allocate tents, four to a tent. I advice you to use your mosquito nets. That was a bit of superfluous advice, if ever there was. The camp was next door to a salt marsh, covered in mosquitoes 10,000 per square centimetre. The moment the sun went down, 5 million moved in for breakfast. One of our lot, Stewart, woke early, stretched with his hands behind his head, elbows touching the net, then fell asleep again, next day his elbows were the size of melons.

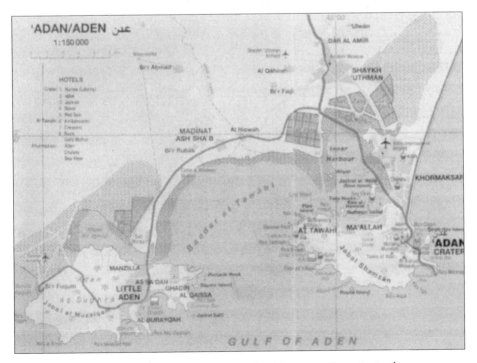

Aden Map (courtesy of the Aden Veterans Association)

The salt marsh, on the west of the camp, sloped into an extensive area of very shallow highly salty water. It must have been teeming with life, because it was teeming with flamingos.

You will eat, wash, and shave at the RAF officers' mess. This was when we realized our status. We were Brown Jobs, inferior people. Aden was an RAF station. They were the top dogs; they owned and managed the Station. The senior officer was RAF. All the rest, Army and Navy, were some thing the cat had just vomited.

'The army tailor will visit you this afternoon; his prices are agreed, they are rock bottom. If he gets up to any tricks let us know, we will get rid of him. There are plenty queuing up to take his place. He makes a living. Order three khaki shirts and shorts. Evening black shoes and socks, pressed white trousers and white shirt, get three each of those as well.

'Service personnel wear a black cummerbund. Afternoon casual wear you can get cheap at Steamer Point, shoes, socks, cummerbund and anything else. Indian and Arab traders are all bastards, they think we are all millionaires; they'll screw your balls of, given half a chance. Barter, barter, barter when you think you have got them to rock bottom, tell 'em to stuff it up their jacksi, and go to the trader next door. When he states a price that would buy a Rolls Royce, tell him what the guy next door had finally offered, start from there, when he won't go any lower, go back to the first guy, and tell him was his mate had offered. One thing you can be sure of, they won't sell anything at a loss. Cameras, watches and such like are tax-free here, gives the traders a head start, take at least a month to argue the price with them. Haggling is an art and sport with them, if you don't do it you will lose their respect.

'Now clear off, I don't want to see either hide or hair of you for three weeks. When you are acclimatized I'll arrange your postings. The water's OK to drink, but tastes vile, it's a dilute solution of Epsom Salts, magnesium sulphate, it'll give you the shits, but you'll get used to it. You can flavour it with army issue lemonade powder, that's just as bad.' He was right on both counts.

There are only two names I remember from the voyage. Stewart, a Scotsman and a chap called Mathews. Stewart who, seemed a very sensible bloke, surprised and shocked us, he signed on as a regular 21 years. Although there was a get-out clause for both sides at seven years. Mathews got stuck on top of the Jebel Akhdar for over 18 months, where I relieved him for three months, he was awarded the MBE. He should have been given a Knighthood. At least it was a proper award.

MBE: My bloody efforts.

OBE: Other buggers' efforts.

Our kit arrived the following day. Desert boots were bought in Steamer Point. Hat, shirt, shorts, socks and boots, everybody regardless of rank stuck out like a sore thumb: White Knees.

Then came the universal taunt, 'GET YER KNEES BRAHN'.

In the street, on the parade ground, anywhere, even for the Regimental Sergeant-Major or Colonel in Command, that phrase would be heard in the air.

The new Company Sergeant taking his men on parade as soon as his back was turned. 'GET YER KNEES BRAHN.' He could turn, demand to know the culprit, threaten severe retribution, no one would have even heard it. Yet as soon as his back was turned 'GET YER KNEES BRAHN'.

There was no point in complaining to his officers, the answer would be. 'Well your knees aren't brown Sergeant.'

A good sergeant said nothing but quietly plotted his revenge. One already a fitness fanatic spent his time running up jebel sides until he could do it in full kit with rifle and ammunition and then took his company on a 10 mile hike in full kit not at the quick march but at the jog trot. Fortunately he had enough sense to have an ambulance following some distance behind. Half a mile from base the ambulance emptied, an intact company entered the camp at the jog.

The phrase was not only used for newcomers, it was also used for men who had been out in Aden for a year or more. Any person who moved to a new post or started a different job was expected to know something about it. If he didn't he was told 'GET YER KNEES BRAHN'.

Transport arrived, tents were allocated, we headed for the RAF officers' mess a few hundred yards away. We were sweating like pigs when we got there. The bar had numerous fans, a round of lager, we were sitting relaxed and cooling off. Suddenly a familiar voice said. 'By God, if it isn't our Wog.' Thinks 'Not that b—dy nickname again.'

Parents be very careful when you christen your child. Grandpa Moses hadn't had a grandchild called after him, so it was decided I would be Moses Goldthorp. Dad, who had grown up near Manchester, for a change firmly vetoed it. 'Not on your Nelly.' Even though it was 1933 a divorce was in the offing. Dad would have gone back to Canada, taking me with him, rather than allow that. Neither he nor I were anti-Semitic, but it is embarrassing enough in the Manchester area with my surname as it is. It's not the Semites who make the mistake but the Wasps. So I was named after dad's dad William with Oates stuck in the middle to mollify Moses.

No problem until I reached the Sixth form and started using my full signature. The physics master started to refer to me as Warrant Officer Goldthorp, the friendly chemistry teacher did much better, Wild Oates Goldthorp, I liked that. But my pals spotted the initials, I became Wog. For the first year at university, I got rid of it. Then early in my second year I was sitting with my friends, in the CAFF, (cafeteria) when up came a gang of freshers from Scunthorpe, 'Hi, Wog. How you doing?' Thinks 'Oh. God.' Student pals, eyes wide open with delight, I was Wog from then on.

It did have its uses. One sunny summer afternoon, I was sitting in a café, near Platt Fields, drinking tea with my favourite girlfriend, the very attractive one, who told me quite firmly the first time I took her out, that she was not going to be just one of the strings on a young man's bow. That is warning me off the others. Although you could not avoid noticing the number of Beaux on her string. She was telling me of a big rave-up the staff-nurses had organized that ended in a large number being carpeted. She proceeded to tell me the names of some of the medical students present. I began to realize that a number were some of my bosom pals. Then she said, 'And there was that idiot they call Wog. Do you know him, have you met him? He's always there when there's trouble, but never gets caught.'

'This is going to be a bit difficult.' thinks I.

One of the Beaux on her string

I was very fond of this one, although it was my intention to have a large number of strings on my bow. I must not tell lies in case she found out; on the other hand I felt it best that she did not know the truth. Evasion seemed appropriate.

'Yes I had heard of him, but I had never MET him. (Which was true.) From what I've heard he seemed quite a decent bloke. Though he does have the reputation of seeing trouble coming and clearing off before it happens.'

We had been married for about five years before she found out, and with two babies under her belt it was a bit late to kick me into touch, though that doesn't mean that revenge was not taken.

I looked round. Oh my god, not those two. Two of my favourite fellow rogues, the number of escapades, carpetings, pub-crawls round Central Manchester, midnight marches back home from dances at the various Nurses Homes round Manchester. The two Brians, Chantyboy and W. B. They were in the group of forty that went straight into second year with me when we started university. I had not seen them since we qualified and hadn't a clue they were there. They were boys in blue, Flight Lieutenants, they had not done obstetrics like me, but gone straight in after their first year, they had volunteered for the RAF which in a moment of corporate mental aberration had accepted them. They were old hands, in Aden for six months. To think that these two mental defectives became highly respected GPs, whose patients were under the misapprehension that they were brilliant, and whose wives, for some inexplicable reason, adore them, is beyond believe.

'What are you drinking?'

'I don't know, what do you recommend?'

'A John Collins, that's good in hot weather, plenty of fluid.'

'That's what you need in Aden, Wog, plenty of fluid.'

Then W. B. W.—, issued that famous statement that I was to hear regularly over the next forty years.

He tapped me on the shoulder, 'Wog', he said, 'In Aden, you don't pass water, it's steam.'

W. B.'s dissertation on the Arabian Fly was a marvel and kept him well supplied with free beer in the pubs of North Manchester for the next twenty years.

John Collins

One large glass, at least half pint.
Shake in a large amount of bitters and swirl round glass.

Ice.
One inch freshly squeezed lime juice.
One measure gin.
Fill to top with lemonade.

A very refreshing pleasant drink, we gossiped away, I was introduced to the other two Flight Lieutenants, of the Khormaksar medical team, together with their boss the Squadron Leader. Several rounds were bought, I had four John Collins. 'It's time we went in for dinner,' said one of my newfound friends. I got off my bar stool, wobbled and fell flat on my face. No one had informed me that a non-alcoholic Moslem Arab barman's idea of a single was a lot more generous than that of the British Government.

I once had a John Collins Special that contained two measures of gin and one of Cointreau; I did not try that a second time.

The RAF medical team annexed me, one brown job in a sea of blue. The Squadron Leader R. F. Lowe, an easygoing guy who let everyone else think they were making the decisions, was married but had no children, so his wife Alison mothered us instead. There was a dark-haired chap, who I did not see much of, as he kept getting sent to outlandish places, this was to keep him out of sight. He had an ability to get half-pissed and cause a furore wherever visiting top RAF Brass were to be found. W. B. reminded me of his nick-name 'Piss Head P—ce.' I last heard of him as a paediatrician in Canada.

The fourth, a playboy and ladies' man, became a Gynaecologist like myself. I couldn't remember his name, W. B. to the rescue – David F—, at the time he hadn't a clue about his future. He had signed on for three years. He was loaded with cash, bought all the most expensive camera equipment, a couple of Rolex watches and a flash car, how he smuggled them back to England I don't know. He was a brilliant car mechanic, buying the clapped out cars of those who were going home, doing them up and selling them to newcomers.

He returned home, continued his playboy lifestyle, became a Senior Registrar, when the big romance finally hit him, the new young female Houseman. His luck stayed on however, he insured themselves against twins, when the first pregnancy started, they won, twins, and again the next pregnancy, won again. Third time the insurance company refused to take the bet, they won again, only one this time.

I last met him at a conference, when I was in my mid-forties; the playboy flash cove was looking a tiny bit care worn. I thought of my parsimonious life compared to his in Aden, and with great inner satisfaction, thought of the large house required for five children under eight, the school fees, riding lessons, dancing and piano lessons etc, etc. - we all get our comeuppance in the end. Though if I ever meet him again he will be crowing about the number of grandchildren he's got, and how many children have become consultants, barristers, PhDs etc. They will have, like their dad, landed on their feet.

I actually started working with my friends at the Khormaksar medical centre before my three weeks acclimatization was up. I deserted my army colleagues; I was found a room in the RAF officers' mess. The RAF gang held discussions with the Squadron Leader who was persuaded to contact my CO; my next posting was arranged, with the two Brians at Khormaksar.

Medical Work

The work, up at 6, sick parade at 6.30, mainly fit young RAF blokes. Breakfast, 0900 hrs. Then families, a mixture of army and RAF, nothing extra special, British General Practice. We had a rota, home visits, an afternoon followed by the night on call. I do not remember any calls after 6 p.m.; we larked about and boozed as usual. There were only two problems that could be serious and cause us to send people back home. The first Otitis Externa, a fungal and bacterial ear infection that we tried to treat with daily ear cleaning and packing, some were totally unresponsive so our only option was to send them home, where it promptly cleared up. The other was the typical Scottish Shetlander, red hair, freckles and white skin. Sunburn and prickly heat, it was stupid to send them out to Aden, we sent them home as soon as possible.

Families

The arrival of a Comet full of army families was a signal for a flurry of activity. 30 to 35 mothers with 90 to 100 children. You could guarantee that one mother would board the aircraft with a child incubating measles, another mumps, another whooping cough, and another chicken pox. The mothers would arrive to find they were coping with an epidemic of all four, with a little bit of diarrhoea thrown in.

For example I will take a Staff Sergeant's wife who arrived with six children. She was given a flat in the stinky Arab quarter of Crater.

I virtually visited her alternate days for over three weeks. She was haggard, tired, drawn, two or three of her children would have one or other of the four diseases described. The air conditioning did not work, her husband was busy, she had no one to help, and laundry was piling up. She had rushed out to the shops and found out that she had paid far over the value for everything she had bought. We were there non-stop for nearly a month. Suddenly it stopped and we never heard from her again.

I bumped into her while visiting the sergeants' mess about two months later. She was relaxed, done up to the nines, glamorous. The air conditioning was working; she had a sweeper to clean the flat, dhobi man for the laundry, an Ayah for the children. Hers was a bit older than the usual ones that looked after babies, she was quite capable of wading in and sorting matters out when the older children quarrelled. She had been a shorthand typist, a skill in high demand by the Indian and Arab traders, she had a well paying untaxed job, they were in clover. They had even started paying off some of the mortgage on their house back home. Once settled in the wives enjoyed it, particularly in winter. Help was cheap; they had skills for which they were highly paid. They had also learnt the art of haggling and were a match for any trader. There was one little problem, summers were hot humid and sticky, the winters were warm dry and pleasant, rather romantic. Many wives returned to England with an unexpected addition to the family.

Crater, itself was mainly the Arab quarter, it was teeming with people, traffic of all descriptions, dry, dusty and smelly. There were two ways into Crater, the main road off the road from Steamer Point to Khormaksar. A canyon that had been blasted through the crater wall some time in the past by the Royal Engineers.

Along the beach from Khormaksar, was the native port at Masalla. It was totally greenless, except for the corner of the crater, where the water channels joined together to supply Sheba's Tanks. Vegetation grew in profusion in the gardens at the tanks, and alongside the outflow, rarely the rain was so heavy the tanks filled up and overflowed. Close to the outflow vegetation was profuse, but thinned out rapidly away from the outflow, into barren typical Aden. It showed how fertile the land could have been, if a little rain had occurred on a regular basis. All the officers' houses had little green patches in their gardens, where water from the bathroom and kitchen was directed.

There was little of the unusual in what we dealt, but trust W. B. to spot it. W. B. has a wicked sense of humour, but he is also very astute, with a mind like a sewer, like mine.

Crater Pass

A young Pilot Officer had seen two medics elsewhere, with rectal irritation and discharge. W.B. was onto it in a flash, rectal gonorrhoea, tested and confirmed in a day. Instant uproar, such activities then were illegal. A ring (for the want of a better term) of Europeans, Arabs and Indians was discovered. We were surprised about the Indians, not about the Arabs. The supposed Arab proverb – a goat for necessity, a wife for a family, but a boy for sheer delight. We thought the Arabs were a gang of puffs, a compliment the Arabs returned. Well, what were they supposed to think of a large number of men who lived together without women, who were always tearing about the area in large raucous gangs.

The poor Pilot Officer was promptly returned to UK court-martialled and discharged ignominiously from the service.

He had just taken delivery of an expensive two-seater sports car. His colleagues promised to look after it for him, and arrange for it to be transported back to England. They kept their word, drove it all over the place and sent it back to England after 18 months when they went back themselves.

Sunburn. This was a chargeable offence, a self-inflicted condition. I have no recollection of signing anyone off-duty because of it. It could be extremely serious especially for recent arrivals. It was so easy to get hot, remove your shirt and continue working, not realizing how long you had been exposed. Severe second degree burns could occur with large areas of the body blistered. A bad case meant hospitalization, with intravenous drips to provide fluid and salt and antibiotics to prevent infection. Just like an actual burn caused by fire at home.

All the senior men were on the watch for it, particularly among the young National Service soldiers. Whether private, corporal or sergeant they would all watch and warn the younger men. 'Hey you! Get your shirt back on. You're already red, it'll hurt like hell tomorrow.'

We were supposed to look after each other; we weren't very good at it. Diarrhoea was very common, here's a bottle of *Kaolin et Morph* sort it out yourself. It always settled in a day or two. W.B. got diarrhoea again, tried the usual treatment, it did not improve, and he got the abdominal gripes as well. He went sick, and stayed in bed, so we all went to the bar, ordered a large number of bottles of lager and joined W.B., for our regular pre-lunch booze up. Laughter and jokes with W.B. making regular trips to the bog. After three days someone said – he's not getting any better – a conference, W.B.'s next production was speedily taken to the Path. Lab. at Steamer Point. Shigella Shigae, Newcastle Strain, the most virulent of all the causes of bacillary dysentery. Appropriate treatment was commenced, his pals promptly deserted him and organized their pre-lunch booze-ups elsewhere.

Garden and Museum at Sheba's Tanks and WB

Rest Gardens, Steamer Point

There was one very common disease we all dreaded getting, Infectious Hepatitis. A viral infection of the liver not usually serious, but you had to go on the wagon for six whole months, with booze at NAAFI prices as well. Fortunately it passed our little band by.

The gulf of Aden was the main harbour, deep water, so large it could accommodate today's US battle fleet several times over. American naval ships often visited. Being totally dry, all the crew headed ashore for a booze up. British warships were different, every time one docked, everybody, officers, sergeants and other ranks, vied for an invitation to board. British warships carried draught beer, every one was fed up with the local lager variety. Here was the main British centre, Steamer Point where there was another green oasis, the Rest Gardens.

Chapter Six

Aden BFPO 69

British Forces Post Office 69. That was the address, postage, as in Britain, three old pence, thruppence, it had just gone up after decades of being tuppence-'apenny. (halfpenny). Serious inflation did not start until our post-war socialist governments started squandering the capital that should have been used to rejuvenate and modernize our worn-out industrial base, on developing the welfare state, resulting in us being overtaken by Germany and Japan. Somebody has to pay, even if it is your grandchildren, that doesn't matter, they will not be voting yet.

There are two seasons in Aden, hot, humid and horrid, mid April to mid September; mid September to mid April hot, dry, with a slight breeze and marvellous. I arrived in the pleasant winter season. For about a week it was too hot, but one soon acclimatized and then the weather was great. The changeover was rapid; it would be pleasant with clear blue skies. A breeze coming in over the Indian Ocean from the southeast. Then two days later it would be hot, humid, sweaty, no breeze, airless, a slight haze over the sun and miserable. This was prickly heat time, tiny itchy red lumps all over the body due to blocked sweat glands; fortunately none of us got it. Bad cases had to be sent back home.

Provided you drank an enormous amount of fluid and took your daily salt tablet the winter season was great. You had to do the same in the summer season. In winter you would feel nice and comfortable and dry. In summer you always felt hot and sticky. Your skin was always sticky, cold showers at every opportunity; you felt nice and refreshed for about 5 minutes. Air-conditioning was available, but no one had told the army or air force, the traders had it in their shops, offices and homes. The services had, by all appearances, just stopped employing locals to sit outside, like they did in early India, with a string attached to their big toes, wagging it up and down to move a fan.

Winter was not too bad; you did not roast wherever you sat.

There was often the breeze, if not you were dry not sweaty. In summer everyone congregated under the nearest fan. We slept under fans the whole year, in winter wearing longis, in summer nothing. A longi is a sheet of light coloured cotton four foot wide and about eight foot long that you wrap around below the waist like a skirt. We usually lay on top of the bed, but most had a sheet, which was occasionally used in the winter. You went to bed with a pint beer mug and a large quart thermos flask. A night time ritual – take the thermos to the bar, pour in a glass of ice, a handful of the horrible army issue lemonade powder, fill up with the dilute solution of Epsom Salts that Aden described as water, and place alongside your bed. Twice during the night during winter, you would automatically waken; fill up the beer glass with the concoction just described. It went down in one gulp, without hitting the sides. Ten seconds later you were fast asleep. In summer two thermos flasks were required.

Micturition, having a pee, even my weak bladder was no problem, you went once a day if you were lucky, not quite steam as suggested by W. B., more like treacle, golden yellow and thick.

In summer we did as little as possible in the afternoon, usually what the army called Egyptian P. T. (physical training), the RAF called it climbing to one foot six inches and levelling off. We made the most of the evening and night, though it was still sticky, often staying up to 1 or 2 a.m.

In winter we were much more active. Afternoons were spent at the officers' club, at Tarshyne, to the south east of Steamer Point, nearby were the sergeants' and other ranks' clubs. The pilots of Aden Airways belonged to the officers club, many being ex-RAF. There we swam, played Volley Ball and sunbathed, no warning of skin cancer then. The officers' club had a large swimming pool, with diving board, a bar selling all varieties of soft drinks and alcoholic ones. There was a shark net about 100 yards out, which gave a large swimming area. The club also had a restaurant, which we visited once a week in the dry season. The food in the officers' mess was alright but got a bit monotonous, the menu at the club quite varied. You could also order the wine list. Somewhat limited, red Chianti and that was it.

Very attractive officers' wives with their families would also be there, no impropriety, but male admirers would surround them. We watched what went on, rather glad we were not married or in my case, my wife was at home. This brings me on to the remnants of what in Indian empire days was known as the fishing fleet. Young ladies who went out to India in search of husbands. In Aden they

*Officers' Club, Tarshyne, the beach and Capt Griff Edwards, Author and Ian
Stewart sat around a table*

were Nursing Sisters, schoolteachers, secretaries and colonial administrators. All single, but late twenties early thirties, a little bit beyond
their sell-by date, so were some of the blokes. All the bits and pieces
required by a young lady, but not of the best quality. What a vicious
vile male chauvinist pig, I can hear feminists say, but it was not
just me, that's what we all thought. However, they were absolute
beauties in Aden, hundreds of admirers.

I well remember on the final trip home, having been discharged
leaving Salisbury plain, arriving at Waterloo Station with eight
other chaps. It was early November but still warm, we had all
bought a beer and were sitting outside the station buffet at 5.30 p.m.
watching all the office girls, blondes, brunettes, redheads, etc. rushing on the platform, when one of our group said 'Oh! The poor
sods.' We said, 'What's up?' He said, 'I was just thinking of those
poor bastards who've got engaged in Aden.'

The Crescent was the central business and shopping area at
Steamer point. One of our other favourite pastimes was shopping,
well not exactly shopping; we had an Arab trader pal, in whose
shop we often passed the afternoon, talking and gossiping. He
stocked all kinds of modern camera equipment, watches etc,
Japanese, German, American and Swiss. All taxfree from our stand-

point. As soon as we entered he would send his boy out for drinks, the regular Stim orange or lemon, bottled in Aden, in bottles the size of coke bottles. He did all right in the long run selling us cameras, watches etc. I felt very envious watching my unmarried colleagues and short service men spend £200 or £300 on cameras or a watch. I bought a Voitlander camera for £15, a Rolex Oyster watch for £20, and one of the newfangled transistor radios. That watch now costs me over £100 to get it cleaned. We did not interfere with his trade, when a cruise liner was in port we would sit there quietly, while he sold a camera or watch for three times the price he had negotiated with us. The traders hated the Australian £10 emigrant ships. The emigrants were as tight-fisted as hell, hanging on to every farthing, in case they needed it when they got there.

This leads me on to the goats. Even in Aden marauding bands of goats. What was there for them to live on, nothing apparently? There was a reasonable amount of greenery at Sheba's Wells, where the collecting channels carrying water from the mountains on the rare occasion that it rained caused there to be a little underground water. There near a small museum was a garden, railed off from goats; there was also some vegetation close to the outflow from the tanks. These goats ate anything vegetable, chewed wooden posts. If a carpenter was planning wood they ate the strips of wood produced, they were street cleaners. Taking your last cigarette out of a packet you threw the packet on the street, the goats ate it. Light your cigarette; throw the match on the floor, the goats ate it. Fag ends weren't tipped. Throw those on the floor still smouldering the goats ate them as well. The dhobie men had to watch the laundry; given half a chance they ate that as well. Anything with a hint of vegetable they ate. The nannies ran round with little brassieres, bags on their udders to prevent the kids having a quick drink.

The other street cleaners were pye-dogs who ate any thing semi-vegetable, and anything protein however rotten. When you see a pye-dog, you can understand why Mohammed said they were unclean. Thin as rakes, with ribs through the skin, unhealed sores and abrasions, covered in flies. There was a little pack of more prosperous ones, near the RAF other ranks quarters. Thin, but ribs covered, shiny coats and eyes, they had worked the doggy charms, which Anglo-Saxons are susceptible to, and Arabs have more sense than to succumb to.

The other cleaner, for which a heavy fine was levelled if you shot one, was the kite hawk. The kite hawk has a similar sounding name to one of its favourite foods; as a result we called it the Shite hawk. Streets were swept and kept clean by the lowest of the low, sweepers.

They swept up the sand and goat dung, the pye-dogs having got rid of the rest and the shite hawks the dog muck.

Kite hawks (It's very difficult not to use the other term.) were very useful birds, particularly in the protectorate. They helped the political officer and his police force, when they were hunting dissidents, our version of the Taliban. Looking over the Adeni landscape it would appear to be bare of people. The political officer would scan the treetops with his binoculars. When he spotted a pair of kite hawks circling, an Arab encampment was usually underneath. Arabs being prone to cat sanitation without the spade. The kite hawks were waiting for breakfast.

We visited the cinema at Steamer Point every week or two. The cinema had walls, admission box and screen but no roof, wintertime pleasant, but summer we did not go much, it was too sticky. Our behaviour was different than that at home, rushing out as soon as the credits started to roll so that you did not have stand while the National Anthem was played. Now we stood rigidly to attention and woe betide any Indian, Arab or Somali who failed to do likewise. One Anglo Saxon thug holding each ear the reluctant native would be hauled to his feet during the Anthem.

Conversation, gossip, was our main recreation, that was developed to a fine art. What did I detest most when I got home? That B—dy goggle box, now nationwide, even my dad had one. You went to visit friends or relatives you had not seen for over two years and all they did was grunt and gawp at that damn box. I felt like making a tour kicking all the screens in.

Many pleasant wide-ranging discussions took place in the Khormaksar mess. In the mess we would get out of our evening gear, back into shorts and flip-flops, the discussion would often include a stroll, through the RAF other ranks barracks, three storey, lit up like a fairground, with the Aden Forces Radio blaring away. We would walk to the beach on the east side of the Khomaksar sand spit, walking bare foot or paddling to the strains of Shirley Bassey, Hey Big Spending it, into the night air. Of all the songs played on the forces radio, that's the only one I remember. I wonder did she get her royalties? Not if the army could get out of it.

Flip-flops, our constant off duty foot wear, I had never come across before. They arrived in the UK about 10 years later, when Mediterranean tourism got started. One shilling a pair, easily replaced if they wore out or the thongs pulled out.

A major search party had to be organized one night, twelve of us with torches, a ribald and raucous occasion, one of our comrades had had a date, and gone skinny dipping with the young lady on that very beach. He had just bought a Rolex watch for £200, and not noticed its loss during what we all assumed had been a very passionate and vigorous wrestling match. It would have been better to accept the loss than suffer the ribbing he subsequently underwent.

If a National Service man was a sportsman he could get away with murder especially in the army. A Medical Officer who had won national fame by breaking an important time record in long distance running came out to Aden. He stayed 2 or 3 months, doing research into body metabolism and oxygen consumption. Running private soldiers, not himself, up and down jebels with airbags on their backs.

He was given the red carpet treatment, none of the Medical Plebs I knew were allowed near him, the top brass kept him to themselves. We listened to reports of his living conditions with envy. He probably went home envying us being able to stay there in such comfort for two years.

For the first seven years as a consultant in my hospital there were only two of us. My opposite number, John, had done his National Service before going to Medical School. I doubt if he did as much square bashing as I did. He was a brilliant rugby player, and as soon as the army found out he was promoted to sergeant and spent two years playing rugby for the army. What good he would have been on the front line if war had broken out I don't know. Probably very effective. He would be able to drop-kick a grenade right on top of an enemy position.

Cars and Transport

No real problem, we scrounged or 'borrowed' it. It is surprising how blind Commanding Officers, Quartermasters, and officers running transport pools became, as soon as they crossed the three mile limit. Short Service chaps and regulars bought cars, they were very cheap, there were Mercedes galore. Provided you had had the car for a year it could be imported into UK without tax. If you could not find a car there were always the local taxis, expensive individually, but not when six got in.

There were two occasions when no one in his right mind would drive in Aden. On the extremely rare occasion that it rained, and on Thursday evenings when the Quat plane had arrived. In all the time I was in Aden, it rained twice for about three hours. The usually hot roads were covered with an extremely fine layer of rubber, wet they were lethal. The Arabs, a rather devil-may-care set of drivers at the best of times, had no experience whatsoever of driving in the rain. There were crashes and multiple pile-ups galore. We stayed at home, no one dare risk the Arabs' driving when it rained.

Quat, a plant that looked like recently cut privet leaves, that the locals chewed contained some drug like cocaine that caused them to behave strangely, perhaps the best would be to say they got drunk on it. It could send them into a mania. It was grown in the Adeni and Yemeni mountains. All the best soil, instead of growing food, was put down to quat. A Yemeni farmer would rather his wife die than loose a field of quat. Friday is the Moslem Sabbath; so on a Thursday night, like England on Saturdays, the men go out on the piss. They then drove cars, almost as bad as in the rain. If we went out we borrowed a three-ton truck or an ambulance, both high off the ground, with thick solid massive bumper bars.

The quat would be flown in fresh by Aden Airways, overcharging freight prices for quat, which produced large profits and enabled it to be run on a semi charitable basis the rest of the time. A mail contract and army contracts covered costs, so they would deliver medical drugs, and carry ill people at low charges. There were many quick lifts given to service personnel that the managers knew nothing about. I believe British Airways was the parent company. Its planes were old Dakotas left over from the war. They were anything but clapped out; Aden Airways had a brilliant maintenance department. Dakotas had been produced in their thousands by the US during the war. Dakotas were an airborne mule.

The pilots were first class, they could land on a postage stamp. An Aden Airways pilot could fly one of these Dakotas, fully loaded, down a Wadi side in a hailstorm and land on a 100-yard strip, then take off again when his plane was unloaded.

Aden Protectorate Levys' Hospital

Another wonderful place to me was the Aden Protectorate Levy's hospital. It was run by the RAF. There were 4 or 5 young docs, all short service commissions, the surgeon, the only surgeon, no specialist this or that, a young man from Edinburgh. He had been a surgical senior house officer for two years. He had his Primary Fellowship examination for Fellowship of the Royal College of Surgeons, which, nearly as old as the Royal College of Physicians, dated from the time the Guild of Barber Surgeons split up, the wealthy London hairdressers of the time throwing the surgeons out because they did not earn enough. The examination was like the primary, anatomy and physiology, 2nd MB all over again but 20 times as hard. Its purpose, to ensure encyclopaedic knowledge of those subjects, and to weed out the less dedicated, so that finals would not be full of no hopers. I was as envious of him as hell, he was doing operations senior British surgeons had only read about, indeed some that they had never heard of. He had to do everything, including dealing with the traumatic aftermath of prolonged and neglected labours. He had had no Gynaecological training, not that it mattered, an English Gynaecologist with 20 years experience would have done no better. Such things as vesico-vaginal fistulas, where the woman constantly dribbles urine, is sore and stinks, had disappeared from British practice a century ago.

At that time in the UK we were just starting to treat severe Ulcerative Colitis, where the whole large bowel is inflamed and the sufferer has constant diarrhoea and blood loss, with cortisone and total colectomy, that is removing all the large bowel. There was a tropical disease Schistosomiasis, where a parasite gets into the lining of the bladder or large bowel, destroying their function. In the case of the large bowel the symptoms are like Ulcerative Colitis. This young man started treating cases of bowel schistosomiasis by total colectomy, and by the time he returned home, he had collected a large series. A year after I returned home I recognized his name as author of an article in *The Lancet* on that very topic. He also had another article published in a quality journal on the repair of vesico-vaginal fistulas. Whether having two such prestigious articles in two prestigious journals, as a junior doctor, in the jealous world of academic and consultant surgical practice helped his career, I have my doubts.

We were invited to join the APL hospital staff in preparing a clinical demonstration for the top RAF doctor, a physician. His rank was equivalent to an army major general, which is as high as a doctor, not being a proper soldier, can go. It had been rammed into us time and time again at all the medical schools. 'There is only one disease, to diagnose two is wrong, it never happens, look carefully and you will find how the one disease accounts for the unusual symptoms.' We had to find four cases which the big boss would come, teach on and show us how to diagnose, investigate and treat properly. Majors, Squadron Leaders and Colonels were not involved; they just knew what we were planning. We collected four candidates, for example, tuberculosis, malaria and tapeworm, or amoebic hepatitis, soft sore and schistosomiasis, or heart failure, leprosy and trachoma, etc.

At last the great day arrived and all who could, attended. The Big Boss aided by two Arab interpreters commenced his consultations, just as he started the last case he suddenly went back and started all over again. We realized he had cottoned on.

He started off his summary by congratulating us on the trick we had played, and proceeded to give the differential diagnoses, investigations and proposed treatments of two of the diseases, each of our volunteers had. He was very pleased with himself, and then we played our trump card and showed him the proofs of the diseases he had missed. Was he put down, was he heck as like, he was delighted and fascinated and promptly organized one of the best clinico-pathological conferences that I have ever been to.

Labourers

Aden was crowded with workmen of different races, though the majority were from up-country, Aden being the only place they could earn cash. Pay for an unskilled labourer, one East African Shilling a day. There were hundreds of them like ants. A contract would be taken with a local contractor, say to dig a ditch, which two Irish navvies could do in a day. Thirty labourers would turn up and take a week. They were all rather skinny things, putting an Irish navvy alongside an Arab was a bit like parking a Centurion tank alongside an Austin Mini. They all used the same tool, like a big adze, which was used as a pick, spade and scraper, to scrape sand and rubble into a small shallow basket to be carried away. At that time there was no hint that the British would leave, and building construction work continued. Tower blocks 8 to 10 storeys high surrounded by scaffolding, not the sturdy tubular steel we use, but constructed of strips of bamboo and any other long bit of wood, tied together with string, or so it appeared. This would be swarming with labourers, men, with the odd woman, carrying shallow baskets with two or three shovels of concrete, like a row of ants to the top of the building. There were so many that even at a shilling a day it would have been cheaper to use modern construction methods. The British authorities had decided that the money spent was better thinly spread over the protectorate, than going in profits to German and Japanese international companies, although as I began to realize later, in that part of the world the profits would most likely be to an Indian owned company.

The Arab workers could live on this wage and send money home, or save up to buy land or a wife. They cooked their own food and slept on the street, it was warm and didn't rain, why should they pay rent. As you walked down a street in Steamer Point, you would see their beds, charpoys, piled up in the alleys. At night, they would be put on the pavements, each one containing a body wrapped up so that it looked like a corpse. Heads and faces always covered, you would not see a tiny piece of human anatomy. I often wondered why they did not suffocate. It was a good protection though against flies and mosquitoes.

Then one day, I can't remember when, the Squadron Leader called me to his office.

'Bill, they want you in Dahla, tomorrow.'

'Where's that?'

'80 miles away up in the Aden Protectorate, near the Yemeni border. It takes all day to get there; a convoy goes up once a week. Up on a Wednesday, down on a Thursday, you've missed it this week. They want you now; you'll be going by air. There's a plane going up tomorrow. Get your kit ready, the flight's at 10.30 tomorrow morning.'

'How long for?'

'Dunno! About two months I guess. You can still work with us when you get back.'

I had heard of these sudden trips from W. B., he had done one to Maseera Island, which was near the mouth of the Persian Gulf. There the officers' mess had a door marked in large letters, Television Room. All newcomers, exclaimed, 'Oh! You've got a television!', walked forward, opened the door and fell three feet on to a pile of sand, while the door slammed shut behind them.

Next morning I cadged a lift to the airstrip, and at 10.30 boarded a small transport cum passenger plane. High wings, two engine, the RAF, 'Jack of all trades', a Twin Pioneer. We took off promptly at 10.30, and I flew back into the Old Testament. That was my impression – I felt that the basic life style of the local people had probably barely altered for the last two thousand years. I thought this is what Palestine would have been like just before Jesus was born. There was even the, in some quarters deeply resented, occupying power The Romans, in other words, us.

Chapter Seven

Dahla

Thirty minutes after take-off the twin pioneer landed on a rough airstrip about three miles from the Aden Protectorate Levy camp. Gabriel, my driver was waiting with the MO's landrover, two large red crosses on either side of its canvas top, adapted to take two stretchers in the back should it be necessary. As the weeks went by, I began to realize that Gabriel was most aptly named after his grandfather, the Archangel, as we rushed along rough tracks at 60 miles per hour and round sharp bends above 200-foot precipices. Someone up above was watching over that landrover otherwise it would have sprouted wings. That landrover could go places, through narrow gorges, to inaccessible villages, dissident tribal territory, with impunity, which a battalion of Levys, backed up by a squadron of Saladin armoured cars dare not enter. It was known to carry the current Hakim Sahib and his Arab and English medical orderlies. That was my new name, Doc still to my fellow officers, but the Hakim Sahib to the rest both British and Arab.

Hakim meaning a mixture of wise man, wizard and healer, Hakim Sahib was my name at Dahla, on the Jebel Akhdar, in the Oman and Sharjah in the Trucial States.

The Western Aden Protectorate

There were two protectorates, the West and the East. The East had an interesting history, but does not concern us. The protectorate treaties had ossified the area in the past. It was a conglomeration of small Emirates and Sheikhdoms, each run by its rulers as a little feudal domain. The area was very mountainous, steep rugged mountains, deep wadis, plateaus and plains, many places isolated and difficult to get to. There were numerous tribes and tribal groupings, many often traditional enemies to each other. They knew their own areas like the back of their hands and made efficient guerrilla

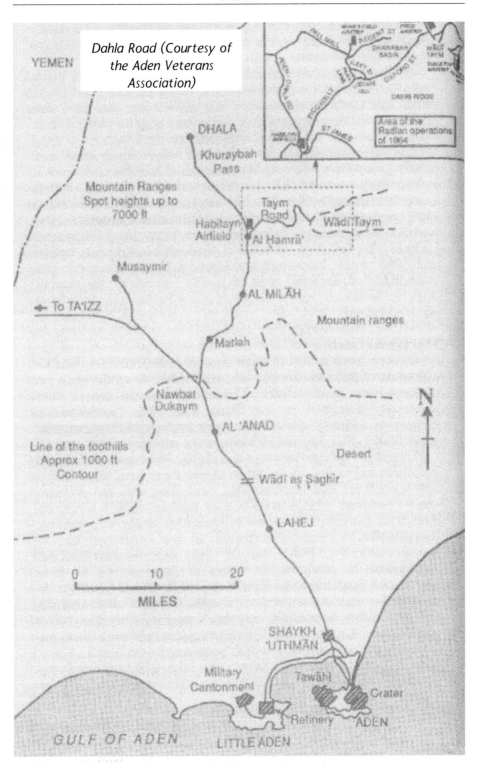

Dahla Road (Courtesy of the Aden Veterans Association)

fighters, similar to how the mountainous parts of Afghanistan are described today. The fighters we called dissidents, being equivalent to the Taliban.

The area was organized and controlled by the RAF. Retribution, for attacks on British Forces or British supporting territories, was RAF style. A message would be sent to the recalcitrant group, 'Your valley will be strafed in two weeks time, and anything alive and moving will be shot at.' Given the warning the tribesmen would have to move out of the valley with their goats, sheep, camels, donkeys etc., no easy matter when the folk in the valley next door hated your guts. They would start shooting at you, stealing your animals, and pinching your harvest, though they may end up being shot at by the RAF, while doing it.

The tribe ended up having a nasty week camping in the mountains returning to find all their houses, watercourses and irrigation systems blown up. During that week the pilots from Khormaksar, flying the latest jets with rockets, cannon and machine guns, would fly over the valley shooting and blowing up everything in sight. This policy did tend to keep the peace. Dissident activity was of a minor nature, or carried out by dissidents based outside the protectorates, as resident dissidents were very quick to point out. Such retribution was unusual, but had been carried out; the threat was always there.

The emirs and sheikhs controlled a certain area of tiny towns and villages, each village or town had its own ruler or feudal owner, who being less rich or possessing less military (gangster) muscle, held that village only under the authority of the big chap. Rather like an English Baron held his lands, from our medieval kings. In order to ensure the junior man's behaviour, a male family member, brother, son or uncle would be held hostage in the senior man's town. Usually in the Lord's castle, or other fortification, where they would be free to wander round. I came across several of these hostages when I visited the Emir's castle in Dahla. They were all wearing manacles on their ankles, the idea being that that the Emir would execute them if his subject did not do as he was told. This did not seem to worry the hostages I met, they were a very happy bunch. In fact, it would have had to be something extremely serious for the Emir to take such action, such as a rebellion in which some of the Emir's own family had been killed. To have executed the hostage for a lesser failure to obey the Emir's authority would have led to a tit for tat blood feud, which would continue until one side or the other ran out of adult males.

I did not find out how the locals dealt with theft, but should one of them injure or kill a tribesman in any way, the consequences were similar to early Anglo Saxon practices: compensation according to the damage committed. For example for the death, accidental or otherwise, of a male Arab, compensation of a monetary nature was required, although actual goods, mostly livestock, usually represented that monetary value. The family of the man who had caused the death had to pay the compensation, which varied according to the status of the aggrieved family. When the family of the man who had caused the death, had paid the negotiated amount, the matter was at an end. In the case of a high status wealthy family, then the only thing that they would settle for was the body of the man who had killed their family member.

Alive or dead did not matter, if the perpetrator's family provided the body arrangements would be made for the guilty party to be executed before the body was handed over. If a clan or family who were unrelated caught the perpetrator, he would be handed over alive. The perpetrator would not be badly treated, or tortured in any way, but his execution would be arranged. If the accused cleared off to a nearby country, where no one could get at him, it did not matter, the family whose member had been killed, would take what was considered justified revenge, by killing a male relative of the man who had done the killing. One day a father, son, brother, uncle, nephew or cousin would not return home, he would be found shot. This applied to the Oman and the Trucial States as well.

Every tribesman carried a gun, many had seen better days, the old Martini-Henry was common, rarely anything as modern as a 303. Nowadays, I suspect they all carry Kalashnikovs. All highly decorated with inlaid silver. The amount of silver on an apparently poverty stricken tribesman was phenomenal, his rifle would be covered, his ammunition belt, his leather belt, and his curved Arab fighting knife, bigger than a Bowie knife, and its scabbard. That poverty stricken Arab tribesman, in his dirty sweat-stained clothes, could have over two pounds weight of silver on his person.

The East African Shilling was accepted in the protectorate, but the currency that was really valued all over Southern Arabia was the Maria Theresa Dollar, two inches across and quite thick. It was said to be worth 5 shillings, and of solid silver. The Adenese did not trust paper money. Maria Theresa was Empress of Austria in the eighteenth century, about 1750. All the inscriptions were in Latin, with a date 17 something or other, everyone had to be identical. They were made in the British mint in London.

Aden, The Protectorate, Somaliland, Uganda, Kenya and Tanganyika all had the same currency, The East African Shilling. 100 cents to the shilling, a cent, a small copper coin, a 10-cent coin copper, about as big as an old penny, with a small hole in the middle. One East African Shilling equalled an English shilling.

Theirs was an agrarian economy, subsistence for many. Sheep, goats, camels and donkeys for riding carrying etc. I don't know what crops; it was spring when I was there. I can't remember seeing cows and there were no draught oxen. Plowing was by donkey power, not as effective as our Anglo Saxon deep-turning plough; their plough merely scratched the surface of the soil. There were a lot of fruit trees, and date palms in the lower areas. The shallower slopes were terraced. Quat seemed to be the main cash crop. Transport was mainly donkey with camels for long distance, and there were rough tracks that could be used by motorized transport. Converted lorries, like the African Mammy wagons, carried passengers and freight.

As Moslems all men were allowed four wives. Girls were married off at 14 or 15 when menstruation was established. A bride price had to be paid, so the girl went to the highest bidder, often ending up as the third wife of an elderly man in his fifties. There was no contraception, so with an average of 10 pregnancies per wife, a wealthy man might have been over-blessed with children. It was not a problem, only two or three children survived. One thing that sticks in my memory is as we drove about the Dahla plain, at least once on every trip some men would be digging a grave. On enquiry it always seemed to be a baby, an infant or a young teenager who just given birth or died undelivered.

Houses were made of the local stone, flat roofed, water sources usually wells. Refuse disposal; throw it outside for the dogs and carrion birds. Latrines appeared to be the nearest convenient place. The first time I visited Dahla I was walking close to the town and passed two laughing little girls of around 7 or 8, defecating at the side of the road.

Dahla Camp

Gabriel drove me to the Aden Protectorate Levy camp; it was surrounded by a dry stone wall five feet high, with a sanger, machine gun post at each corner. It was situated on a small hill, the road came up the hill parallel to the wall, turned 90 degrees to the left, passing an eight foot dry stone tower, another machine gun position, beyond which was the guard room.

Machine guns were not kept in these positions; they were only

Entrance, Dahla Camp

to be placed there if attacked. The main use of the sanger close to the officers' quarters, was sunbathing during the day and sitting talking at night. Beyond the guardroom was the MI Tent on the left and the officers' mess tent to the right. The camp contained a battalion of Levees, with their machine gun and mortar sections. A section of British heavy mortars, a REME outfit, a squadron of British Scout Armoured cars, two Royal Artillery 15-pounders, a large transport section, with all the support staff, signals, catering, quartermaster etc. I was part of the etc.

The view from the southeast sanger, the one the officers used for relaxation, was over the Dahla plain to the east, from the south wall of Dahla itself, to the west more mountains, and the cavalry camp. Close to northeast sanger were two small villages on the top of very steep hills, probably for defence, reputed to be permanent enemies, so that in spite of their close proximity they had never intermarried.

The large MI Tent had the usual equipment of a doctor's surgery, with many extras, for crude surgery, anaesthetics and resuscitation. Another tent next door was a nursing ward, for casualties and more serious cases that needed extra supervision. There were plenty of flies, so we had a resident chameleon, Horace, what a tongue, six inches, almost as long as its body. Adeni Arabs would never touch a chameleon, it made them impotent. They were useful to catch flies, not to be harmed, but not touched. The chameleon became part of my Hakim Sahib, witch doctor outfit; it clung to one side of my stethoscope, catching the odd fly that landed on me. Little Arab boys and girls stared at me in awe as I examined them.

My staff consisted of: two scousers, National Service, life-long pals who had joined up together, Corporal Moorish and Corporal Griffiths. How they had wangled it so that they were posted together I could never fathom. They were Liverpool working class, not well educated, but intelligent and canny, real reliable Englishmen; Ali my bearer, two Arab orderlies whose names I have not recorded, and of course, the archangel's descendant Gabriel.

My own tent was about 9-foot square, with camp bed, large desk, chair and camp ablution set so that I could wash and shave. The officers' showers were in a block of their own.

No discretion, we all stripped buck naked and showered for all, English and Arab, to see. The tent at night was lit by a Tilley Lamp, which I became a dab hand at lighting. If you got up after going to bed, it was moonlight or starlight.

The mess tent provided an English breakfast. There was light

Dahla Medics.

Back row: *Gabriel.* Front row, left to right: *Ali (my bearer), author, Cpl Moorish, Cpl Griffiths, Arab orderly*

My tent during the day and at night

lunch with locally bought ingredients, plenty of fresh chillies; how anybody could eat those with a salad I hazard to guess. I once tried a tiny piece; my burnt mouth took all day to recover. A hot three-course dinner at night, the myriad ways the cooks tried to produce eatable cold and hot concoctions of goat and sheep did them credit. Fortunately no one was old enough to have false teeth.

Two thirds of a mile away was a small camp, on another hilltop. This totally English Cavalry unit contained a squadron of Scout armoured cars, Ferrets, and another of Saladin armoured cars. The Ferrets were light fast vehicles, thin armour about the size of a landrover, the Saladins big heavy things, six massive wheels, machine guns and a great big cannon, like a tank. They always belonged to a posh lot, one of the Guards regiments.

The Photograph on My Desk

When Margaret qualified her family asked her to have a studio photograph taken. Copies were distributed to friends and family, I got one. A week later I was in the large lounge in the Men's Student Union at Manchester. The Men's Union was like one of the old

London gentlemen's clubs, financially independent of the university, owning its own premises. Many senior members of the professions in Manchester were life members and used it as a club. The lounge, full of leather easy chairs, always had several copies of all the daily papers. Late one afternoon I went into the lounge, and picked up the *Manchester Evening Chronicle,* one of our two evening

The page three girl, the photograph on my desk

papers that no longer exists. I read the front page, turned over, my eyes went blank, my heart stopped for about five seconds. Pictures usually meant something serious had happened. My eyes focused, it was Margaret's photograph.

Manchester Beauties number ???. *The Evening Chronicle* invited people to send in photographs of local girls to be selected as beauties, unfortunately no prizes except publication. The picture included a short resume of the young lady's background. At that time Margaret was one of my best pals, although Margaret probably viewed the situation somewhat differently. In view of my subconscious reaction I should have realized that Margaret was going to be more than a best pal.

Margaret was furious, someone had sent her photograph without her permission, she was even more furious when the fan mail started to arrive. Suspicion fell on you know who. I had to produce my copy to prove my innocence. At the time I could be described as rather upset. Now it would not upset me in the least, for decades I have accepted with equanimity that when anything goes wrong, it is my fault. That photograph went everywhere I went for the two years of my National Service.

Jebel Jihaff

My first job two days after I arrived was to climb the Jebel Jihaff, a further 2,500 feet. We were already about 3,500 feet or more high, and, I suspect I had a little altitude sickness, as I found the latter part of the climb tough going, and I wasn't all that unfit. What made it worse were my fellow officers saying, this is a dangerous place Doc, you must be armed. In addition to my Doctor's bag and the kit for inoculating a company of soldiers, I carried a 303 rifle and bandolier with 200 rounds of ammunition up that bleeding mountain.

My language was much worse at the time. I was not being conned by blokes up to no good either, it appeared to be a regular arrangement. The scouse corporal who accompanied me carried a rifle as well. The last part of the path was almost vertical. That was the first and very last time I carried a rifle with me everywhere in the various parts of southern Arabia I went to. I was not going to lug that bloody heavy thing around with me wherever I went. I reckoned the only reason any Arab would have attacked me was to pinch it. Our team drove all over the place unarmed, so we walked unarmed as well. I may have been ignorant and stupid, but

Starting the climb up the Jebel Jihaff. Carrying that bloody rifle. On the right, Peter King, my guide

At the top looking down

we felt save and secure, if anything nasty had happened we would not have known about it, we would have been dead. However to this day I believe that the locals were well aware who was in that landrover with the big red crosses on it. Imshallah! It's the will of Allah, the locals said when illness struck, but were aware that Allah was glad of a bit of help from time to time.

I had to carry out the annual inoculation of the company with TABT. Once I got there we had a pleasant day. My scouse corporal and I had had plenty of practice. We made an efficient team. The whole lot was done in less than two hours, the rest of the day to ourselves, he in the sergeants' mess, and me in the officers' mess.

The plateau was well populated and heavily farmed, a lot of the fields growing quatt. There was a large village, Shima. Most of the area was terraced. The rainfall was high enough not to require much in the way of irrigation. There were plenty of wells; the water table must have been high. There were English wives in Shima. Girls who had married Adeni seamen or dockworkers, under the impression that they were from landed families, which they were, peasant landowners. The women were isolated and allowed no contact with their families or any British people. The odd letter had been smuggled out asking for help, but was totally ignored by the British authorities. 'They have made their own bed, they must lie on it.'

Left: *Mike Hudson, Gunner RA.* Right, rear: *Peter King, Aden Protectorate Levees.* Front: *author*

A bit of bribery would soon have located them, and we had the military hardware to rescue them, but locals may be killed and unfriendly but untroublesome tribes converted into troublesome ones. The women were all from a working class background whose families had no influence, it would have been different if it had been a Member of Parliament's daughter.

There was a wonderful view all directions. North the Jebel dropped sharply onto another plain, which stretched to more mountains, where the disputed border with the Yemen existed. To the south, 2,500 feet below the Dahla plain stretched for miles, Dahla camp and airstrip easily made out.

Two days later a runner came from the Jebel camp, 'Doc, you've got to come back,' said the message. 'The whole camp's gone down with some illness. Get the CO to send up a platoon to act as our guards.'

Another climb, this time without a rifle. All the Adenese soldiers were either in bed or sitting round looking and feeling miserable, but not the British. What was wrong, I hadn't a clue, aspirins and paracetamol all round, then back to base. The illness lasted three days then all was well. Discussing it in the mess, a couple of days later, an officer said. 'Don't you remember last week before our regular MO went on leave, the generator conked out, it took us two days to get it repaired - the Doc's fridge is an electric one.' Most fridges used in the protectorate were run on kerosene.

I had only gone and injected a whole company of soldiers with TABT vaccine which had been cooked at 120 degrees Fahrenheit for 48 hours. The medics in Aden had a saying, 'You might get shot, but you won't get sued, and if you get shot then you've nothing more to worry about.'

Dahla

The first Thursday after I arrived, Captain Bordass took me round Dahla. Thursday the day before the Moslem Sabbath was market day, a soukh was in full swing. Arabs from all the surrounding area were buying, selling, and bartering.

There were also a few permanent shops, six foot wide and about fifteen deep, crammed with everything you could think of, the proprietor sat at the front. When closed the doors were massive with numerous large chains bolts and locks. The owners did not trust anyone.

We visited the Hubs, an old Turkish fort; the Turkish Empire had stretched down to Aden in the past. In general architecture it was

The Soukh, Dahla

The Hubs
A Turkish built fort

Dahla from the Hubs

like a medieval castle, but with very thin walls. It would not have
stood up to one of Edward the Third's trebuchets never mind a
cannon. It was high on the hilltop with good views in all directions.
It was also the Emir's jail and we met six of his hostages wearing
ankle irons. My orderly introduced us to a well-dressed young man,
about 10 years old, in bare feet, fancy turban, and decorated belt,
the Emir's son. Dahla was to the north of the Hubs, at the bottom
of the hill, stretching a short distance, to an outstanding white
painted building, with a large square three-storey battlemented
tower on a small hill just beyond.

The plain was covered with scattered small villages and hamlets,
all on small hills. Here and there on isolated small hills were white
painted buildings, which were said to be the tombs or shrines of
old but named saints. This seemed strange in a Muslim country; the
shrines were revered, protected and very old. Most of the area had
belonged to strange early Christian sects before Mohamedanism
swept over the country, and early beliefs had not entirely gone.

We were to some extent isolated, air transport could arrive
quickly from Khormaksar, but normally most personnel and all but
very urgent supplies came by weekly convoy from Aden. This was
a complicated affair, which came up from Aden one day and went
back down the next. There was an unsealed road from Aden to

Main road to Aden

Dahla winding through high steep-sided wadies, ideal ambush country. A battalion of the APL and two British battalions with two squadrons of Ferrets and Saladins picketed the lower half of the road, and our battalion of the APL with Ferrets and Saladins picketed the upper half. Fast convoys of landrovers and Ferrets went through any time; their timing totally irregular, so that the dissidents would not know when to mount an ambush. They had land mines, but did not know when to place them, if they did, they could blow up a mammy wagon and kill some locals. The political officers were usually able to work out who had planted the land mine, when their male relatives started to be killed from ambush.

It did not happen while I was there, but a dissident would line up a rifle like a 303 with the camp during the day, pack it round with stones, so that it would not move and during in the night fire half a clip at the camp. Then pick up his rifle and run like hell. The artillery and mortars had all the surrounding features marked out on a grid. An officer would estimate the grid reference, call it out, and all would have a jolly time blasting all hell out of the area. By this time the dissident was long gone, but the odd camel, goat or pye-dog got hit. There was no compensation for the tribesman who owned the camel; he had to get that from the tribe the dissident belonged to. A dissident was not very popular with his brothers, uncles or cousins, when a third party came, and quite legally by Arab law removed one of their animals.

Medical Work

Sick Parade started at 0600 hours, continued until 0900, when we all went for breakfast. Before breakfast, we queued up at a side table and swallowed two 1 gram tablets of sulphaguanidine, to prevent diarrhoea, one Paludrine tablet, anti-malarial, and a gram salt tablet to replace the sodium lost through sweating. The regular Majors always had a large gin and tonic, which looked like a quadruple to me. Except for one occasion to be described shortly I never did.

After breakfast, I saw any local Arabs that cared to turn up. They reported to the guardroom where they were disarmed, knives, the highly silver decorated daggers, rifles etc. They then queued outside the MI tent. Numbers varied from 10 to 30, men, boys of all ages, small girls under about 9 but no women. The majority of seriously ill women had to rely on nature at home. I did see a few, but always at home. It was mostly routine stuff, but there were some exotic cases. In a mixture of Arabic and Anglo Saxon swear words, the odd bit of Arabic and English, sign language, exaggerated facial grimaces

Civilian Sick Parade
Weapons handed in, under guard. A foretaste of the modern NHS

and the assistance of an interpreter, I could take a pretty accurate history.

The consultation started by shaking hands and giving the local Arabic greeting. It consisted of six phrases, three each, said alternately; I can only remember two.

Patient, or patients father	Me
Salaam Alicum	*Alicum as salaam*
Hickory dickory dock	*Dock dickory hickory*
Etc	Etc
Words	
Wogga	Head
Ras	pain
Wogga ras	headache
Tammaam	good
Muche tammaam	no good
Jhetrush	combined with an open mouth, retching movement and hand open with palm upwards, moving from mouth toward the floor. That should be obvious to the reader – vomiting.
Plenty shit, Sahib, plenty shit	I don't think I need to translate that.

The Only Case I've ever treated

Ageing Adenese was difficult, infants, boys, young men, men of indeterminate age and old men. This man was of the indeterminate variety, anywhere from 35 to 55. After the greetings, he sat in front of me, looked straight into my eyes, made a fist of his hand, held his forearm at a right angle to his upper arm, flexed his arm, saying *muche tammaam sahib, muche tammaam*. He repeated the gesture a few times, an idea started to occur in my brain, I looked up, saw the broad grins on the faces of the two scousers and Arab orderlies. I knew I was right.

'Is he saying what I'm thinking?' I said to our interpreter.

A discussion took place between both parties for about a minute. Then the interpreter, 'He says, Sahib. Old wife, fourteen babies, too big, no good. He buy new wife, only fifteen, very nice, but he can't do anything.'

One of our lady feminists would have been incensed. I admit, I was a little taken aback. What stood out was the matter of fact way in which my Adenese orderlies took it, more amused than anything.

In my opinion the attitude of the average Adeni male to his women-folk was by far the worst in all the places I served in, in Arabia and East Africa.

As a peasant, boys and men were the only humans, but animals were necessary for him to make a living. Animals being camels, goats, sheep, women etc. He took no interest in his daughters until they had menstruated, when they were ready for sale to the highest bidder. The wishes of his daughter had nothing to do with it, if she was lucky she would be the first wife of a young man, or the third wife of a man in his sixties. Women were valuable when young, when they could be used for copulation and breeding, having the disadvantage from other animals, that they could not be killed and eaten when no longer able to breed. Their most important use was copulation. There would be no way an Adeni male would use a condom, or refrain from intercourse, when a doctor had told him his wife would undoubtedly die if she had another pregnancy. That had nothing to do with the husband; it was the will of Allah, Imshallah.

When I visited the Aden Protectorate Levy Hospital, described above, while discussing the complications of childbirth I was told of the problem of vaginal strictures, caused by the custom of packing the vagina with rock-salt after delivery to make it nice and tight again for the husband. This attitude to women was reflected in the attendance at my morning clinical session for the Arab civilians. There were always plenty of proud fathers with their sons of varying ages, but not many girls. Whenever I saw a girl, she was usually the sister of a little boy, who had been brought at the same time because it was convenient. It was extremely rare for a father to bring a little girl on her own. It was also reflected in the follow up. If I asked that a boy be brought back in 5 or 6 days, he was always brought back. If I asked that a girl be brought back, she hardly ever was.

Lieutenant Goldthorp's principles for treating impotence

After 36 years as a gynaecologist you will not be surprised to learn that my experience is limited to one.

1. The cause may be physical or psychological. A full examination did not reveal any physical problem.

2. Play for time.
   'Tell him I will need some very special medicine. I will have to send a radio message to Aden to get some. There is a plane due on Saturday, with luck it will arrive then, can he come back to see me on Monday.'
   Hoping he would not come back, unfortunately he did.

3. Make it difficult so that if it doesn't work, which is what usually happens, you can blame him for not following the instructions.

4. Find some really vile medicine. I did, has anyone seen or smelt 1960 army issue vitamin B complex tablets. You will all have gone to the chemists and got those nice little round dark brown sugar coated tablets. Army issue, was pure rancid yeast, supplied in flat round screw top tins. When you screw the top off, they stink to high heaven.

5. Those were the tablets supplied, two at dawn, as soon as he woke up, and two at night as soon as it was dark for 28 days, if he missed one dosage it would not work.

6. Build up a high head of steam, a complete and absolute ban on any attempt at sexual intercourse for a month, if he tries and fails, which he will, he will remain impotent for life.

7. I'm a Hakim, a wizard; throw in a little bit of black magic. Treatment must commence with the next new moon, for a full length of a moon cycle, that's why everything is for a month.

8. Blame Allah. Imshallah, it's the will of Allah. Only if Allah wills it will the treatment work. Both Allah and I know that he has to work his land, so cannot go the mosque seven times a day as is required, but he must go first thing in a morning and last thing at night, and the full number of times on the Sabbath, Friday.

He attended on the Monday, the tablets were supplied, and the regime carefully explained and memorized. He went home and we hoped to God we would never see him again. To our initial horror he turned up six weeks later, grinning all over his face, shaking hands all round, and bringing me a present of four rather scraggy chickens. *It had worked.*

Scraggy chickens, all their chickens were scraggy, like undernourished bantams. I did very well with scraggy chickens, and supposedly new laid eggs. The eggs were bantam sized as well. I kept the officers' mess supplied. The chickens were kept in a pen at the back of the mess and fed up with scraps. They made a nice change from the usual goat.

I will be describing a number of cases and recording incidents which will catch the reader's interest. We British, being sentimental, are always interested in a happy ending, so what happened? In most cases I have not got a clue, the person, the patient or I moved on, there were no follow up letters.

The Placenta Praevia

While we are on the topic of attitudes toward women, I will record this case. Placenta = afterbirth, praevia = in front of. This was my only obstetric case whilst doing my National Service. When the afterbirth is in front of the baby it has to separate and be delivered before the baby. Severe haemorrhage is inevitable. In traditional societies death before delivery was inevitable, the birth attendants, the granny midwives were usually aware of this.

The lady in question was in her twenties, and had started bleeding when about 30 weeks pregnant. Aware that his wife would die, she had been, not deserted, but discarded by her husband and sent back to her own family. I must add that not all husbands behaved in this manner. I saw a number of wives at home, and their husbands did show genuine concern and it was not because they would have to buy another one if anything serious happened.

Nor were all Adenese women frightened dominated creatures subject to their males every whim. My patient was fortunate in her sister, who could be best likened to the actress, Peggy Mount, but without the foghorn voice. This dominating person had decided that her sister was not going to die.

Just before lunch one day, a young man came to the MI tent and told me that an Arab lady was outside the main gate and wished to speak to me. They had set off just after dawn, and walked all morning to speak to the Hakim Sahib. I went out with my interpreter, and met the lady. She was not the usual Adenese lady, 5ft 2 or 3 inches; weighing about 7 stones, shy withdrawn and reticent. She was 5 foot 7or 8 inches, sturdy, broad shoulders, 8 to 9 stone, a square firm face, neither masculine or feminine, a ready smile but eyes that could be hard, and bored holes when others disagreed with her. Others being Arab males.

Her sister was at home, pregnant, with about two months to go, but having repeated bleeding attacks. We agreed to go. Gabriel got the landrover, and together with the interpreter and one Arab orderly we set off with our lady and the young man, who did exactly what she told him. I wasn't aware we were going into prohibited territory. The village was about 10 miles away, to get there we had to go through an area where the wadi narrowed down to about a hundred yards before opening up into a wide valley. This was a dissident tribal area; they were traditional enemies to the Emir of Dahla. They were the enemies of Britain too. A British no go area, you would need a battalion of Saladin armoured cars to go there. The locals knew the Hakim's land rover with its red crosses meant the same as the Red Crescent.

We reached the village, there were several men hanging about, it was obvious that our presence was not welcome. That's when I saw the jaw on our lady's face tighten, and the gimlet eyes appear. She did not have Peggy Mount's shout. Her voice was firm deliberate and slow, each word stressed, the men turned round and went inside.

Her sister was still bleeding, and strangely I was allowed to examine her stomach. Soft, non-tender, all the parts of the baby could be felt, this was placenta praevia without a doubt. Death from haemorrhage was inevitable. Through our interpreter I told Peggy this. She answered that she knew that, I must do something to stop it. I told her that I could do something to stop it now, but the bleeding would come back again, her sister's only chance was to go to Aden where her tummy would be cut open and the baby removed. Talking through an interpreter who did not understand what I was talking about, things had to be kept simple.

I injected that good old standby that I also used during the numerous GP, locums in my youth, that GP's today are too scared to either carry or use, ¼ grain of Morphia, 15 milligrams today. It was not for pain control, it was to flatten the lady out for 12 to 15 hours, send her to sleep, relieve anxiety, and keep her resting, so that the bleeding would stop for the moment. I told Peggy that I would speak to our headman (as I described the colonel) and see if we could arrange for a plane to take her sister to Aden. Road transport was contra-indicated, she could not be crammed in a mammy wagon, in any case the roads were too rough, the bouncing would start the bleeding off. The journey would be over 10 hours, if they were not stopped at the many custom posts set up by the local rulers. Should bleeding start; she would be dead by the time she got there.

We left not knowing if we would be contacted again. I spoke to the adjutant; he contacted Aden Airways by radio. There was a Dakota flying down from the Yemen proper, every day, it could be diverted to the Dahla airstrip any time. Incidentally Aden Airways did not expect payment for the trip.

Four days later the young Arab arrived again, the woman was bleeding. Aden Airways were contacted and a pick-up arranged for the following day. I went back with the young man, injected another ¼ grain, and told Peggy that we would be fetching her sister tomorrow.

The following morning, the medics set off with a driver and mate in a three-ton truck.

On arrival, another ¼ grain of morphia, then the woman was placed on a stretcher and put on the back of the truck. A deputation of angry men arrived, who appeared to be objecting to our efforts. Peggy came into her own again and won the discussion. We were told to wait awhile, one man about 40 went into his house and came out with a bedroll, he was Peggy and her sister's escort. I told the truck driver to travel very slowly and avoid all bumps as much as possible. He did very well. When we arrived at the airstrip, the plane was waiting for us. Patient, Peggy and escort, went aboard, the plane took off and that was it.

What happened, I do not know.

What might have happened?

Treatment: resting as much as possible, to try and get the patient as far as 38 weeks so that the baby would not be premature. If bleeding persisted then an operation would be carried out earlier, resulting in a premature baby. It would be most unlikely that the mother could be persuaded to leave the baby behind. In which case being premature it would very quickly die. Should the baby be left behind, a little boy would be collected in a few months time, a little girl would be forgotten about. Tribes invariably had some relatives in Aden, which is where Peggy and her escort would stay.

The mother herself: we had merely postponed death in labour by a few years. As soon as her husband knew she had got over the pregnancy and was well, he would reclaim her. She would then be subject to pregnancy, after pregnancy, after pregnancy, after pregnancy, until such time that the scar in her uterus gave way during labour and she died before delivery from internal bleeding. It might be the next pregnancy or six pregnancies down the line. With extreme luck 10 pregnancies later she might reach the menopause and survive.

Lest we be too complacent with regard to ourselves, and are over critical about Adeni peasant society we ought to remember we too were peasant societies at one time, Europe longer than England. I record two European rhymes about a peasant's attitude toward his wife.

The first from Hesse.

> If the cow kicks off, mighty cross.
> If the wife kicks off, no big loss.

The second, from Franconia,

Got a dead wife? No big deal
Got a dead horse? How you squeal.

The European peasant had a great advantage over an Adeni peasant. A new wife for a European peasant also meant another dowry, a financial gain, for the Adeni, it meant a bride price, a financial loss.

The Cripple

A hefty man came to see us; he was at least 6 foot, and sturdy with it, Henry Cooper style. There was a lot of Negro in him, slavery was supposedly abolished. He was the servant and body servant of our patient who was a wealthy man. Would the Hakim Sahib please come and see his friend, no reason given. We went that afternoon, taking the man with us. We were ushered into an average sized house, as soon as we got in, everything was very different. The room our patient occupied was clean and bright, recently painted. There was furniture, curtains, cushions etc, obviously a wealthy man. Sitting in a chair, near a large window with a magnificent view over the plain was a severely crippled man.

There was a certain amount of movement in his muscles, but the bones of his limbs were grossly distorted, his joints, except one hip, were movable. He could use one arm, but was otherwise unable to move. He spent his time sat at the big window watching the world go by. His servant had to do almost everything for him, carrying about as necessary. He had many visitors whom he entertained at his house. He wanted me to examine him and give my opinion.

The only thing that could have been done was for him to come to England or Europe see a Specialist Orthopaedic surgeon, have all his bones broken and reset. I mentioned the work being done by Charnley at Writtington, where hip replacement was being carried out. This was all done via an interpreter. After that we went through the usual coffee ritual, which I shall describe later. The gentleman was very pleased with our visit. We found out that whenever he heard that a new Hakim Sahib was at Dahla camp, he always asked him to visit to give his opinion. My advice was the same as all the previous Hakims had given, except for the news about Charnley. Whether he ever took our advice and went abroad for treatment, I do not know. He may have been a wealthy man in the protectorate, but whether his wealth was enough for foreign travel and treatment, I have my doubts.

The Thoracoplasty

This was the only time I ever saw a man who had had a thoracoplasty done. In 1959 it was old-fashioned treatment. It was used to treat more advanced tuberculosis. As TB progresses, the lesions in the lungs coalesce and form cavities which are in the upper part of the lung, the apex of the upper lobe. Pre-antibiotics, treatment included attempts to close or reduce the cavities. This was often done by putting air into the space between the chest wall and the lung, called a pneumothorax.

In severe case the cavities could become lined by hard fibrous tissue and would not collapse with temporary measures. This was when thoracoplasty was used. A large cut was made from the axilla downwards, on the chest wall down to the ribs, then a large piece of each of the top six ribs was removed, the remaining portions of rib were fixed together so that the upper part of the lung was permanently collapsed, and a cure hoped for.

It had obviously worked in this man's case. The operation had been done over 15 years ago. He looked fit and healthy, well nourished for an Adeni; you never saw a fat one. He was living a full and vigorous life. I cannot remember why he came to see me or why I examined him. I have never forgotten the appearance of the left side of his chest.

Beneath the left clavicle (collar bone), was a large hole, three inches long by an inch wide. It led into a conical hole the length of a forefinger, three inches, terminating in a small hole ½ inch across that led into a TB cavity at the top of the lung. It had been present a long time and was covered by thick skin, down to the small aperture. When the man breathed out small bubbles of mucous-enclosed air could be seen coming out of the top of the lung. What did I do, nothing. He was happy, he seemed to be cured, and he didn't want anything done about it. Why should I interfere, he'd been like that for years, he wasn't complaining about it. He came to see me about something else and that is what I treated. It has just stuck in my mind, as an example of the unusual pathology that could turn up in places like the protectorate.

Dentistry

One morning I was happily minding my own business, and getting on with my morning sick parade. An Arab soldier came to see me; he had bad toothache and wanted it removed. I said, 'Give him some aspirins. He can go down to Aden on next week's convoy, I'll give him a letter and he can see one of the dentists at Steamer Point.'

He said 'Can't you take it out, Sahib?'

'No, I'm not a dentist.'

'The other Hakim Sahib does,' says he.

Thinks, 'Aw, SHIT. How do I get out of this one?'

'Right,' I say, 'We're a bit busy just now. Come back at 11.00 hours when I have finished with the civilians. I'll sort it out then.'

He left the tent.

'Does the other MO take teeth out?' I said to one of the scousers.

'Yes Sir. There's a dental roll in the basket.'

This was a massive wickerwork trunk found in all out stations; it contained everything including the kitchen sink. It was about four foot long, two foot deep and three foot wide. If we wanted something that you could not find, it would be in the basket provided you were prepared to empty it. It might have been put in twenty years ago but it would be there.

He opened the basket and took the roll from the top indicating its recent use. A large leather roll tied round with black tape. Pull on the bow; roll out on the desk, marvellous - there was everything one needed to remove teeth. There were two rows of forceps, fourteen in each row. It was obvious, top jaw and bottom jaw. Starting with the left upper wisdom tooth round to the front incisors and round to the right upper wisdom tooth. The bottom row matched the top. There were three extra pockets on each row, these held levers of various shapes for prizing out roots. So far so good, but what about the anaesthetic, that had to wait.

Breakfast time, I went to the officers' mess and did what I did not normally do, but all the regular Majors did. Except that they usually asked for a large gin, I went and poured myself one. It was the usual gin and tonic but for the fact that on this occasion, it was a measure of tonic topped up with a large amount of gin. I took a large gulp and retired to my tent, where after another gulp, I placed the glass on the table alongside my bed. Lay down, put my hands behind my head, closed my eyes and tried to imagine a skull. Slowly an image formed, there were two little holes on the upper jaw just beneath the nostril hole, front teeth upper jaw sorted out. Lower jaw, mandible, the bit that sticks up at the back, two thirds of the way up on it's inner side is a hole for a nerve, lower jaw sorted out. All I could think of for the upper back jaw was an area just at the back of the upper jaw, the pterygoid fossa.

The pterygoid fossa, I was explaining all this to Bateman, an RAF dentist, when I got back to Aden. 'Pterygoid fossa!' he screams, 'It's a wonder you didn't paralyse half his brains. It's full of veins, arteries, ganglions and nerves. All you need to do is inject into the gums on either side for the upper jaw.'

I gathered the pterygoid fossa was not a good idea, I'd got away with it so far, but now I knew what I was supposed to do, I left the fossa strictly alone.

Why had no one thought to give us an hour's lecture on rudimentary dentistry during our six weeks basic training?

By 11.00 hours the large gin had worked wonders for my confidence. The soldier arrived. The tooth was a lower right molar. (Big one at the back on the right.) I injected local anaesthetic at the place I had thought of on the inner side of the upright part of the inner side of the lower jaw. Glory be, it worked. Somewhere, sometime, someone must have given a talk on tooth extraction, from inside a little voice said shove before you pull. I selected the forceps from the roll that matched the molar on that side, applied the forceps, shoved then pulled, Good god, the tooth came out. I WAS A FULLY QUALIFIED DENTIST.

I moved into dental practice, and pulled teeth in Dahla, Somaliland, on the Jebel Akhdar and at Sharjah in the Persian Gulf. I have just made a serious error actually as all Arabs will tell you it's the Arabian Gulf. If you pull out the tooth that your patient says is hurting you do not always pull the correct one. I went to the Royal Electrical and Mechanical Engineers (REMEs), and got them to make me a tiny steel hammer. With this I would play on my patient's teeth as if they were a xylophone. Tell me if it hurts I would say. When my patient had climbed back down from the roof of the tent, after 'b—=*(*&ˆ%$$#!@**=-\|?88%6,' he would say 'Yeah that's it doc.'

I became s dab hand at it. The front four were alright with a shove and a pull, the back three needed a shove, wiggle and a pull. That's when a root sometimes broke off. Then I had to sweat to get it out if it was an Arab, if it was a Britisher I'd say, 'See I told you I wasn't brilliant at teeth, I'll give it a go to get the root out, but don't be surprised if you end up at the dentist's after all.'

When I arrived in Sharjah, the local non-army British civilians came to me for extractions. There was an Indian dentist at Dubai but they would not go to him. They popped into the MI room with all sorts of problems. They were used to the Health Service, I was free, well almost. Just a couple of pints when they popped in to visit at the officer's mess.

The Arabs all over the parts of Arabia I went were chary about loosing teeth, and were prepared to put up with a lot of pain to avoid loosing them, the reason being that they could not get or afford false ones. One came to see me with a painful abscess under the stump of his back molar on the left. The three teeth in front were just rotten brown stumps and roots. They really needed to be out, but he absolutely refused, he could still eat with them. There was no way I could use a forceps on the tooth, it was broken, just a stump. I had to use a lever; it was tough, as hard as hell to shift. I was straining and sweating, suddenly the stump popped out, and my lever ripped down the rest of the jaw, in a second removing all the other stumps. To say that my patient was not best pleased would be an understatement.

Lost fillings, if there was no pain, they were easy, back to base at the earliest opportunity for a proper dentist to deal with. Painful lost filling had to be kept going until I could get them to a dentist. Have a look at the hole, without a mirror do the best you can. Put in a drop of Oil of Cloves and rub on the gums, good for toothache, tell him to fetch his toothbrush.

When he gets back, the Oil should be effective, give the cavity a good scrubbing with his brush. That should clean out debris because you cannot see into it. With dropper put two or three drops of Hydrogen Peroxide into the cavity. That should clean it up and the oxygen bubbles released get rid of any bits left behind. Clean with bit of cotton wool, then put several drops of blue methylated spirits, into cavity. We had plenty; it was used to light the Tilley lamps, which ran on kerosene. Leaving the meths in the cavity for a few minutes, I mixed a thick paste with zinc oxide powder and Oil of Cloves, when ready I dried the cavity and packed in the mixture. That would last about two days, after which I packed it again. I was able to keep the soldier going for a week or so, until we could get him back to base.

Captain Goldthorp's Patent Dental Chair

Take one ordinary straight-backed dining table chair and one one-inch bandage. Wrap one inch bandage firmly round left thumb, to make mouth gag and to prevent patient biting it off.

Place victim (sorry patient) on chair. Stand slightly to the rear and right of the chair, so that right side of victim's (sorry patient's) face will fit into the gap between the upper part of the pelvis and lower ribs. If you do not know what I am referring too, it's that bit of the body that used to dip inwards when you were young. If my memory serves me correctly it used to be known as a waist. You know that bit that's filled up now, where what are known as passion handles can be found.

The upper left arm goes slantingly behind the victim's (sorry patient's) head; your elbow sticking out to the left of your patient (or should I say victim)'s head. Flex forearm sharply and place bandaged thumb on patient's (victim's) lower jaw. Assuming you have given a local anaesthetic, because it would not alter matters if you had not, gently put forceps on offending tooth.

Suddenly with great vigour, clamp down tightly with a Half-Nelson, fixing victim's head solidly into torturer's (sorry operator's) waist.

(Vigour, i.e. that of a healthy 26 to 27 year old, who is either playing Polo, hunting, or walking miles over jebels and up wadi sides every day.)

It wouldn't have mattered if I had not had local anaesthetics, that tooth came out. There were times when it was difficult, the owner of the tooth, ramming his feet hard on the ground, lifting his body into a rigid arch from the chair, but the grip held, the forceps stayed on and the tooth came out.

Counter Irritation

This has been part of medical practice; witch doctoring and local wise womaning for thousands of years. It works on the principle that all nerve messages from an area have to pass a particular collecting point, like a telephone switchboard. Too many telephone calls the switchboard gets overloaded and only a lower number of messages get through. Cause other painful stimuli in that area and the original pain doesn't feel as bad. We still do it. A hot water bottle for tummy ache, heat to the sacral area for backache. Hot water bottle for toothache, etc, etc.

In Southern Arabia it became a useful diagnostic aid. The Arabs used little cones of gunpowder, which were placed on the appropriate area and lit, a sudden flare and a small round burn about ½ inch in diameter was left behind. When the burn healed it left a round mark, darker than the patient's skin. The burns showed where pain had been felt, and the number of burns gave an estimation of frequency and severity.

For example, indigestion, the epigastrium, that is the triangular area at the bottom of the breastbone, with the ribs spreading slantingly on either side to make a triangle. Stomach, duodenal ulcers, acid regurgitation into the gullet (hiatus hernia) cause pain here. This was a common site for the old burns, 2 or 3 meant occasional discomfort, but there could be over 30 burns, new scars overlapping old ones, obviously a constant recurring problem. Rarely scars would be found on the temples, indicating headache, commonly over the sacrum, repeated backache, sometimes the loins, kidneys, over the knees, elbows and ankles, arthritis, and other areas.

A Marasmic Baby

This was the day when, 'Me guts wus tied inta knots, and me 'eart damn near ripped out.' Marasmus, a description of a baby suffering persistent vomiting and diarrhoea, weight loss, the chubby cheeks have gone, there is no spare fat, ribs highly visible. A triangular face, pointed chin, sunken cheeks, the prominent bone under which the jawbone goes, sunken temples, very prominent eyes. The baby dehydrated, short of water, salt and sugar, the child will die in 24 to 48 hours. I had only seen pictures in textbooks.

We were tearing along as usual, Gabriel at the wheel, one of the scousers, an Arab and I, returning to the camp from some trip out, laughing and joking, in a grand mood. We were just over a mile from the camp about to pass a tiny farmhouse (hovel), when a young Arab stepped out and waved us to a stop. He was joined by a young woman in her early twenties. She wore the all covering black dress and head-scarf, but like the others she did not have a veil so her face was clearly visible. She was carrying a little bundle of cloth. That young face wore a look of despair and desperation, seeing me her sad brown eyes showed a little twinkle of hope, soon to be dashed. She opened the bundle; there was a baby about four weeks old, with all the signs of marasmus. If it lasted 36 hours it would be lucky. What could the great Hakim Sahib do, absolutely nothing, I would like to use a more appropriate Anglo Saxon phrase, but this is not the place to do so.

I put on a grave face and shook my head, noticing that there were no other children crowding around us as usually happened, what you would expect with a woman of her age, (How many had died?) and said 'Imshallah' It's the will of Allah. I could have kicked Allah's teeth in, but that is blasphemy, because Allah is also my God, the god of Christians and Jews as well as Muslims. To say I was upset is an understatement; my eyes are wet even now as I write this 43 years later. All that baby needed was water, salt and sugar, intravenously admittedly, treatment should have been easy. How I wished for a magic carpet from the Arabian legends or a pair of seven league boots from Grimm's Fairy Tales, that could whisk that baby and me to the Special Care Baby Unit at Fairfield General where I had last worked.

What could I do? What could I feed the baby on, we had no teats and bottles, no dried baby milk, and the only thing was breast milk. If that young mother had passed through the camp gates she would have been ostracized for life. The locals would have assumed she serviced the whole camp. The honour of the men whose family she came from, would have been besmirched, they would have taken revenge on the husband for permitting it, perhaps even the ultimate sanction, shot from ambush.

Where were my experienced nurses, there were only the two helpful but hardly nurse-trained scousers. We had the sugar, dextrose, the water and salt, saline, but only massive needles for adult men. Tiny disposable little needles for giving sets did not exist then.

The mother had successfully gone through a pregnancy and labour, without proper midwifery help, delivered an apparently healthy baby, which would soon be dead. I could do nothing. We tried, I took the husband back to the camp and boiled up some water, salt and sugar, put it into sterilized 8 ounce bottles, pinched a teaspoon from the mess, and told him to get the child to take 10 spoonfuls an hour, and come back next day for a refill. We were not surprised when he did not.

The Dissident, upsetting the Colonel and the Political Officer, a Major

Late one afternoon two Arabs brought another Arab in on a home-made stretcher. The Arab was unconscious; he had been like that for two days. Unconscious for two days, naturally he was dehydrated, pulse raised, temperature normal, what's going on. I hadn't got a clue. Well let's treat the dehydration, intravenous dextrose-saline. (Salt, water and sugar) 1, 2, 3 litres, he's young his kidneys should be OK; we'll pour it in.

In my tent writing home, 21.00 hours, one of the scousers rushes into the tent. He doesn't knock; there is nothing to knock on.

'He's just peed Sir, right funny colour, dark brown almost black, we managed to collect some before he stopped.'

This was a reflex action because we had overfilled his bladder while he was still comatose. I went and looked, sure enough it was deep dark brown, suddenly it clicked. Black water fever = cerebral malaria.

What had we got, paludrine, a preventative, and chloroquine, oral tablets. He can't swallow he's unconscious. Can we grind down chloroquine, will it dissolve, and will the undissolved bits block important arteries? Is there anything we can do? Almost unanimously, let's look in the basket. The basket was almost empty, contents strewn all over the place, at last right at the bottom, a 50 cubic centimetre ampoule of quinine, strength I cannot remember, and wasn't bothered. One problem, it was old, years past its sell-by date; the contents had turned yellow with age. So what, 'They might shoot us, but they won't sue us, let's give it.' What's the dosage, who knows, give the lot and keep our fingers crossed. I injected the lot, continued the dextrose-saline, and went to bed.

Next morning there was a little improvement, semi-comatose, but able to drink some water by mouth. Grind up a double dose of chloroquine, shake it up in the water and get him to drink it. He does but a lot dribbles out of the patient's mouth. Repeat with normal dose at night. Second day, conscious but weak, can take an ordinary dose of chloroquine by mouth. Third day, improving, drinking, takes proper dose of medicine. Fourth day, early morning, gone. At first. I shouted, 'What the bloody hell's happened, did he die in the night, why wasn't I told?'

'No! Sahib,' says one of the Arab orderlies 'About 02.00 the patient got dressed, they went to the guard room, asked for their weapons and walked away.'

We checked with the guardroom, they agreed with everything that had been said. Ten days later, the trouble starts.

'The colonel wants to see you in his office, the PO's (political officer) there with him.'

Our colonel was a full colonel, one of the right posh lot, a Staff Officer, been to Staff College and all that crap, with a red band round his cap.

I won't try and reconstruct the conversation; it was a bit to embarrassing and argumentative. Suffice it to say that the PO starts off by asking if I had had an Arab patient who was brought in unconscious. I said I had. Was I aware that the police had being trying to catch a certain dissident for years, without success, and that was my patient? That was the general drift of the conversation, but with a certain degree of acrimony, vociferousness and Anglo Saxon expletives. The impression being given, that the fact that he was still at large was my entire fault. The PO, a major, let's call him Major Grim, supported by the colonel seemed to be under the impression that I was fully conversant with all the goings on of the intelligence section. Since intelligence is supposed to be part of the Secret Service, I did not see that I should be.

Unfortunately although I was quite used to giving all Glory, Laud and Honour to hospital consultants, I did not appreciate that the same 'Yes Sir! No Sir! Three bags full Sir' was also expected by full colonels and their minions, disgruntled majors who wanted to blame me because they could not do their job properly. Firmly of the opinion that I had done a brilliant job in making the diagnosis and curing the patient, my natural ability for self-preservation failed to exert itself. Here I was listening to two God almighty, self opinionated, lay idiots who had not a clue as to what they were on about. The fact that the dissident I had so recently treated might at this very moment be laying a land mine on the track that led to Major Grim's headquarters did not occur to me. In the mood I was in, had I known I would have gone and helped him. Eventually I exploded. 'How the hell was I to know? What was I supposed to do, shoot every Arab that came through the gates?'

'That's not the right attitude to take, remember who you are speaking to.'

'Yes! Two soldiers.'

'That's no way to speak to senior officers. Why did you not report it to the colonel?'

'What for, he takes no interest in our section, he's never visited us, all the time I have been here, or for the past year according to my orderlies.' This was absolutely true; up to now our colonel had not taken the slightest notice of the MI section, as long as we carried on as usual, he took no notice.

'No one met me when I arrived, no one told me what was expected of me. I just got on with it.'

'Enough' said the colonel 'We, especially you, are getting a bit overheated. Remember it's the rank you respect, not the man.'

I said nothing, thinks, as *I* still think, 'That's a right load of the proverbial. There're all toffee nosed bastards when they get to that rank, almost as bad as consultants.'

The colonel said 'I can understand the major being upset.'

'A bit,' said the major shuddering, looking up into the air in despair.

'Well it can't be helped, we were all doing our job' said the colonel. 'They might not like us, but it shows they trust us, the Medics anyway.'

'Winning over the locals,' said the major. 'That's a laugh, they hate each other so much, we'll never get them all on the same side.'

Whooping Cough, And the Political Officer Again

We had just come bouncing back from one of Gabriel's magical mystery tours. A message, 'The PO's with the adjutant, he wants to see you.' Hell, not him again. I went over to the adjutant's office. I keep writing about the various offices of various officers, they were just glorified tents.

'Where've you been Doc, the PO's been waiting hours?'

'Oh! We had a call to go to such and such a village.'

'God, not again, it's too dangerous, you're not supposed to go there, why did you go?' Says the PO.

'Because they sent a bloke round to ask me.'

'Doc's as safe as houses,' says the adjutant. 'Once he's gone with them he becomes their responsibility, matter of honour. If anything happened to him, they'd take revenge the usual way. You know, shoot the chap or one of his relatives. That's right isn't it Doc?'

'Gee thanks very much,' says Doc.

'Major Grim wants a word,' said the adjutant.

'We've had word that there is an epidemic of whooping cough, in "name forgotten" village. They're a right bad lot; even you would-n't be safe there. I have been asked to find out and make sure the children are OK. Will you come with me?'

'Yeah! That's fine by me,' I said.

'Good. I've got the National Guard with me, we'll go now.'

National Guard, god knows who they were, another armed gang, he might have meant the Emir's army, I don't know. I never found out.

Off we went, quite a convoy, my landrover, the PO's jeep and three three-ton trucks. The PO leading and me safely sandwiched between the second and third truck. Name forgotten village was about ¾ of an hour away. What a home visit, an escort of 50 who surrounded and attacked the village as soon as we got there. I said attacked, I mean attacked. We halted about 100 yards outside the village, The PO virtually arrested me on the spot. I was left in charge of a sergeant and ten troopers. The sergeant was given the impression that he was responsible for a congenital idiot who was intent on committing suicide by walking unarmed into every dangerous place under the sun. In actual fact I was not that daft, we did take care and made sure the duty officer was aware where we were going, and why.

The guardsmen spread out, surrounded the village, and then

The whooping cough visit

attacked it, giving the best example of World War Two Street fighting I have ever seen. The only thing they didn't do as they smashed down doors was throw in a hand grenade before they went barging in. If it wasn't a dissident village beforehand, it certainly was afterwards. All the children were gathered together in the main square, if you can call an open patch of ground amongst a scattered group of mud and stone dwellings, (?hovels) a square. A flag went up, on the highest building on the highest mound. I was allowed in.

I examined the children and anyone else who wanted examining. It was not whooping cough, just a general bad cold all round. Then a guardsman came rushing up, 'I've found two children with smallpox.' They had been hidden away, in the hope they would not be found. What I believe was the last epidemic of smallpox was on the go at that time. The epidemic had started in Ethiopia, crossed the Red Sea to the Yemen and was working its way down toward the protectorate.

Once I knew the difference between smallpox and chickenpox by heart. I can still remember how the vesicles differ, but I am no longer sure about the distribution. One was centrifugal, the middle, on the body, chickenpox, I think, the other centripetal, hands and feet, smallpox. These two, a boy and a girl about seven or eight, covered in a rash, were far too chirpy and giggly for it to be small-pox, a closer look, chickenpox, panic over.

Return to camp, happy and gay, all satisfactory, no aftermath. Like hell there was no aftermath. There had to be retribution for that attack on an undefended village. They got me, trust those b—dy Adeni dissidents, they had a word with their Mullah, he complained to Allah, and I got **Bl—dy Shingles, yes Shingles**. That's a complaint old people get when their grandchildren get chickenpox. A great inch-wide band, half way down the left side of my chest, stretching from my spine to my breastbone, and it hurt like hell. 'You'd better see a doctor, and get signed of for a week or two.' Laughter all round the officers' mess. No such luck, no locum for me, I was the locum. Sick parade and civilian sick parade as usual. I was too bad tempered, the British lads stayed away; it was the poor Arabs that bore the blunt.

What's the best treatment for shingles? There isn't one. However in my extensive series of one, I swear by Ultra Violet light. No warning about skin cancer then, providing I did not take my under-pants off, I could have been mistaken for an Indian. We were nearly 4,000 feet up, where the Ultra-Violet light was stronger so we were even darker. It's difficult to sleep at night with a massive band of shingles; we were already tanned so it did not matter if you fell asleep in the sun. I spent most afternoons in the officers' sanger, asleep or half a sleep, on my right side on a deck chair, with my left arm over my head, giving the shingles a good dose of Ultra-Violet I think it worked, or was it just another form of counter irritation. They say you only get shingles once; I had another dose about thirty years later.

Stand To

No dissident in his right mind would have organized an armed attack on our heavily armed camp; it would have needed a small army. Practice stand-tos did occur, though not while I was there. An alarm like an all-clear would sound in the middle of the night, the men had to dress, collect their weapons and go to various assembly points. It was always timed, with rewards for the best performing group, the results were good full assembly in about 12 to 15 minutes.

The colonel had gone on a week's leave, the second in command, a major, was in charge, particularly of the colonel's black Labrador bitch, which was on heat. The second in command and the other

British officers were under dire threat of severe retribution if any of the male pye-dogs got anywhere near his beloved bitch. Immediate posting to the Gobi Desert or the South Pole had been threatened. The local male pye-dogs catching the scent of a bitch in an attractive frame of mind had been serenading us all week, all night. The whole officers' mess being pig sick of both bitch and the pye-dogs, sleep had almost become an impossibility.

Saturday night a gathering in the officer's mess with second in command, having had a few bevvies, was discussing the problem, when a whole pack of pyre-dogs opened up their evening chorus.

'Christ, what a bloody row,' said one.

'We'll be awake all night again,' said another.

'Let's shoot the Buggers,' said a third.

'Good idea,' said the number 2-I-C.

We all headed for the guardroom, told them what we intended to do. We took a sten gun, two 303 rifles, some revolvers and a Verey light pistol with a some Verey lights. Verey lights are fired into the air at night, the light hangs there for about a minute and gives a good view of the surrounding countryside. They can act as warning or emergency lights. We all repaired to the sanger at the officers' corner of the camp, fired three Verey lights at intervals to light up the surrounding area and opened up on the pye-dogs with everything we had got.

The result had been unforeseen; it was the fastest stand-to ever, five minutes flat. The walls lined with riflemen, 50 calibre machine guns, loaded and ready at every machine gun post, except our sanger where the sergeant in charge of that squad called the number 2-I-C, words that sergeants do not usually address officers by. The Ferrets were fully manned, engines running and revving, mortars manned and the two 15-pounders ready with shells up the spout. The officer of the guard standing at the door with a cup of coffee, wanted to know what all the fuss was about. They of course did not stand-to. Admittedly the uniform of the soldiers left a bit to be desired, helmets, longis and flip flops, but what a stand-to, any attacking force would have been decimated in seconds. Panic over, everyone went back to bed leaving us some what red-faced. You can imagine the comments we overheard from British soldiers, fortunately we could not understand the Arabic ones. We should have been in for right rollicking, but where was the senior officer, who had to do it? There with us in the sanger firing the Sten-gun!

The posh cavalry outfit in the company camp two thirds of a mile away saw the flares, also stood to, there was no way of communicating except by runner. They were not going to risk one, on the Dahla plain at night when it was crawling with enemy fighters. They remained stood-to all night until dawn, when two Saladins came slowly over to us in full combat readiness. The others were drawn up in combat array outside their camp.

'What's happening?' said their major from inside his turret.' Has there been a crisis, do you want our help?'

'No thanks,' said the 2. I. C. 'Everything's fine, no problems.'

'What happened?' said the major, now popping out of his turret.

'Nothing,' said the 2. I. C. 'Just a minor misunderstanding.'

2. I. C., second in command, that was his code, on open-air wireless. I have been trying to remember some of the others; mine was easy, Doc. The big boss, the commanding officer, the source of all life, or so he thinks, SUNRAY.

Pets

I have mentioned the chameleon, Horace, part of my witchdoctor outfit. Corporal Griffiths was bringing up a hyena pup. God knows what he would do with it when it grew up. I have a lovely slide showing him feeding it from a home made device made out of a pop bottle.

Charlotte

The unit is full of healthy young men, Doc's got nothing to do, let's find him something, which is often someone's pet or the officer's mess mascot. Charlotte was a two-thirds grown female baboon, quite a pleasant little creature in actual fact. The current Doc was her keeper. She was named after the Colonel's mistress, the lady he visited by plane each weekend, when he said he was going to Aden on official army business. I suppose he was in a way, it was a matter of improving morale. His!

Charlotte lived in a large box on the end of a stout five-foot pole behind my tent, there was an iron ring round the pole to which a light long chain was attached. The chain was fastened to a little leather belt around Charlotte's waist. It was very effective; Charlotte was able to bounce around to her heart's content.

Charlotte did have her uses; she was our early warning system. The RAF pilots in their Hunter jets (I think they were Hunters) thought it great fun to scare the SH*T. out of us by beating up the camp. Coming out of nowhere, at a high rate of knots, flashing over

Corporal Griffiths and his hyena

us at 25 feet with one hell of a bang, if you weren't expecting it, you damn near crapped yourself. Charlotte could spot them when they were a pinprick in the sky over ten miles away. She would start jumping up and down on her box screaming her head off. Charlotte was of the opinion that the Hunters were a new kind of hunting eagle intent on having Charlotte for breakfast. Just as the plane was about to fly over the camp she would dive into her box, to reappear five seconds later as the plane climbed away, giving it hell in baboonish Anglo Saxon. Occasionally this tirade would end in horrified silence for 30 seconds, Charlotte had spotted the fact that the plane had turned round and was coming back for another go, Charlotte's early warning screech would start all over again.

I spent many a sunlight afternoon in a deckchair, reading with a book in my right hand, Charlotte on my knee supported by my left hand. Fortunately for Charlotte I am a very hairy sort of bloke. My wife says I am living proof that the Neanderthal man never died out. Charlotte spent the afternoon rooting through my hairy chest looking for nits, fleas and salt flakes as baboons are want to do. She never found any, I hope, but did nibble the odd bit of dead skin. I never felt like reciprocating as you are supposed to do in a grooming session. I had a half toothless comb and a stiff useless brush, from the human viewpoint. Once a day I gave Charlotte a good going over. Talk about baboonish bliss, Charlotte sitting on

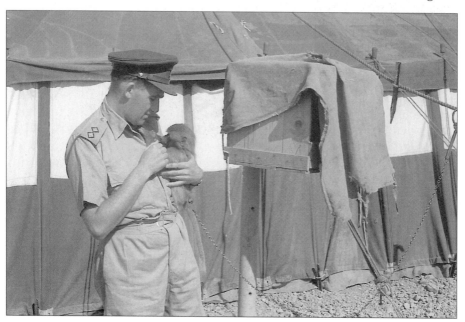

Charlotte looking for fleas

your knee, with glazed expression on her face and adoration in her eyes, arm held in the air, so you could do her armpits, was a sight for sore eyes.

Like Griffiths' hyena, what on earth would the officers do with Charlotte when, she grew up? Especially when as lady baboons do, she started issuing the pheromones (stinks) that large aggressive male baboons are interested in. Baboon pheromones are not usually picked up by human nostrils. Just imagine, a future Hakim Sahib, going for a walk in the country after Charlotte had sat on his knee, inadvertently passing a troop of baboons. He would find himself surrounded by a group of puzzled male baboons with romantic notions.

Company Barber

One aspect of life in Dahla was how the senior NCOs looked after the National Service lads. One particular Royal Artillery sergeant, I remember, acted as company barber.

He was in his early thirties, his lads as he called them 18 or 19. He was their big brother, uncle, father, advisor and counsellor. He did not have to discipline them, they did it themselves to please him. They would have gone through hell and back for him. A good way to lead, though probably not in wartime. They were too dependent on him.

Patrols

Ramadan, this was the first one I had been associated with, unaware of it prior to visiting Aden. Ramadan occurred while I was in Dahla. Followed by the three-day party, the Aed. They were strict in their observance of Ramadan, unfortunately for one chubby half Arab, half Indian soldier. He found Ramadan particularly trying, and was always hiding away trying to have a quick nibble or quick drink. His comrades, well aware of his foibles, kept a careful watch on him; he was caught with monotonous frequency and beaten up. At times like that it was British policy to ignore it and mind our own business.

Travellers at Ramadan according to the Adenese are exempt from its daytime restrictions so it was the only time when a patrol was organized that there was a surfeit of volunteers. I do not know what Mohamed would say about travelling in a three-ton truck, but our

Royal Artillery Sergeant also acted as the Company Barber

soldiers were absolutely certain, as soon as the driver started the engine out came the cigarettes, water bottles and chapattis.

Patrols went out regularly but in a totally haphazard fashion, so that dissidents could not lay mines without the danger of blowing up a mammy wagon. One patrol went out in battalion strength, plus Ferret, Saladin armoured cars, mortar section and both 15-pounders, and me. This was an aggressively gay affair, everybody English and Arab, except me, was hoping something would happen. The patrol headed by Ferrets and Saladins, armoured underneath so that no one would be hurt if a landmine did go off, set off for the border between the Yemen and the protectorate. The only problem being that no one knew where it was, a difference of ten miles between the Yemeni version and our version. We went as far as possible into the Yemen until we were nearly on what was definitely their territory, to everyone's disappointment nothing happened.

The tribes on the Yemeni side were traditional enemies of the tribes on the British side. The Adenese soldiers were itching to have a go at them. I was told that occasionally a Yemeni tribesman, with more guts than common sense, would fire his rifle at the convoy, or a new young inexperienced army officer would order his troops to oppose us. Then all hell would let loose, retaliatory raids were permitted; the whole shebang would fire everything in the general direction that they had been shot at from. Looting was not permitted, but disarmament was. The Adenese disarmed everyone with a silver encrusted rifle or dagger including the scabbards. The odd sheep or goat disappeared into the backs of trucks. Letters of complaint would pass between Salah the Yemeni capital and Aden. Eventually all the arms removed by the British returned, except those removed by the Adenese, as described above. There was no record of their capture.

Chapter Eight

Somaliland

Send off

Second week June 1959. I was called urgently to see Lieutenant Colonel Matheson - my 'proper' commanding officer. By 'proper' CO, he was RAMC (Royal Army Medical Corps). There were two Lieutenant Colonels in Aden at that time - Colonel Matheson, a nice bloke who knew a bit of medicine. The other one - a right pillock whom we will discuss later. I had a word with Squadron Leader Lowe, borrowed the ambulance and driver, who took me to Steamer Point. I knocked and entered the Colonel's office, little

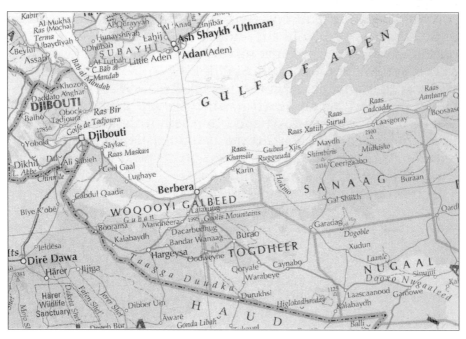

Somaliland
Collins-Bartholomew, 1997. (Reproduced by kind permission of HarperCollins)

knowing that I was about to start the best six months in the whole of my National Service.

'Bill, sit down, we are in a mess. I want you in Hargeisa, in Somaliland, tomorrow afternoon. You're going to have to go to the Somaliland Scouts. They've kicked their MO out – God knows why! Captain so and so – I've met him. He seemed a decent bloke, he's certainly a good doctor, but it seems as though he spent most of his time with the colonial medical service doctors and neglected his regimental duties. Their CO has written to me two or three times, complaining about him. He's had him on the carpet a few times, but he took no notice, so they got fed up. Last week, an aeroplane landed going from Nairobi to London, to pick up two or three people. They grabbed hold of him and his kit, chucked him on the 'plane and sent him home. You've got to go look after the place until they send a replacement'.

'Right, Sir,' say I.

'At the moment, we're the dregs, right persona non-grata', says the Colonel, 'You're going to have to sort it out, I don't really know what's gone wrong, I don't know what advice to give you; it's up to you. I don't know how long you're gonna be there, it might be a couple of months, it might be four or five months, we'll just have to see. I can't really afford to send you, but I've no option.'

'That's a load of bullshit,' thinks I, because Aden was crawling with doctors with hardly anything to do.

'You can help the colonial service out, if you want, I've no objection to that, but make sure you don't overdo it. Make sure that you sort the Somaliland Scouts side out first.

'Now, go back to Khormaksar, sort your kit out, take with you what you think's necessary, and I don't know what's going to be necessary, except that Somaliland's a bit like Aden in the Winter – relatively hot, pleasant and dry. You might need the odd sweater 'cos it gets a bit cold at night-time.

'Tomorrow morning, get to Khormaksar Airfield by eleven thirty, when there'll be transport to take you over to Hargeisa Airport, where they'll be picking you up. What you do after that, is up to you.'

'OK, I'll do my best.' I got up and went towards the door of his office. He rose, came round his desk, shook me by the hand, put his hand on my shoulder and said, 'BILL, THE HONOUR OF THE CORPS IS RESTING FIRMLY ON YOUR SHOULDERS.'

I went out of his office feeling like General Armstrong Custer, about to lead the Seventh Cavalry in a charge at Shiloh in the American Civil War!

I took four or five steps away from his office and a thought suddenly struck me. I turned back, walked to the office, knocked on the door, opened it, stuck my head round and said, 'Excuse me, Sir, but do you think you could let me have the taxi fare out of petty cash to take me to Khormaksar? It'll be quicker than having to ring up and get them to send the ambulance out for me'.

'That's a good idea, Bill, how much is it?'

I can't remember how much it was, we used to think it was a bit steep and didn't usually use a taxi unless about three or four of us got in at once. I pocketed the fare, walked through the administration building, out through the front door, turned left, down the street, turned left into another street, opposite the main NAAFI, walked in and picked up my ambulance driver and he drove me home! He drove me back to the Medical Centre at Khormaksar. I told the Squadron Leader what I had to do, and scrounged a big canvas bag off him - well not exactly off him, it wasn't his, it belonged to the RAF, but I ended up with a nice canvas holdall to take my kit in. I went back to the RAF Officers' Mess, went through my kit. Took what I thought I needed, put it in the holdall. Packed my truck, locked it and shoved it under my bed.

Next morning, I didn't to join my RAF pals at 6.30 sick parade, but stayed in bed and had breakfast as usual. I went with the two Brians to the Medical Centre, and helped them with a few families until half past ten, when the ambulance driver took me out to the airfield. At least I was expected. The aircraft was a Beverley, a massive four engine transport, with wings high on the body, a big square body with a ramp at the back, up which jeeps and lorries could be loaded.

'That's your aircraft,' said the Flight Sergeant, 'go up the ramp and make yourself comfortable. We're not sure when we'll be taking off, but as soon as she's loaded, we're off to Hargeisa'.

I walked up the ramp, looked for my seat, and safety belt - there wasn't one!

'Park yourself on top of them boxes,' says the Flight Sergeant. So I did.

We set off about twelve o'clock, I'd gone wearing my usual tropical kit. The flipping aircraft climbed God knows how high, and I started freezing to death! There was nothing to wrap round me.

Arrival

After a couple of hours, we landed at Hargeisa International Airport, taxied to one side of the runway, where two of the proverbial three-ton trucks were waiting to be loaded. I got off and looked round Hargeisa International Airport - it was built on a small plateau, 300 feet above the surrounding plain. To the North was the capital of Somaliland, Hargeisa. It consisted of thousands of little beehive huts, like the kraals that Zulus lived in. They were made of curved branches from acacia bushes and covered with animal skins, plaited woven mats, tarpaulin, blankets - you name it, anything that the Somalis could get hold of. There was a slight haze over the city, if you can call it that, from the cooking fires. Here and there, the odd grey building made from concrete-type blocks and the odd white painted one, sparkling in the sun! These were the houses of the Indian and Arab traders. The European area was to one side, where there was the Governor's mansion (if you can call a rather large bungalow a Governor's mansion!), the hospital, other European houses, the Court, Judge's house, Police Station etc.

I stretched my legs, warmed myself up in the sunshine, and looked around the rather extensive Hargeisa International Airport. There was a massive runway, and I thought 'Well, where are the repair hangars and places that you keep planes in?' There weren't any! 'Where's the ambulance?' There wasn't one! 'Where are the Fire Brigade and the fire engine?' There wasn't one! 'Where's the repair shop?' There wasn't one. There weren't any storage tanks for aviation fuel either. Any aircraft that landed at Hargeisa had to have enough fuel on it to get back to where it came from!

In the distance was a little white bungalow with a control tower on top. I picked up my kit, slung it on my shoulder and headed toward it. As I approached, I noticed that there wasn't the usual radar detection apparatus turning round on top of the control tower. I got closer, and noticed they didn't have any radio mast on the control tower. When I got even closer, there wasn't anyone IN the control tower.

I went through a door marked IMMIGRANTS TO SOMALILAND. There were two Somalis - one a policeman who was fast asleep, and the immigration officer. He looked at me, saw I was in uniform and ignored me. I strolled round the reception area and came across what I eventually discovered were the only two Water Closets in that part of Somaliland. One marked 'European Style Gentlemen' and the other marked 'Asian Style Gentlemen'. Looking round, it became obvious that Ladies in Somaliland neither defecated nor urinated! I opened the door to the 'European Style Gentlemen' - it was the usual sit down water closet. I opened the 'Asian Style Gentlemen', it was a big hole in the floor, two standing points on either side and a flush – the first time I had seen one of those. I thought 'well, I can understand really, because the locals walked around in big dresses – the Egyptians called them dish-dashers. They wore no underclothes, so all they needed to do was hitch it up and squat. How the hell an Asian Style Gentleman wearing trousers, or shorts and underpants would manage, was beyond me! 1. If he took his trousers and underpants down and squatted, they would be on the floor and get mucky. 2. Well, you can't aim with your backside! He'd probably do a dollop in his underpants!

What a filthy lot these Asians are. Of course, the Asians, think that the Europeans are an equally filthy lot. Fancy, going and having a 'tish' and placing your bum on a seat where 2,000 people had placed their bums previously. They think we're disgusting, but what's equally disgusting is the appearance of a toilet when an Asian Style Gentleman has gone into a European Style Gentleman's toilet, not knowing how to use it, has balanced on top of the basin and crapped all over the place!

There was a dispensing machine for the universal Stim Orange and Lemon. I got a bottle and drank it. No sign of any activity; then the policeman woke up. I went over and said, 'Can you tell me where the public telephone is?' He answered, 'What's a public telephone?' I thought 'God, where am I?'

After three quarters of an hour, a tattered old, one-ton truck came trundling up the hill on the road leading to the airport, driven by a Somali soldier who was getting on a bit. This turned out to be my transport. The driver, Mohamed, was my driver. It was my main transport for the whole time I was in Somaliland – that one-ton truck was very efficient, it kept going for mile after mile after mile, maximum speed, foot flat on the floor, 34 miles an hour. It did have the advantage that, in bottom gear, it could go up an almost vertical hillside at 10 miles an hour. It just kept on going. I did thousands of miles in that one-ton truck. The driver asked if I was the Doctor Sahib. I said I was and he said 'I've got to take you to the Officers' Mess'.

We set off down the main road, into Hargeisa. Little did I realize that that strip of tarmac was the only strip of tarmac in the whole of Somaliland. It stretched the magnificent total of three miles from Hargeisa International Airport to the Governor's 'Mansion'. After a mile and a half, we turned off onto a rough, bumpy track, which I later found out, was the main road to Boroma. Shortly afterwards, the road divided; we took the left hand track and reached the Officers' Mess. It was the most beautiful Officers' Mess I have ever seen!

Single storey, white painted, with an emerald green corrugated roof. At the front, was a white painted balcony with a balustrade, uprights and roof painted green. A brick wall painted white, with uprights every ten yards, surrounded the whole compound, in between, a wooden, green painted fence. There were two gateposts, but no gates. To the right of the gatepost was a little lean-to, the size of a kennel for a St Bernard, the night watchman's hut. A dry-stone construction of bricks, concrete blocks, stones, and wooden roof covered with a tarpaulin. Inside, a bunch of rags – the night watchman's bed – in front the remains of a little campfire.

There were several large trees in front of the officers' mess. Somaliland did have some big trees. The whole area where the officers' mess was sited was well covered in bush and trees. Some were large acacia thorn trees, others had long, thin, dangling branches like a willow; they were some sort of bean tree. During the time I was there, they produced big pods, like broad bean pods, with beans, the size of broad beans. This was a bit of a nuisance because we would be visited by troops of baboons intent on having dinner. The grass in-between was sparse, and varied in colour between light brown and green, according to whether the Somali bearers remembered to water it. It was grazed by gazelle in the early hours of the morning or late at night, when all was quiet. It was often raided by marauding gangs of goats, either the responsibility of a little boy of about 8 or 9, or a teenager of about 12 or 13. This caused great joy to everybody in the compound, all the bearers came hurtling out accompanied by the two dogs kept by a couple of the officers, making a hell of a din, chasing the goats off. If they were in the charge of a little boy of 8 or 9, he was reprimanded. The teenager would be beaten up! Marauding gangs of goats in Somaliland were quite a problem and need a paragraph on their own.

The Mess And History

The officers' mess consisted of a large dining room and a massive lounge leading onto the balcony, full of ancient but comfy armchairs. There were playing cards, draughts, chess, backgammon and other games to play to pass the time. Beyond this were the quarters and kitchens for the Somali mess orderlies and where our own bearers lived. The orderlies had a nice uniform, white shorts and shirts, green cummerbund and a high conical Somaliland Scout hat in green. Behind was a garden quadrangle, mown lawn surrounded by flowers. On two sides were the officers' bedrooms. Beyond, the

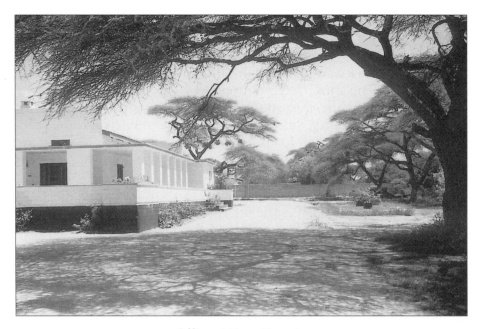

Officers' Mess, Hargeisa

stables where the officers kept two or three ponies and the quarters of the syces that looked after them.

Behind the stables were some lean-to huts, where the Dhobi men, sweepers and other people who made a living on the officers' mess slept. The lounge contained a large library. Mainly travel books and the autobiographies of the early Europeans who had ventured into Somaliland. When Somaliland was first explored, it was a very beautiful place. The human population was sparse and it was teeming with game. They had their own versions of everything – there were Somaliland elephants and Somaliland rhino. Some of the early aristocratic hunters had recorded their hunting exploits. Their daily 'bags' were obscene – twenty warthogs, thirty gazelle, two lions, three elephants. The mind boggles that you had a group of people that could slaughter to such an extent! I know I did my own bit of slaughtering there, but it was mainly for the pot! There was one old photograph – they had been out shooting sand grouse, and there were about 3,000 sand grouse all piled up. It looked like an old potato pie that we made when harvesting potatoes during the war.

There were accounts of fighting a gentleman known as the 'Mad Mullah' who ruled over the Eastern part of Somaliland, which was almost desert. He wasn't a freedom fighter; more a robber baron/bandit leader, who operated between 1900 and the First World War. He preyed on the local Somali tribes, taxed them, taking

50% of any crops grown and 50% of the annual increase in their herds.

He led the British Army and the Somaliland Scouts a pretty dance. Then they were known as the Somaliland Camel Corps. He and his pals knew all the small water sources and the tracks in the Eastern desert, which was also mountainous; they could slip away and hide without any difficulty. The English had to carry their water with them. It took two camel-loads of water to keep one Somali soldier going. Reading the logistics of the campaigns was interesting - how they built up water supplies, special strong points, every hundred miles, which were filled with water. The Mullah could see what was going on and as soon as the British campaign started, he hopped it! When the campaign was over and the British returned to base, he came back. The merry dance went on until 1914 and the beginning of the First World War. That's when the British made a big mistake.

They told the Somali tribes that they would have to defend themselves, supplied them with some old rifles and retreated to the main port Berbera. Here they kept a small company of Somaliland police, 5-6 English police inspectors, and a magistrate. In 1919, when the First World War ended, they moved back to re-organize the protectorate, they found that the local Somalis had got going against each other. Like most old-fashioned societies, each tribe had its traditional enemies. When they fought in the past, they used shields, spears, bows and arrows and hadn't caused too much damage. Now, armed with modern although antique rifles, they were more effective. When the British moved back into Somaliland, they found a dearth of adult males between the ages of 18 and 55.

There was a quick end to the Mullah. The British had just fought a major war and there had been fantastic improvements in transport. They imported four clapped out old bi-planes, a lot of modern trucks, a REME (Royal Electrical and Mechanical Engineers) section to keep everything going, large petrol bowsers and massive water bowsers and moved out after the Mullah. The Mullah couldn't hide any more. The clapped out old aeroplanes found him every day. Eventually, he was ambushed twice, not many were killed - the first time; he lost his animal transport and half his weaponry. Next time he lost his treasury! He couldn't bribe people anymore.

The typical Somali soldier doesn't believe in being on the losing side. His fighting men promptly went back home. Those that came from the Ogaden, Kenya and Italian Somaliland, where the British Somaliland authorities couldn't get at them, went home. Those that belonged to British Somaliland surrendered, their rifles were taken off them, they were sent home, leaving just the Mullah and his lieutenants. He was last heard of in the Ogaden, and then disappeared.

Five years later, the Intelligence Service found out what had happened to him. He had gone to the Ogaden, where the local tribes had kept an eye on him until they had squeezed every last penny from him. Then told him to clear off, tipped off the Somali Chieftains, they sent a bunch of blokes down armed with rifles, who caught him near the Kenyan border and that was the end of the Mad Mullah and his lieutenants.

Living Conditions

The officers' rooms were good sized bedrooms, well furnished, with an attached bathroom with a bath and washbasin. For people who could afford it and the British Authorities and Army, there was a fresh cold water supply in Hargeisa. But, surprise, surprise, we also had hot water! It looked great, until you looked out at the back. The front of the officers' rooms, facing the garden, had spacious balconies. At the back were small balconies and steps, and spaced between the rooms were brick plinths, on top of which was a 50-gallon oil drum, beneath a fireplace. That was your hot water supply. We had hot-boiling water from 3.00 p.m. onwards. It was filled up by your bearer in the morning, and a fire started underneath. All the European houses had hot water, but it was always this primitive affair that required a lot of wood and a fair amount of labour.

It wasn't the safest regime. A young Italian doctor, his wife and two children, of 3½ and 2 years came to work for the Colonial Medical Service. Mum decided to bathe the children; got the bath ready; put the two kids in it and popped out to fetch a towel. Whilst she was out, one of the children turned on the tap and boiling water poured into the bath. Both children received 100% scalds, and died about 24 hours later.

You were able to have a nice bath at 5 or 6 o'clock in the afternoon, when the days activities were over. There was also hot water to get washed in, just before you went to bed. In the morning, your bearer in a grimy old smoky bucket provided it! The latrines were long drops and away from the mess, this was a bit of a problem if you woke in the night wanting a pee, because they didn't have any gazundas (goes under). You could always open the back door!

I had three personal servants, well two and half, no, two and a

Driver, Mohamed; Bearer, Mohamed; Laundry Boy, Ali

bit. There was my driver and mechanic, Mohamed, my bearer, Mohamed, whom I tipped about £2 (40 East African shillings) a month, and Ali the laundry boy who did all my laundry and ironing every day. He was paid 30 shillings per month. He looked after four officers at a time.

My bearer would check my clothes, stitch any buttons on and do any repairs that were necessary etc. He was jolly good at it as well - when one of your shirts or shorts was a bit dog-eared and grotty, you thought, 'Oh, I don't want that any more', and you gave it to your bearer. Next time you saw it, he would be wearing it and you wondered why you had given it to him, because he had set to and repaired it with meticulous care.

I put my uniform on in the morning, came back round about lunch-time, the day's work over, got undressed - underclothes, uniform, everything - kicked it into a corner of the bedroom and put the afternoon stuff on. Went off, and did whatever I wanted to do, return about half past five, strip off again, kick it into the corner, have a bath and put on my evening dress. When I went to bed, same again, kick it in the corner and put your longhi on. Next morning, Ali would collect, wash and press everything, hand it to your bearer, who would put it back in the drawers in your bedroom.

Unfortunately, this became a habit that I got rather used to. It caused problems when I got home! For the first fortnight, my wife appeared delighted to see me, but after a further fortnight, she noticed at night-time, when getting ready for bed, I took my shirt and underclothes off and kicked them into a corner of the bedroom and left them there. After about three weeks, there was a sudden explosion! My polite, charming, darling wife started swearing like a Staff Sergeant in the Royal Marines. 'What on earth do you think you are doing? I'm not your b—dy Dhobi man!' I had never heard her say 'b—dy' before. 'If you think I'm picking them up, you've got another think coming! Either take them downstairs, or put them in the laundry basket.'

I did try to comply, but the habit had become too ingrained, and over the next 3-4 years, similar explosions occurred quite regularly. I began to realize that I was no longer the high and mighty, highly respected Hakim Sahib or Doctor Sahib. I was just an ordinary run of the mill, pain in the arse, husband, the usual stupid, idiotic, lazy, ignorant, male that charming young male fiancés turn into! My presence now, of course, was necessary, I had to help her to bring up the kids. The result of suffering from a high level of sex hormones when young, which clouded her judgement into making the serious mistake of thinking she had got a bargain when she got married.

War cemetery

The little corner of a foreign field that is forever England.

It was within easy walking distance to the east of the officer's mess, close to the Italian War Memorial. An attractive little garden,

Military Cemetery, Hargeisa

a little run down but a beautiful peaceful place. Not many graves, mainly British, a few Italian, not the massive cemeteries that always bring tears to my eyes in Northern France. It was a serene place to sit in the late afternoon just before it became dark.

Nearby was a roofless squash court, but no one appeared to use it. It was far to hot for that game. I played squash from the age of 18 to 67 but was never tempted to use it. Nobody asked me to play tennis so I don't know if there were any courts. I am sure the officers would have played if there had been. There was a golf course, made of sand, no greens, just sand raked smooth around the hole. I am one of those people who believe that golf just ruins a pleasant walk, so I took very little interest in it.

Night Watchman

I have described the night watchman's hut. All European compounds had a night watchman. There was one around the Police Station, the Hospital, the Governor's Office and European married quarters. Three or four houses together made a little compound, inside the compound you would find the night watchman's little shelter. He was paid the regular Somali salary of 100 East African shillings a month. He'd turn up around dusk with his dinner and water supply, build a small fire, cook his evening meal and make a cup of tea. Then wander round the compound, talking with the syces and bearers. At 9 o'clock, he went go to bed and slept soundly until dawn, when he went home. What good did he do? He didn't watch, he went to sleep. It was the same with all the night watchmen. If you didn't employ a night watchman, things would be stolen; if you did, nothing was stolen. If something was stolen, the article would be carefully described to the night watchman. Next week, next month, or four or five months later, he would return the article. You were not just employing a night watchman, you also employed his family and clan, more importantly, you employed the clan's honour. They usually ferreted out the thief, recovered the article, applied whatever the Somalis accepted as an appropriate sanction to the thief. The thief was never be reported to the authorities – they sorted the matter out themselves.

How to make your officer's early morning tea – Somali style

Returning at dawn from my only night call, all the time I was in Somaliland, I arrived in time to watch Major Thorpe's bearer prepare his early morning cup of tea. I had occasionally watched what happened when I got up at dawn (as soon as the top rim of the sun appeared above the horizon) whilst we were out on manoeuvres.

The Recipe

Take one large old, smoke-grimed saucepan.

Turn over, bang on sandy ground to get out remains of previous day's brew.

With dirty hand, wipe round saucepan to remove sand that is now sticking there.

Wipe hand on back of trousers.

From one large, cracked, dirty enamel jug captured from the Italians in 1940, pour a pint of goat's milk.

Bring to boil.

Put in a pint of water. It might be straight from the tap at the Officers' mess, or when bivouacking, already browned and rusty from having spent six months in a jerry can.

If water is in short supply on manoeuvres, and it has rained recently, skim water off top of a nearby pool; as the resultant beverage will be dark brown and milky, officer will not notice if water is that colour to start with.

Bring to boil.

Put dirty hand into dirty Hessian sack, remove two large handfuls of tea, and throw into boiling mixture.

Place dirty hand into another dirty cardboard box, remove one handful of less than white sugar, and throw into mixture.

Boil for ten minutes.

Place on ground and go to talk with pals for 10–15 minutes, during which time 20 thirst-crazed flies will drop in for a drink and scald to death!

Return from friends, observe flies, wipe nose on back of right forefinger and dry on back of trousers.

With dirty thumb, forefinger and black encrusted nails, delicately pick out flies. This must be done with care; otherwise tips of finger and thumb will be scalded.

Take muslin cloth net for straining. Pristine when given to bearer five years ago, by a previous Captain. Now a dark brown, but kept sterile by daily pouring of scalding hot tea through it.

Pour from saucepan, through muslin, into the cracked enamel jug, and then pour back into saucepan again. Test heat with dirty finger, then boil again.

Finally, pour direct from saucepan into Officer's nice white enamel pint mug, which hasn't been washed since it was last used, yesterday.

Using any nearby rag, wipe outside and rim of Officer's mug, so that it is sparkling white.

Take one large mouthful of tea, to see if it is not too hot. If it isn't, swallow it. If it is too hot, spit it on the ground. If it's boiling hot, promptly regurgitate mouthful into officer's mug of tea.

Place on ground to cool further and allow five more flies to commit suicide.

Return, remove flies, and take another sip to make sure it is not too hot.

Mug of tea now ready.

Take to Officer's room, during which time another fly will probably commit suicide, but knowing that officer will not fully awake and his eyes focusing, you assume that the fly will be mistaken for a floating tealeaf.

Hand cup to Officer.

Officer takes big mouthful and swallows fly.

As this solid mixture of sweetened caffeine and tannin hits his stomach, officer goes rigid, eyes pop out and hair stands on end.

Officer takes sharp intake of breath, followed by another sip of tea. Sits on side of bed and relaxes.

A minute later, officer is stupid enough to drink the rest of the tea, by which time he is on the edge of caffeine poisoning and wide-awake.

Officer now realizes he has been in bed all night, hasn't had a pee since he went to bed, and is bursting. Goes through the back door, over the balcony, down the steps, crosses the twenty yards of hard packed sand to the wall and fence round the officers' mess compound, and pees through a hole between the slats. Bearer sees nothing wrong in this, as that's the hole that he pees through, which accounts for a nice, small patch of green grass just outside, whereas everywhere else, it's dry sand. Officer now returns to bathroom to get washed, shaved and brush his teeth. The caffeine has taken effect, he holds his right hand with his left hand whilst he brushes his teeth, lathers and shaves himself. Otherwise, the tremor is too great for him to carry out these acts.

Officer now gets dressed and heads off to work, trundling along in his old one-ton truck, if it's me, or haring along at 60 miles an hour bumping over everything, if it's the Major in his brand new land-rover.

Officer returns at 9 o'clock, having recovered from caffeine poisoning, goes to the Dining Room, says 'All fried' to the orderly, who returns with a massive trencher with two fried eggs, several rashers of bacon, sausages, kidneys, tomatoes, whole pile of toast, butter and marmalade, all washed down with a large amount of thick, black coffee to renew his caffeine level.

All Fried

When Colonel Matheson came over to review the situation a few months later, he made this comment:

'We all went into the officers' mess in the morning and said "All Fried".'

There were only four or five of us in the Mess at the time; young lieutenants or captains, and Major Thorpe, an old bachelor. The rest were all married living at home. He couldn't help noticing that, in spite of this, everybody was as thin as a rake. The other officers would load up in the morning and not eat again until they came back at night. Sometimes, in the rainy season, they would get marooned somewhere, couldn't cross a Toug (Somali name for a dry water course) and get back, so that breakfast might have to last for a couple of days. You could always take rations with you, but then you had the problem of carrying them. The officers of the Somaliland Scouts thought that the best way of carrying rations was already eaten inside your stomach!

Colonel Matheson visited after I had been there for three months. I took him on a tour of inspection around the establishments in Somaliland. At least that's what he called it; I thought it was just an excuse to join in on one of my swanees. I had been having no success in trying to persuade the adjutant that a Medical Officer should have one of the nippy landrovers instead of my trundling one-ton truck. He was well aware what it would be used for, extending my hunting trips, but with a Colonel to impress I had no difficulty in acquiring one. My driver was left in charge of the truck at base, while I belted over the rough tracks called main roads at 50 to 60 miles an hour. It would have cut journey times by half if we had not stopped to do, or admire things along the way. I thought it best not to tell Col Matheson that I didn't have a driving licence.

As usual I went to the armoury to collect the rifle I used. It wasn't there. I searched, couldn't find it. The one alongside looked new so I took that. I told Col Matheson, that I usually went after a gazelle on the way. He gave the impression that he thought Medical Officers would not be very good at that sort of thing, and graciously declined when after showing him how to load and aim a rifle, I suggested that he have the first go. Later we saw some dhero. I took careful aim as usual at its chest, the heart region, up to now I had never missed. After a chest shot the animal always ran a few steps, this one dropped down where it stood, it was still twitching when Mohamed ran to it and slashed its throat in proper Muslim style. The colonel walked over, while I unloaded and put the rifle in its holder, on the landrover.

'What a brilliant shot,' he said when I got there. 'You've shot it right through the head.'

So I had. Thinks, 'Keep your gob shut Bill. You've got to make the most of this.'

I had missed my target by over two feet, which is how far the dhero's head was from its heart. That showed how much one should know the eccentricities of a gun. As a target the dhero's head was about one fifth the size of its chest, no way would I have aimed for that. The colonel was highly impressed, for the first time in his army career; he thought he had a top class sniper under his command. He was still talking about it a year later. No way after that was I going to try another shot with that rifle. Two days later on our way back, we saw some dhero in the distance, the colonel said, 'Are you going to have a go?'

'Not with that gun,' thinks I. A legitimate excuse was required. There were some heavy dark clouds over the mountains to the right, not the usual jet black ones that preceded a rainstorm, but the colonel would not know that.

'Well, Sir, I'd like to, but I'm worried about those black clouds over there. It looks like it's going to rain, if it does there'll be a flash flood, down the Red Toug, it may be in spate, and we'll be held up for hours, we might not get back until after midnight.'

A demonstration of inaccurate shooting was thereby avoided. Colonel Matheson probably retired believing he had had a crack shot in one of his units.

Driving

I was driving tractors about my uncles' farms from the time I was 10 years old, and carrying messages and massive buckets of hot sweet tea to the farm workers in an old van from the age of 13. Driving cars and lorries about from 16. At seventeen I got my provisional licence, thinking I'll soon have my licence, my dad can teach me. Far from it, my dad's only thought was the safety of his car, if I went about a yard from a wall, immediate demise of his car was imminent. I learnt a lot of Anglo Saxon words I had not heard before, but did not get very far with driving. I gave up in despair, and as a student had neither money nor the time. Now on the rough Somali roads, with little traffic, and bored with sitting on my side of the truck, I started driving again. I was soon driving everything the Scouts had, including the three-ton trucks. Every one assumed I had a licence, until we were chatting one day and I told them I hadn't.

'There's an army licence,' said one.

'Yes! and you can use it in England,' said another.

'But only with army vehicles,' said the first.

'Not very useful if you are not in the army,' says I.

'But you might as well have one, while you're here.' Said a third, 'Go And See The Adjutant.'

Next day I went to the adjutant's office.

'They tell me you want an army driving licence, Doc.'

'Yes please.'

'Well I've seen you driving around. Hang on; I should have some licences in my desk. Here we are, I'll sign one.'

In four minutes I had sat and passed my army-driving test.

Riding

I've mentioned the ponies that most of the Officers kept, and the sergeants for that matter. It had been a tradition ever since we first moved into Somaliland. Each officer owned 2-3 ponies and most of them played polo. I had ridden a bit - mainly bareback - on the farms as a boy. Later I didn't have time, you could never call me a 'horsey' type of person. I started riding in the afternoons at Hargeisa. I asked for the mildest pony, and I believe he was, but he was certainly difficult to handle! He loved to bite!

If you went riding, you had to take care. The officers' mess being a single storey building with lots of trees around it, if you were two or three hundred yards away, you couldn't see it. When I went riding I took a note of the time, position of the sun and position of one or two nearby hills. Then I did a circular ride and eventually got back where I started. On one occasion, the pony threw me and my right foot was stuck in the stirrup. Frightened, he headed off home, trailing me behind him. I must admit, at the time, I felt 'Well, Bill, this is it'. I thought if he's going to drag me all the way back to the officers' mess, I'll be dead by the time we got there. Fortunately, he had a typical saddle, which is made so that if you were thrown and dragged behind, your stirrup would pull out, and that's what happened. I limped back to the mess, feeling somewhat disgruntled. I got there one hour later and found the mess in an uproar. A search party was being organized.

I was pig-sick with the pony. I asked the syce to use one of the vicious bits they had for newly broken ponies - not a nice thing to do. I already had a whip, I went into the officers' mess, for some old spurs there, which I fixed to the back of my boots. Although my hip was hurting, I got back on and I galloped that pony for the next hour, heaving on the nasty bit, raking him with the spurs and whipping him. Not very nice, but I was in a bad mood. I brought him back when he was absolutely lathered and tired out. I was aching all over.

After that, the pony and I came to an agreement. He only bit me when I was not looking; he would let me ride him provided I wiped off the sweat and lather for ten minutes afterwards, and got him a nice big bucket of water and spent thirty minutes curry combing him. He was happy to let me comb him in a very vulnerable position. I don't remember the names for the chest and front leg of a horse - I've never been that much of a equestrian, but when you're brushing those, your bum sticks up in the air and this was one of the few occasions when he refrained from biting it! He also expected me to visit him each night after dinner, with a slice of bread and a few sugar cubes. There was no way, I would allow him to take the bread or sugar cubes from the palm of my hand, like most horsemen do. That pony would have had my hand off! He became my favourite polo pony.

'Why didn't you get a quieter one?' The answer was simple – the others were worse. These ponies were the ponies that the Somali fighting men would ride, before the British arrived. We suspected that they'd been bred and trained to fight alongside their riders, because they all bit everything they could see. When there was a melee in front of the goal playing polo, the ponies would be busy biting each other.

Polo! Yes, I have played polo, but somehow Prince Charles and his friends never got round to inviting me to join them. In my early life, I seem to have drifted from place to place that was always a little understaffed when it came to maintaining the team for their favourite game. When I was 14 or 15 years old, I was a regular member of the Crowle Brickwork's Cricket Team. I joined the Louth Hospital Hockey Team. Now, to my horror, they were short in one of the polo teams. There are only four members in each team, but there were numerous polo teams and a league in Somaliland. It seemed that every male under the age of 60 played polo. My team had three regular players, but were one man short. If they didn't get a fourth man, they couldn't play. They were desperate that I should join them! I was desperate that I should not!

Anyway, I ended up playing polo. 'What use will I be?' says I. 'It takes me all my time to stay on the blooming' pony, never mind try and hit a ball with that bloody great mallet.'

'It doesn't matter, Doc, just ride your pony in front of the goal and get in the opponent's way.'

That was all very well, but they hadn't counted upon Major Brown. (I will call him that; it may have been John Harper-Nelson.) He was nearly fifty years old, from somewhere in the South of England – a smallish chap, a little bit chubby, he was a mad polo player.

Twenty years ago, he realized he'd reached the height of his profession. He'd spent the years doing tours in various parts of the African empire, – the Gold Coast, Nigeria, Nyassaland, which is now Malawi, North and Southern Rhodesia, King's African Rifles in Kenya and now in the Somaliland Scouts. In each posting, he had been a mad polo player. There was no way his pocket could go towards playing polo if he went back to England, but in the African colonies, he had found playing the game was well within his pocket.

We were discussing what he was going to do in the future on one occasion. He was a little bit despondent, because he knew that the empire was coming to an end. He wasn't sure where he would be able to go to next; he was thinking about the Trucial Oman Scouts. He knew that as soon as he returned to England he would be promptly retired. On the other hand, he'd had a marvellous time and lived life to the full. Seeing Major Brown set off like a rocket from the goal at the other end of the pitch, on a pony travelling at 75 miles an hour, standing up in his stirrups, waving a mallet round his head, screaming his war cry like a dervish, didn't encourage me to stand in front of him as he approached the goal! He could gallop at top speed, stand up in his stirrups, whirl his polo mallet round his head, lean over and strike the ball, EVERY time he tried - never missed. What's more, it went like a cannonball in the direction in which he intended it to go.

There were often crashing melees of eight horses and riders in front of the goal, with balls and mallets whizzing round in all directions. I'd been told to get in the opponent's way! Well, I did. In fact, I got in everybody's way. There I'd be, with my knees clamped to my pony's side, both hands holding grimly onto the saddle, the reins in my teeth, the polo mallet dangling from my right elbow, trying desperately to stay aboard. With monotonous frequency, I found myself dumped on the floor, two or three times every match, where I'd lay with my hands round my head while 8 x 4 sets of hooves bounced up and down and 7 polo mallets whirled round. How I survived, I've no idea. Well, perhaps I have. It was the pony. It must have been inbred in them, as soon as I fell on the floor, the pony would stand over me, which allowed me to recover and get up, during which time, he would bite anything and anybody that came within biting distance.

Fortunately, Mohamed had everything prepared when I returned to the officers' mess; there was twice as much boiling water in the oil drum. I staggered to my room, covered in bruises, aching in every muscle in every limb in my body. I soaked in a hot bath for an hour, with plenty of hot water in the oil drum to keep it topped up.

After that, and about six pints of lager in the officers' mess, I began to feel human again. My team mates were very encouraging. They had to be, without me, they couldn't play. Normally, we lost, but we drew a fair number of times and, on the odd occasion, won. We would return to the officers' mess where we'd find Major Thorpe, the senior officer, who had far more sense than play polo, or even own a pony.

'Doc's played a blinder today. You know the winning goal, he was just in the right place when we scored it.'

Yes, I was - on a pony twenty yards away, bolting in the opposite direction. I tried to use my biting regular pony on these occasions. Ponies have far more sense than human beings. When you're having a full polo competition, there are several games (chukkas) played. They are played so fast that the ponies get tired; it's only human beings that are daft enough to keep on playing. At times, I had to use a pony that I wasn't used to. That tended to prove a bit difficult, because the pony would head off, full speed, in the wrong direction. At times, I felt as though I would end up in Nairobi.

Chapter Nine

Down to Work

The following morning, I reported to the adjutant and Colonel MacWilliam the Commanding Officer. The way they greeted me and from the way they acted, you wouldn't have thought there had been any problem with any doctor at all. I went to MI room and was introduced to the three sergeants, Abdullah Hersi, Hassan Egen and Ibrahim Mohamed, and the senior medical orderlies, making a total of six.

I carried out a sick parade and then sat down, wondering what on earth I was to do. I wandered round, and came across a sick bay with eight beds. It was being used as a junkyard. I started on that.

Before, I go any further, for non-Army people; I'd better explain how the Army is organized. In peacetime, the Army assumes that

MI Room, Hargeisa Fort
Abdullah Hersi, author, Hassan Egeh and Ibrahim Mohamed

anything that is lost, destroyed, damaged or disturbed in any way is the responsibility of somebody and, therefore, must be paid for. The art of being a peacetime soldier is to make sure you palm the responsibility off on to somebody else, and if you can't avoid the responsibility, then you make sure you don't pay for it. It starts off like this. One Field Marshal signs for one British military establishment intact. He promptly divides it into armies and hands it down to his generals. General A gets Army A intact, etc. He promptly palms it off to his Brigadiers, who palm it off to the Colonels and Regimental Commanders, so that it eventually lands up with me, in the Somaliland Scouts. One medical establishment, Somaliland Scouts, intact. The first thing I do is palm off the responsibility. Count up all your sergeants; find out what you've got, where it is, divide it up into equal amounts, make a list and the sergeants sign for it, its their responsibility, so that if anything gets lost, I don't pay for it. The sergeants promptly hand it down to their corporals, who hand it down to the lance-corporals, who finally, hand it down to the PBP (Poor Bloody Private), who if he hasn't got the skill to prove that it hasn't been damaged, lost or destroyed, usually has the skill to avoid paying for it. The PBP, all he can do, is go out and kick the cat!

The first thing I did was to say 'Whose responsibility is this?' The sergeant in charge came along and I said 'Where's your list?' He brought me a list of how many blankets etc. that was in the place. We cleared out the rubbish and looked at what was there. The blankets must have been twenty years old, amid a pile of stuff – pillows and mattresses; there weren't any sheets. I examined them and I thought 'Well, in for a penny, in for a pound. I've been told to modernize the department. I'll condemn the lot'. We only had enough left to make two beds. Having condemned the blankets etc., how were we going to dispose of them? That was simple. The Somali sergeants signed a form saying they'd destroyed them Then I shared the blankets, mattresses and pillows amongst the orderlies. They were delighted! I had them on my side from then onwards.

We washed the walls down, swept and generally tidied up, got some black enamel paint, re-painted the beds, and made everything shipshape. Then, I produced a report saying how old the equipment was, that I had no option but to condemn it, included the statements from the Somali sergeants, saying that it had been destroyed, and that we required replacement blankets, mattresses and pillows, to this amount.

I spoke to the adjutant, borrowed a typist, and made out two reports – one to the Commanding Officer, Somaliland Scouts, and one to Lieutenant Colonel Matheson. I moved on to my MI room, the GP surgery itself, where we did a full survey, looked in every drawer we could find. It was surprising what we did find. I found ampoules of Salvarsan – a substance made of arsenic, invented about 1905, which was the mainstay treatment for syphilis until the advent of penicillin. I went through all the drugs, found the old and expired ones, piled them on one side – the non-dangerous ones I gave to the Somali orderlies, the others I destroyed. I made a record of what I'd found and what we'd got rid of. But not how I'd given anything away. The same applied to all the equipment. Then I went through all the modern drugs, worked what we hadn't got and what we needed. I was supposed to put in a monthly request for drugs and equipment, but I put in a supernumerary one. I finally had two reports – one for the CO Somaliland Scouts, one for Colonel Matheson, together with my demand for further equipment and a fresh supply of drugs. This took about three or four days.

I then went to the Armoury, found a nice, reasonably new 303 rifle that fitted me nicely, persuaded them to hand over forty rounds of ammunition, went to the rifle range, where I surprised an English Armoury Sergeant, who in this case, was delighted to see me! No other officer of the Somaliland Scouts, never mind the MO, had ever been to see him, to do a bit of rifle practice. We spent a couple of hours cleaning and sorting out the rifle and making sure I understood how it fired, so I could use it accurately.

Monday morning, I packed a three-day supply kit, took my bearer Mohamed and my driver, went to the MI room, told the two

Dhero

*Adadlem Camp Officers' Mess
chewing pomegranate seeds*

*Adadlem Camp Officers' Mess
CO, Major John Harper-Nelson*

Somalis to hold the fort and if anybody needed treatment, to send them to the hospital in Hargeisa. I then disappeared into the bush of Somaliland. Two hours drive, to the east, was a company camp, Adadlem, out in the bush. On the way there, I made my first mistake. There were a lot of what we called dhero - a gazelle, the size of a goat but the body was bigger. They had a black and white stripe down the side. The first one I aimed at, I shot, but it was still kicking when I got there, so I put another bullet through its head to finish it off. The driver, who had been coming up behind with a knife in his hand promptly spits on the ground, grunts and won't touch it. Mohamed comes up and says,

'You can't do anything now, Sir, its dead. It must only be killed in a proper Mohammaden fashion. It must have its throat cut and bleed'.

I said 'Can't we take it back?'

'No, there's no point, nobody will cook it'.

That was the end of my first day hunting.

We drove up to Adadlem camp; it was tented and surrounded by a high thorn hedge - a zareeba. By a hedge, I don't mean the thorns were live; they were acacia thorn trees that had been chopped down and built into a thick, high hedge around the camp. It was to keep out lions, hyenas and jackals. The company commander - Major John Harper-Nelson - his captain and a couple of lieutenants were delighted to see me, they didn't often have visitors. We started off

Buroa Army Hospital. PSM Abdi Farah

by having a rather alcoholic lunch, which resulted in my sleeping the rest of the day.

The following day, the English Staff Sergeant that ran the MI tent and I did the same there as what we had done at Hargeisa. Then, I sat down and wrote a report that was later typed out for the two colonels. That night, the officers arranged an impromptu mess dinner. Under the starlit night, lit by Tilley lamps, we dined. They had some wine and had cooled it, in bags soaked with water that evaporated.

Next day, I trundled on to Buroa, at thirty miles an hour, a further 100 miles – a 4 or 5 hours drive, again to the East. This time, I shot a dhero and let the driver get there and slit its throat. This was acceptable. When I arrived at Buroa, we carried the gazelle into the kitchen and that night we all had a good feast on gazelle instead of the usual horrible goat. The Somali cooks and orderlies didn't do so bad either – being strict Mohammedans, when you kill an animal, you have to eat it the same day. Four officers weren't enough to eat a whole gazelle at one go, which meant there was plenty left over for the Somalis to take home to their families.

Buroa had been a major centre. A small army hospital had been built there, but it hadn't been used as a hospital for years. It was just an MI room run by another staff sergeant. We did the same again, destroyed equipment and other things, put in the usual demand, and I made my report.

There was surgical and anaesthetic equipment that would have made exhibits in a museum! One room contained a lot of hundredweight bags of salt tablets – about 12 – they had been captured in 1940 when the Italians were chased out of Somaliland, and handed on from staff sergeant to staff sergeant ever since. I decided not to destroy them, but ask permission to destroy them, and got a message back saying, 'What the on earth are you asking me for?' I spent two days in Buroa having a good look around. There was a colonial medical hospital, run by an English Sister, an SRN (State Registered Nurse) and SCM (State Certified Midwife). I made the acquaintance of the Major in Command's wife, George. George, her husband Nipper Harris with small daughter Mandy were to become good friends.

George gave me an idea that allowed me to leave Hargeisa on a swanee for two or three days through the bush, every fortnight. After general pleasantries, she asked me if I would be coming again in the near future. I said I didn't know, probably in about a fortnight, after I'd finished my survey, but we'd see. I did visit Buroa again a fortnight later, on this occasion she invited me to tea with herself and the other officers' wives. I visited again a fortnight later and was asked to tea with the officers' and sergeants' wives, and that's how it continued. I visited Buroa for two or three days every fortnight, calling at Adadlem, for a chat and lunch. The doctor was entertained to tea, it gave the wives the opportunity to ask questions and discuss their families.

George, Bob Foulkes, Mandy and Nipper Harris

By total accident, I had hit upon the way in which the RAMC could be put back on the top of its pedestal again. I regularly visited and talked to the families, the wives and mothers, and discussed the kids. I didn't plan it. I just fell into it. The wives sang my praises to their husbands and the sun shone out of my bottom. I went on swanees all over Somaliland; I'd take a couple of days off and go shooting here, after sand grouse there, having a glorious time; and the Colonel and other the senior officers thought I was marvellous. The honour of the Corps was back.

Borama

The following week, I headed in the opposite direction, to a place called Boroma, where the training camp for the annual intake of recruits was located. Again, the officers were delighted to see me, because they didn't get many visitors. I stayed a couple of nights. The staff sergeant and I went through everything, chucked a lot away, put in a demand for every bit of equipment we could think of and ordered new drugs. The major, Norman Rankin took me shooting; we went after gazelle called Auwl, big things, about as big as donkeys, and another glorious time was had by all!

Hunting Auwl

Going after dhero, was what one thinks of as hunting, working up close until you are in range. Auwl were different, two people were needed. They were found in large herds, on the plains near Boroma, particularly in the rainy season, when the plains were covered in lush grass. There were 2 or 300 in a herd; they kept away from all cover. Then I and another officer tried to wreck the company landrover. It was a landrover, and over the land it roved. Over the grassy plain, potholes, small sand hills, warthog wallows, at 30 or 40 miles an hour. Bouncing up and down, sharp turns that nearly threw you out; there were no seat belts. We headed out onto the plain; as soon as the auwl saw us they were off, galloping at high speed. Third gear, foot down we were after them. We took it in turns, one driving, and the other shooting. The shooter, marksmanship was impossible, stood in front of the passenger seat, lashed with belts and rope to the landrover. The driver raced the landrover alongside an auwl, twisting and turning with it, while the shooter tried to shoot it. About one shot in four was successful. Halt immediately, bearer out to slit its throat, gut it. Chuck it in the back and off again before the auwl had disappeared over the horizon. We usually shot two or three, so there was gazelle meat for all the recruits at Borama. We resembled Sioux horsemen doing a buffalo hunt. Borama was quite close to the Ethiopian border, I am sure we strayed into Ethiopia on those hunting forays.

Having carried out the survey, I gathered everything together, presented a massive report to Colonel MacWilliam, and posted one off to Colonel Matheson, together with demands for equipment and extra drugs. I developed a principle that has stood me in good stead for the rest of my life, dealing with NHS administrators. That is, put up a large barrage of bumph, and do what the hell you like behind it!

Dr Deering

Then I decided it was time I introduced myself to the Colonial Medics. I headed off to the Hargeisa General Hospital, where I met the surgeon to the Somaliland Protectorate, that is surgeon to an area the size of England with a population of over a million. He did everything. His name, Doctor Deering - he was very quickly to become infamous. Doctor Deering was a Polish doctor and had been in Somaliland since 1946.

He featured in the book *Exodus*, which had just been published and dealt with the concentration camps where the SS had slaughtered thousands of Jews during the war. Doctor Deering had been sent to one of the concentration camps, I can't remember which. It was one at which the SS doctors decided to experiment on young Jewish girls - to sterilize them. Their pelvises were exposed to X-Ray radiation, and their ovaries removed so that they could examine them. Doctor Deering was told to remove the ovaries, which he did, without an anaesthetic. There were other Polish doctors in the concentration camp that were also ordered to do the same, but managed to avoid it. Doctor Deering's subsequent defence was that 'he had been forced to do it, otherwise he would have been shot'.

When Somaliland became independent, Doctor Deering returned to London and joined a general practice there. *Exodus* came out and he sued the publishers. The publishers made a substantial offer to settle the matter. With legal advice, he refused and proceeded with the case. There is a problem when the defendants make an offer into court, if the plaintiff continues with the case. If he wins, and the money he is awarded is less than what the defendants have put into court, then he loses the case and has to pay the costs for both sides.

The English jury decided on Doctor Deering's side. They agreed that he had been slandered, and then decided on the quantity of damages. The quantity of damages they awarded Doctor Deering was one farthing. For those that don't remember the old currency, one farthing was a quarter of a penny, there were twelve pennies to a shilling, and a shilling is equivalent to five new pence. Dr Deering went bankrupt, and died shortly afterwards. When I met Doctor Deering, he seemed a very honest, pleasant, charming, hard-working doctor. To find that he had the history that he had was quite a shock.

Signals

There were no telephones, we communicated by letter. There was a very expensive radiotelegraph if you wanted to contact anyone at home urgently. Otherwise it was by Morse code. That was how we contacted Aden and communicated between the out stations.

I was not aware of this at first. I assumed the contact was by radio using the spoken voice. I sent a few short messages and then received an urgent request from one of the Staff Sergeants for advice regarding treatment. My advice included a long and complicated prescription, which must have given the Somali radio operator with his Morse code a fit. A special visit from the signals officer resulted, explaining radio communication was more primitive than the Doc thought. The message was to Adadlem, two hours away. A letter was sent instead, as an urgent answer had been requested, it made a heavy load for an otherwise empty three ton truck.

Medicine

The medical work wasn't anything extra special, there weren't any particular tropical diseases that bothered the Somalis. It was dry and arid; there was malaria about, it wasn't much of a problem, except in the rainy season, when we had epidemics of malaria. I continued with my Paludrine as did all the other officers; I didn't need to take the Sulfaguanadine or the salt tablets. It was like an English general practice, with covering Casualty and a bit of Dentistry, plus veterinary work.

Rabies, hydrophobia, was endemic, hyenas, foxes, dogs, ground squirrels and other predators were all potential carriers. Any bite that broke the skin was considered dangerous. You were supposed to catch the offending animal, tie or lock it up to see if it got hydrophobia. Of course by the time it died it might be too late to start prevention. Rabies then, as it is now, was 100% fatal. Officers and sergeants tended to be very careful not to get bitten, not because of the fear of getting rabies but of landing in my sympathetic (Ha Ha) hands. I only had one to deal with. I cannot now remember details, but it was a series of 14 injections. They were very, very, painful. Into the abdominal wall, starting at the top on one side then the top on the other the next day and so on alternate sides working downward to a new area every day. It was the same vaccine that the famous Frenchman Pasteur had invented about 1870. It consisted of the ground-up spinal cords of rabbits. Toward the end of the course the victims sometimes got sensitivity to rabbit protein making the injections more painful.

What annoyed the recipients was that the chances of actually getting rabies was very small, but with a 100% mortality rate we couldn't take the risk. A delighted MO assisted by beaming highly amused Somalis did not help either. Nor did the comments and lack of sympathy of the recipients fellow officers improve matters. Any sympathy offered went to me for putting up with the moans and groans.

As for sickness rates, the officer who had the anti-rabies injection in spite of the discomfort refused time of duty. That is one thing I remember particularly about the British officers and sergeants in the Somaliland Scouts in the six months I was there – not once did I sign any of them off duty. That reflected the high morale of the unit. The Somali soldiers were no different, they were just as proud, not many of them went sick either.

There wasn't a veterinary surgeon in Somaliland, so guess who got landed with it! It was a problem, because I hadn't a clue! I was all right with dogs if they'd had cuts – I could stitch them up. If they got infected, I gave them antibiotics; if they got worms, I made a mixture containing all the vermifuges I had to treat humans. Having mixed it up, got everything in it, we gave it to the dog and hoped for the best. As regards dosage, that depended on how big the dog was. It was more of a problem with horses, but I had a way round that – the head syce. When somebody brought a horse to me, unless it was a cut that needed stitching or an infection that needed antibiotics, I bided my time, had a quiet word with the head syce and found out what he recommended. I made the appropriate

Training Fred Payne's camel

mixture and added the appropriate human treatment to it. For instance, if a horse got bunged up, then I got the syce's mixture for it and chucked in a few ground up tablets of cascara or added some castor oil. I did draw the line with veterinary surgery, when Captain Payne at Buroa asked me to look at his riding camel. I thought that was a bit beyond me! Apart from which, it smelt, if you went near it, it spat at you and had big yellow teeth that it was quite prepared to bite with.

Why he went and bought one was beyond the rest of us. Admittedly the Scouts had been 'The Somaliland Camel Corps', but this was taking things just too literally.

Dosage for a horse

Stand one Somali alongside a Somaliland pony, divide Somali into pony, and multiply human dose by the number of times the Somali goes into the pony.

Painkillers

There was one problem, - painkillers - aspirin, common-or-garden aspirin. The Somali soldiers and orderlies saying 'It works sometimes, but not always, we need something a bit better'. When I made out my next monthly order for supplies, I requested paracetamol. The answer came back 'too expensive - use aspirin'. Next month, I asked for codeine or PAC (phenacetin, aspirin and codeine). The answer came back 'too expensive - use aspirin'. I tried one or two others, and got the same answer. I was a bit stuck. The next month when I put in my order, instead of asking for the usual one thousand tablet bottle of aspirin, I asked for a couple of 500 tablet bottles. I arranged with the quartermaster that as soon as the supply box arrived, I would be notified. The adjutant had two labels printed, similar to the ones found on the bottles supplied from Aden. The first one said 'Painkillers - Strong', the second 'Painkillers - Extra Strong'.

When my supplies arrived, I was notified; I removed the two 500 tablet bottles, went to the adjutant's office, acquired four bottles of blue ink and four red and returned to the officers' mess. In the sanctuary of my bedroom, I poured blue ink into one bottle and red ink into the other. I allowed half an hour for the ink soak in. Then spread the tablets out on the top of the dressing table to dry. I steamed off the proper labels, put the other labels on, put the blue aspirins into the 'Strong' bottles and the red aspirins into the 'Extra Strong', and returned them to the supply box.

Later the next morning, our monthly supply box was delivered and my sergeants started to empty it. All of a sudden, one rushed in and said 'Look, Sahib, we've got some new painkillers'. So we had. We prescribed them just like you'd prescribe aspirin tablets and if the pain was a bit heavy; we prescribed the red ones, just like you'd prescribe aspirin tablets. And they worked!

Then I had ample proof that they were very effective; I found them for sale in the local Souk (market). In England, when we prescribe antibiotics, we always give a 5-day supply. We never gave more than three days. Soldiers and their families always had to come back on the third day to see how they were getting on. We gave them two more days if necessary. The reason, as soon as they started feeling better, the Somalis stopped taking the tablets and sold them in the Souk, where there was a special stall which made medicines and sold every sort of modern medicine that you could think of - cortisone ointment, aureomycin, everything was for sale on that stall. There I found my blue and red aspirins.

Whilst talking about drugs, I ought to state how we treated typhoid in Somaliland. The treatment for typhoid fever was chloramphenicol capsules, one six-hourly × 5 days. Each tablet cost 1 shilling and 6 pence, which was 6 shillings a day. It cost one shilling a day to nurse a Somali in hospital. Unless a Somali was seriously ill with typhoid, he was never treated with antibiotics, but by nursing for three weeks, at a cost of 21 shillings, instead of 30 shillings. When we or the Somalis had conjunctivitis, treatment was different. I was supplied with chloramphenicol eye ointment for use in European officers, soldiers and their families only. The Somalis had to make do with Golden Yellow Eye Ointment, a mercury-oxide preparation that had been used with success for a couple of hundred years. We still had things like Gentian Violet, which even in those days was used in England for treating vaginal thrush. For dermatitis, there were paints like Brilliant Green, which was a type of dye.

The lead swinger

The Somalis were Mohammedan, allowed four wives each, but most of the Somali males thought that one wife was enough and looked down on man who had more than one wife. There was a stocky Somali sergeant (fat would be more appropriate) who had three wives, whom most of the Somali soldiers disliked intensely. He came to my MI room frequently, with recurrent headaches, sacral backache or a bit of an ache in an arm or an ankle. Exactly what GPs in England were quite used to, amongst the lead-swingers, when you knew but couldn't prove that they were just after a week off work. The Somali sergeant was just as bad! But I didn't appreciate this at the time. Finally, the senior sergeant Abdullah came to me and said,

'Sergeant Ibrahim making a fool of you, Sahib. He also make fool of us.'

I said, 'What do you mean?'

'Sergeant Ibrahim always come here, you give him time off. Nothing wrong with him. He make fool of both you and us. Last time, he came with backache and sore ankle. You gave him a week off; he leaves with two of his wives, with a large herd of goats and walks three days and sells them in Borama.'

Sergeant Ibrahim and his wives were very efficient traders and had built up quite a substantial holding, obviously my orderlies were pig sick of him.

A few weeks later, he came in again; I noticed that instead of having a nice head of curly hair, his was short and stubbly. I asked him what had been the matter. He had been to see the Mullah (Muslim priest) because he'd had a headache. He would have had to pay the Mullah. The Mullah told him that headaches could be due to the weight of the hair pulling on the roots. If he shaved off his hair, then it would get better. He'd shaved his hair off and, sure enough, his headache got better. I thought for a moment and then said 'Well, that is correct. But the Mullah hasn't done the full treatment. He should have treated the hair roots, while the hair wasn't there, so that the roots would be nice and fresh. They wouldn't pull on the head again and the pain wouldn't come back. Whereas, it's bound to come back again when the hair grows'.

As soon as he'd gone, I took my uniform jacket off, told the sergeant to take his off, I painted one arm with Gentian Violet and the other arm with Brilliant Green, did the same with the sergeant's arm. We each gave it a good scrubbing. The Gentian Violet scrubbed off easily, but the Brilliant Green stayed, staining the skin. The stain was unremarkable on my white skin, but was quite prominent on the Sergeant's.

After discussion with the other Somali orderlies, a plan of action was decided upon. The next time Sergeant Ibrahim turned up complaining of a headache, his head would be shaved and painted with Brilliant Green. He would be informed that this would soak into the roots of the hair and guarantee a permanent cure. The orderlies were told not to paint just the top of his head, where it could be covered by the Somaliland hat, but to paint down to the level of his eyebrows, ears and the back of his neck.

Whilst I was away in Boroma, Sergeant Ibrahim turned up again, complaining of headache, requesting further time off. He was told that the Doctor Sahib was away and would return in two days time. In the meantime, Doctor Sahib had left special instructions and a special medicine to treat the hair roots. The orderlies shaved his head, and painted it with Brilliant Green, which took over a week to wear off. The effect was brilliant. Sergeant Ibrahim never complained of headache, sacral backache or anything for the rest of the time that I was in Somaliland.

How to immunize a 120 man Company in 90 minutes

Take

One magnifying glass

One candle

One box of matches

Two sheets of emery paper

One effective nail file

Ten ½ inch stainless steel needles, of the non-disposable type we had then. These needles are on a small square stainless steel base, which is attached to the syringe.

Two non-disposable glass syringes, disposable ones have not yet been invented. Cylinders and plungers must not be mixed up. Otherwise one plunger will stick in the cylinder, and other plunger will be loose and contents escape.

One Spencer Wells artery forceps

Two stainless steel 1½ inch needles

One bottle of surgical spirit, if you haven't got any, go to quartermaster and get can of methylated spirit, same stuff only blue.

Two large packs or rolls of cotton wool

Seven twenty-cubic-millilitre bottles of TABT or whatever else is recommended, plus a spare

Self

Four Somali medical orderlies

Getting ready
One orderly tears cotton wool to bits and rolls up into small balls for use as swabs.

Self takes magnifying glass and examines the ten-½ inch needles, which have been used on 25 occasions before. Any small spots, stains or rust removed by polishing with emery paper.

Taking nail file, examine points for snags and bluntness with magnifying glass, and then sharpen needles. It is also useful to examine the 1½ inch ones, once in a blue moon.

Careful examination with magnifying glass reveals one needle without point, discard, two hardly any point, points bent to one side, discard. Two kinks in middle of shaft, query straightened last time used, put on unused syringe and jab left forearm, both bend, one breaks, neither penetrate skin, discard.

Problem, now only have 5 needles for 120 injections. Say, 'Sergeant how many boxes of ½ inch have we got?' Each box contained ten stainless steel needles.

Sergeant answers 'Two, Sahib.'

'When did we last order a box?'

'Two months Sahib.'

Knowing that you will now be able to ask for another box when this month's supply request is sent to Aden, without Colonel Matheson, crossing it off and writing alongside. 'You had one last month. Don't waste army supplies, we're not made of money.' I said 'Right we'd better open another box then.'

Box opened, and you wonder at the bright newness of the needles, and the pristine sharpness of points without snags, being aware that each needle will have to average forty injections.

Make sure fridge has been working and TABT or whatever has been kept in fridge ever since it arrived. If it hasn't do not tell anybody.

Notify officers in command, that you will start prompt at 10.30 the following morning. Taking single dose ampoules and new needles to officer's mess. Immunize them that night provided they buy the beer.

10.30 the following morning, a 120-man company of Somali infantry line up outside the MI room. Sergeants and corporals are done first while the needles are still sharp.

The line of infantry starts in front of self, sitting on the front of his desk. On the right hand side is a Somali orderly with a basket full of cotton wool balls and a tin of methylated spirits. His job is to wet the ball with methylated spirits and put into your right hand as the soldiers walk past. On the left side is another orderly with the two 1-½ inch needles and the seven bottles of stuff you are immunising with. His job is to remove the empty 10cc syringe form your hand when it is empty and replace it with a full one. One orderly remains in the MI room to assist if necessary, such as remove anyone who faints, tough soldiers often do that. The remaining orderly stands at the door, guiding the victims in, and keeping people with urgent messages, such as commanding officer's orderly, out.

I have practised my stab on the odd volunteer to get the angle correct. So that it goes under the skin and not into muscle.

On my right side, on a recently laundered and ironed towel, so it is still sterile, place the ½ inch needles after being boiled for two minutes, in a row. Just in front of needles place candle. Tell orderly with the methylated spirits, be very careful. Orderly with matches lights candle. We are now ready.

We start off, first orderly hands me swab, soaked in spirit. Soldier with left hand on hip, stands in front. I swab middle part of upper arm, and delicately, to start with, I push needle through skin, at angle to skin so that it only goes into fat underneath, squeeze in 1 centimetre dose.

Put needle in candle flame until it turns red-hot. Remove needle with Spencer Wells forceps and place at end of row of needles. It should be cool by time you come to it again, but in case it is not, pick up needle at front of row of needles with forceps, put on syringe and we are ready for the next soldier.

The syringe contains 10cc, that is ten doses; you never get ten out of it, usually nine, rarely eight. As soon as it is empty you hand to the orderly on your left, after removing needle, he hands you a full one and proceeds to fill empty one.

A rhythm starts:

Swab, stab, squeeze,

Put in candle flame, turn red hot,

Remove with forceps, end of row,

Pick up front, and off we go.

Swab, stab, squeeze etc. etc., etc

Rhythm starts, going great guns, sudden hiccup, soldier faints, third orderly grabs him pulls him out way, while next soldier steps over him and –

Swab, stab, squeeze

Gets going again.

Later a soldier faints as he steps through MI room door, no problem, that does not interrupt the rhythm, as two of his mates prop him against a nearby wall.

Hey presto, in 90 minutes it's done.

Faintees are sitting in chairs outside in fresh air, suffering ribald comments from their friends, you walk outside and do them while they are sitting.

It's done. Take magnifying glass and with emery paper clean the needles removing any bits of soot clinging to them. One of the new ones is so badly bent, it has to be discarded. Two of the old ones look a bit ragged so they go as well, leaving twelve for next time.

Disgusting, racial prejudice that, no it wasn't. I did a company of the Highland Light Infantry in an identical manner the following year, though then I only had one orderly to help me. On second thoughts, maybe it was racial, Scots being known to be inferior members of the English empire, wanting to be independent. Unfortunately if they ever get round to having a referendum, it will not be democratic, it will only be held in Scotland. Ordinary Englishmen like myself will not be allowed to vote for Scottish independence. The Scots won't, they like having their hand in someone else's pocket.

Dentistry

In addition to my efforts every six months a dentist came from Aden for a month. We had a visit whilst I was there. Because of the restrictions placed on him there was very little for him to do. British military staff and their families already had well kept teeth. Apart from inspection, cleaning and the odd filling there was not much else. He was not accompanied by a technician but knew how to make dentures and part-dentures. It did not matter he was not allowed to provide them. The Somali soldiers and families were allowed extractions and fillings and that was it. He told me that an awful lot of work was needed among the Somalis. Teeth beyond repair needed removing, but the Somalis would not allow extraction because they were the only teeth they had.

Within a week he had done all he could do and got bored. I got landed with him. Whether he was supposed to visit Burao or Boroma I don't know, but as he latched onto me like a limpet he did. Sergeant Abdullah Hersi who became my self-selected mentor and advisor (I always had one of those wherever I went) may have been acting on his own or on behalf of the other Somalis, when he told me it was a waste of time sending a dentist. The Somalis knew they needed treatment but it was no point going when all the dentist could do was extractions and could not replace them with dentures. Maybe I was being primed and recruited to act on their behalf, but I did act. I arranged an interview with Col MacWilliam and took the dentist along. We explained what needed doing and persuaded him to put in a request on our behalf. Col MacWilliam tried but no luck. 'Not army policy. There's no money, besides it's the job of the Colonial Medical Service to provide that.'

The fact that there was not a dentist in Somaliland was ignored. A Somali medical orderly could have been sent to Aden to train as a dental technician, but no, Somaliland was run on a shoe-string.

Marauding Bands Of Goats

These, and collecting firewood, the only source of heating and cooking, could be described as the biggest curse on the ecology of Somaliland. Somaliland appeared to be semi-arid bush desert, scrubby little acacia thorn and similar trees. The Somalis had to live on something and goats are a major source of food. These bands of goats could be found anywhere, eating everything! As they browsed, they ate every new shoot and all the green leaves below a certain level. The smaller, lighter goats were picked up by the herdsmen and put into the trees. They also carried a massive knife, known as a panga. With this, they chopped off large branches at the top of the tree, the branches fell down and the goats could eat the leaves. These branches would be picked up and taken into Hargeisa or the nearest village, for firewood. Gradually the countryside was converted into a desert.

British policy, combined with the agreement of local tribes, was that certain areas would be declared off limits for a period of 20 years. These areas covered anything from 20 to 50 square miles. This allowed the area to regenerate, and it was surprising how much greenery there was. There wasn't much grass but the number of trees and bushes was remarkable. They were full of game and that's where you would often see gerenuk. Gazelles with long legs, not a very big body, a tall neck, allowing them to browse on the top of the trees and shrubs. They stood on their long hind legs, propping themselves up with long forelegs, stretching their necks to browse on the top of the shrubs. They were graceful creatures. I was often in range with my 303 rifle, but I never felt like shooting them.

For a while the area was left alone, but certain Somalis, being individualists, and prone to take advantage of a situation, when they saw a little bit of greenery, they moved into the prohibited areas with their herds of goats. Every 2-3 weeks, all new areas prohibited to sheep, goats, donkeys, camels, cows etc., would be patrolled by a three-ton truck containing a platoon of Somali soldiers and sergeant, all armed with 303 rifles, and twenty rounds of ammunition. Any animal belonging to the above group, would be shot. There would be no recompense to the tribe or village concerned. It only had to happen once or twice for the locals to obey the law.

That didn't stop the odd bright spark, after an area had 15-20 years of growth, taking his goats in an area well away from the roads. Invariably one of the local villagers tipped off the authorities. A platoon of soldiers would be sent to the area, bivouac overnight, and next morning when the herd of goats or sheep were taken into the prohibited area, they were shot. In such a way, a man of 55 - 60 might lose his pension, or a young man who has been working abroad 5 or 6 years, lose his bride price.

Hunting

Whenever I went on one of my peregrinations, to Buroa, the Eastern Protectorate, or Borama, I always took a rifle with me. I shot a gazelle - usually a dheero or an auwl - on the way, which I took to the officers' mess and we had a pleasant meal, a change from the usual goat, tough grisly sheep, or awful camel.

SOMALILAND PROTECTORATE

General Game Licence
(Ordinance No. 18 of 1955)

NOT TRANSFERABLE

Licence No. 000280

Station *HARGEISA*

Date of issue *15 July 1959*

This GENERAL GAME LICENCE is issued to *Lt. W.O GOLDTHORP.*

of (address) *OFFICERS MESS. SOMALILAND SCOUTS   HARGEISA*

and entitles him to hunt the animals shown in the Fourth Schedule to the Fauna Conservation Ordinance, 1955 subject to such restrictions as may be imposed under the Ordinance.

All game killed on this licence must be recorded in the space provided on the reverse of this licence.

This licence is valid for one year from the date of issue unless cancelled or suspended.

This licence does not entitle the holder to capture animals nor to be in possession of live animals.

Fee paid Shs. 40/= Resident.

~~Fee Paid Shs.100/= Visitor.~~

....
(signature of holder)

....
(signature of issuing officer)
DISTRICT COMMISSIONER, HARGEISA

AUTHENTICATED

....
ACCOUNTANT GENERAL

ORIGINAL .. To be handed to holder.
DUPLICATE .. Voucher for Accounts.
TRIPLICATE .. Fauna Conservation Officer.
QUADRUPLICATE Office Copy.

Having developed my secondary profession as mess butcher, I was often be asked to go looking for dinner. Eventually I bought a Somaliland hunting licence. It cost 40 shillings and it allowed me so many warthogs, so many dheero, auwls, gerenuk, kudu, buffalo and an oryx, plus a couple of lions and a few other things. In fact, I only took the dhero and auwl. I never found a kudu or a buffalo. You couldn't eat lion, so there was no point shooting one. I once came across a herd of oryx, which I knew were getting rare. They did look marvellous and I was a bit tempted to shoot one, mainly for the horns. By that time, I had quite a collection of horns, which I tried in various ways to preserve, hoping to bring some home to get them mounted. All I ended up with was a stinking set of horns covered in ants. There didn't seem to be any point shooting an oryx. Instead, I shot them with my camera. I was too far away and the photographs didn't come out very well. I should have had a long focus lens. There was a little gazelle that ran around in the underbush, a dic-dic. I shot one of those with a shotgun. We had a stew made, but didn't like it, so I didn't bother with dic-dics any more.

There were game birds – they were supposed to be greater bustards and lesser bustards. The greater bustards were protected and off limits. I was allowed two lesser bustards, but didn't find any. There was another nice tasty bird, in shape resembling a partridge, but in size a pheasant, known as a yellow neck.

There were also sand grouse. Shooting sand grouse, you had to be near an open water at dawn. There was a place, about two hours

A Yellow Neck

away from Hargeisa. We usually slept there overnight, to be present at the crack of dawn when the birds came in for a drink. Thousands came; you had fifty minutes to do your shooting. For a shotgun, I used a single barrel Greener gun, a rather heavy, long barrelled gun, used for riot control. It fired something a bit longer than a twelve-bore cartridge.

I got a supply of twenty cartridges from the Armoury every time I took one of these Greener guns with me. When the sand grouse came, they flew in large dense crowds above the open water. I'd fire a couple of cartridges into what we called the 'black'. Each cartridge would bring down 20-30 sand grouse. Then, we spent the rest of the morning firing at individual sand grouse as they flew past, fast on the wing. The sand grouse were taken back. My bearer and some of the others were bribed to do the plucking and gutting. They were fat little birds and three provided a good meal, the rest I distributed around the officers' wives in the married quarters.

I have a letter, addressed to the Commanding Officer, Somaliland Scouts, 'Shooting Incident at Arapsiyo.' I had taken the dentist with me, shooting sand grouse. I had warned him to always shoot into the air, he got a bit excited and shot along the tuog (a dry river bed). The Somalis dug down into the dry river bed to get water for their own use and to water their animals. On this occasion, a Somali lady was bending down, digging in a hole in the riverbed and my dentist colleague hadn't noticed her. She was a fair way off, but her rear end and other bits got splattered. As soon as I reported the incident to the commanding officer, the dentist was promptly sent back to Aden - the Colonel being fully aware that in a day or so, a complaint would arrive from the tribe involved and they would demand compensation. The complaint duly arrived and strangely enough, the dentist couldn't be found!

Exploring beyond the east of Buroa, myself and the Staff Sergeant would go with Mohamed, my orderly, and one of the Somali soldiers and stay out for a couple of days. We'd take a rifle with us, as we'd been told that the area contained kudu. It was mountainous, so we always took a compass and maps. Somaliland had been mapped from the air. The maps were extremely accurate. Wherever we stopped, we left the Somali soldier looking after the truck, and took compass bearings and walked into the mountains. If possible, we tried to keep the truck in sight, but if not, as we went along we left markers, breaking a branch or making a little pile of rocks. We never walked more than three hours, if we hadn't got where we wanted to or found anything, we always returned via the way we came. We never did a circular tour as we felt we might lose our

M. I. ROOM,
HQ SOMALILAND SCOUTS,
HARGEISA,
SOMALILAND PROTECTORATE.

District Commissioner,
HARGEISA.

Commanding Officer,
Somaliland Scouts.   28 Nov 59.

Re Shooting Accident ARAPSIYO

1.   Between 0815 hrs and 0915 hrs I was shooting sand
grouse at ARAPSIYO, using a 12 bore shot gun.

2.   At 0930 hrs as I was preparing to depart, a Somali
girl was brought to me complaining of being hit with shot
gun pellets.

3.   On examination I found that she had a perforation
wound of the upper lip, an exit and entry wound being
seen, the pellet not entering the gum, I could not feel
any pellet in the lip.

4.   There was also a mark on her Rt arm, whether a
pellet had entered or grazed I could not say.

5.   I applied dressing and supplied some tablets to
prevent any infection. The wounds were only of a minor
nature.

                                                    Lieut
                                                    RMO

bearings and not get back to the truck, except on one occasion
when we took a guide with us.

Returning from one of these treks, hot, sweaty, unshaven and
dusty, we met the nursing sister in charge of the local hospital. A
rather attractive young lady - half Somali, half Indian, who had
just returned from England after five years training to become a
State Registered Nurse, and State Certified Midwife, accompanied
her. I can still remember the sneer as she looked down her nose at
myself and my companion with deep disdain, being more used to
the better-dressed gentlemen that she had met when training in
England, than the sweat and dust stained, unshaven, young men
she had just been introduced to. My friend was quite smitten by
her. Training a local girl as a fully qualified nurse and midwife had

been a good idea, but I could not imagine that highly sophisticated, westernized young lady settling in Somaliland, nor taking a local Somali as a husband.

A different type of hunting

It is surprising what jobs get landed on the Medical Officer. Everyone thinks he's got lots of time to spare. I mentioned previously that I had become the officers and sergeants wives 'little darling' by popping down and discussing family matters with them. I received a deputation from the wives in Hargeisa. They had been giving serious consideration to the following topic – the Governor's 19 or 20 year old daughter who was at University had come to stay with her parents for the three months long summer vacation. It had been decided that the Doc would be an appropriate and respectable escort; the wives had come to inform me that I had been selected. It was a bit of shock when I told them I was married and my wife was due a baby in a month or two's time! Needless to say, they didn't press on with the idea.

Pets

Whenever anybody went anywhere, I got landed with their pet. For a full 3 months, I acquired a Heinz 57 black dog, by the name

Afternoon relaxation in the officers' mess. Major Bill Thorp, Big Black Bob, and the author in his longhi. Fortunately the cigarette was in his right hand!

of Buster. One of the Captains and his family, having been out three years, had gone on leave. Pets were numerous.

In Borama, they kept a ground squirrel, rather dangerous, if a ground squirrel bit you, you might get rabies. There were numerous pets in the sergeants' mess - a baby dic-dic, an oryx calf, a cheetah kitten and lion cub that played together. There were a few young ladies working in the colonial service - one would walk around with a full-grown cheetah on a lead. Major Thorpe had a large black Labrador, who was with him constantly - Big Black Bob. I have a nice print of Major Thorpe and Big Black Bob, on the main balcony. It shows me in my longi, doing something that I have reprimanded my patients for doing for years, that is, smoking. It must have been one of my Players Perfectus.

Recruits

A recruiting party went around the tribes once a year. There was little employment in Somaliland, being a soldier was good, steady employment and considered a worthwhile profession. There were far more volunteers than needed. Each tribe had its quota. It was not a case of forcing a tribe to fill that quota; it was preventing a tribe from over-filling it. The troops were always high-class recruits, mainly from the Chieftain's families and their close friends. They spent six months confined to the training barracks, where they learned the principles of drill and using a rifle. They were also taught to read and write English. The Somaliland Scouts weren't a fancy outfit. There were 303 rifles, bayonets, a few bren-guns and that was it. If there were any heavy machines guns I never saw any. They didn't have mortars, and certainly no artillery!

Trouble

As was usual in my various jobs, I ended up getting into a couple of scrapes. The first one was extremely serious, involving the Colonel's lady. The second one should have been serious, and would have been serious back in England - it was more embarrassing serious than serious, as I stood there with two gentlemen, supposedly reprimanding me, trying not to break down into hilarious laughter.

The Colonel and his wife were a nice, Northern Irish couple. They had had about six children - one or two of which were with them most of the time. Periodically, four hooligans from various boarding schools in England, descended to create chaos. The Colonel's lady developed superficial thrombo-phlebitis, a red, extremely tender, hard strip down the leg. Treatment was to apply a dressing of Glycerine and Ichthammol, an oily black tarry substance. Dressings had to be applied to the vein, which were then bandaged on. I had been visiting the lady at home and applying the dressings for a week, when I ran out of Glycerine and Ichthammol. I got a new 500 millilitre bottle went round to the house, into the bedroom, where they had just had a brand new carpet (admittedly they hadn't paid for it, it was an Army carpet) fitted. I was in the process of applying the dressing, when the tip of my toe knocked the new 500-millilitre bottle of Glycerine Ichthammol all over the new carpet! I was not popular, for the rest of her treatment, she attended the MI room. An Indian trader was called in to clean it all up.

Smallpox

As far as I know, I was involved in the last epidemic of smallpox. This was the same smallpox epidemic that I had come across previously, when I was in Dhala. Smallpox was endemic in Ethiopia. Smallpox had been reported in Djibouti, port and capital of French Somaliland – a little province to the west of British Somaliland. The colonial medical authorities were worried that it would spread into Somaliland itself. They had a word with the Colonel; he contacted me and asked if I could help. They couldn't get any smallpox vaccine. This was usually supplied from Nairobi. Their samples of smallpox vaccine were in thin, capillary glass tubes that could be used for one or two people. Army vaccine came in large ampoules, already dried and water was added to reconstitute it.

When vaccinating against smallpox, you put the vaccine onto the outer aspect of the upper arm, and gently prick through the little drop of vaccine to puncture the skin several times without bringing blood. A proportion of cases would take, but about 10% had to be re-done. My way was a little different. In view of the fact that I might not see the people again, I wanted to make sure it took. I always used a sharp needle and made a tiny cross in the middle of the vaccine bubble and made sure it bled. This guaranteed a 100% take. I had been re-vaccinated again when it was known I was going to Aden and we re-vaccinated each other every 6 months. Once or twice, I actually vaccinated myself. My antibody level for smallpox at that time was very high. I got hardly any reaction – just a little red spot where I had done the vaccination.

Nairobi had run out of vaccine. I contacted Colonel Matheson and asked him to send a supply. He responded quickly and within a day, an aircraft had brought a large box of Army vaccine. I gathered my Somali orderlies together. We got a map, worked out the main routes that the mammy wagons and other traders would use from French Somaliland to Hargeisa. There were four main routes. I re-vaccinated all the Somali soldiers that were in the fort at that time, using the medical orderlies to do the vaccination so that they knew how I wanted it done. I selected the best four, had a word with the adjutant and he lent me 8 other soldiers. I made them into teams of three, worked out the best place to go, on the main roads and signed the forms so that they could collect their rations.

I arranged with the transport officer that a three-ton truck would take them, deposit them at the four points selected, and pick them up two weeks later. They were under instructions to stop all vehicles, explain the situation, that there was smallpox in Djibouti, where they had come from, and we would like everyone who hadn't been vaccinated to be vaccinated before they reached Hargeisa, and they would do it for them. Everything went well; we didn't have any cases of smallpox in Hargeisa or the eastern part of the protectorate. Three weeks later Colonel MacWilliam asked to see me. He gave me a message of congratulations from the Governor, and asked that I give the Governor's thanks to the MI section for their help.

3-4 weeks later, there was an entirely different interview in the Commanding Officer's office. I was called to the Colonel's office and, on entering, I saw Colonel MacWilliam with a gentleman in a white civilian tropical suit.

'Hello Bill.' I wasn't asked to stand to attention.

'Will you sit down, but before you do, I would like to introduce you to Mr So and So, who is the secretary to the Judge So and So, who is our senior magistrate in Somaliland.'

'Pleased to meet you,' says I, as we shook hands.

'Now, Bill,' says the Colonel, 'why did you arrange armed road blocks on all the four roads leading from French Somaliland to Hargeisa?'

I said 'What armed road blocks? All I've done is send my bearers out accompanied by a couple of soldiers, asked them to stop every vehicle coming through and advise them to be vaccinated'.

The Judge's representative then informed me 'We've had a complaint. It was from an Indian trader, who was coming with a load of goods from French Somaliland. The men you sent out had set up a full road block, made him get out of his truck at gunpoint.

When he refused to be vaccinated, they told him they'd shoot him if he wasn't, and forcibly vaccinated him'.

Horrified, I said 'But I never arranged that!'

The Colonel said 'You did arrange that there would be somebody on all the main roads into Hargeisa, that they would have some smallpox vaccine, so they could vaccinate, didn't you?'

So I said 'Yeh'.

'And you signed the request for rations for all of the twelve soldiers involved, didn't you?'

'Yes,' I said.

'You are aware, Bill, that when you sign for a Somali soldier to be given a week's ration, you also authorize him to draw his 303 rifle from the armoury together with 20 rounds of ammunition'.

'No,' I said. 'I just get sent out here to sort a problem out for somebody else, I have received no instructions and I've never been given any information about the rules and regulations of how the Somaliland Scouts are run.'

They were good Somali soldiers. They were good orderlies. I had asked them to make sure as many people as possible were vaccinated, so they did. Very efficiently, although it wasn't legal by British law! Each group, when left, built a dry stone post each side of the track, found a long branch that was laid across. Every passing vehicle was stopped in front of the branch with two soldiers pointing their 303 rifles. Everybody was told to get out, and everybody was vaccinated, regardless. As the legal representative told this story, the Colonel nodding and listening, bigger and bigger grins began to appear on their faces. It was just typical behaviour of a Somali chap, doing his best to help at the time.

'Ah, well,' says the legal secretary, 'I think what we had best do is keep our heads down, say nothing and hope to God nobody has a word with the press in England, or the Government finds out. If it does, all hell will be let loose.'

Then I really upset them. I gave them the bill that Colonel Matheson had sent for the smallpox vaccine he had supplied. No one had thought of that, it was army property and had to be paid for.

When I think about how the Somalis behave, when we looked at them from an English point of view, our relationships and expectations were a bit strange. I don't want to upset anybody in the Republic of Ireland, but we English called our Somalis 'African Irishmen'. Both races have the ability to drive Englishmen up the wall, but in spite of that you can't help liking them.

Gun Running

It was illegal for a Somali to own a gun. Well, at least own a gun without a licence. We kept an eye on our own 303 rifles, but most of our soldiers could be trusted with them. If they went out on patrol, they were allowed to draw their 303 rifles and 20 rounds of ammunition. On rare occasions, one would desert with rifle and ammunition and hop it into the Ogaden, part of Ethiopia. There, he could get £200 for his rifle and ammunition, if he wanted to sell it, which for a man earning £5 a month was a lot of money. It had the disadvantage that he would not be able to come back to British Somaliland.

The Somalis considered the Ogaden as part of their territory. We had taken it over in 1940 when the Italians had been chased out and the Somalis were extremely upset after the war when we gave it back to the Ethiopians. The Somalis of the Ogaden weren't very friendly with the Ethiopians and there was a bit of fighting going on. There was a regular market for rifles, which were smuggled through Berbera and carried through into the Ogaden. We had received information that a caravan of camels carrying rifles would be travelling from Berbera through the eastern part of the protectorate to the Ogaden. It was decided to send a company of Somali soldiers to stop them. I was talking this over with Nipper Harris, when he said:

'It's a pity you can't come along, Bill. It should be interesting. We're not looking for any fighting or anything like that.'

I thought about it for a minute and then said:

'Leave it with me.'

I was planning another trip into the bush. I went to see the adjutant, mentioned this trip, and said:

'We've never had the opportunity or any experience in setting up a regimental aid post. This would be a marvellous opportunity for me to take four or five orderlies, organize everything, get the equipment, and practise setting up a regimental aid post as we would if you were planning an actual battle.'

It was all a con on my part. The adjutant said, 'Right, Bill, that's a good idea. I'll have a word with the Colonel'.

Later that day, the message came back, 'The Colonel thinks that's a jolly good idea. You get it arranged'.

We did it properly - organized the tents, worked out the appropriate equipment that we would need to take with us, borrowed a jeep and a three-ton truck, I took my 303 rifle out as usual, because I intended to go shooting, and we set off.

There were several tracks and paths, some that would take vehicles, others only camel caravans, leading up from Berbera, on the coast to the mountains in the higher areas of Somaliland. We camped at the top of one of these. A conference was held between the senior Somali sergeants, and the British Army officers. Once the conference got going, it was obvious that the Somalis were well aware who was transporting the rifles and where they were going. It was pointed out that none of these rifles were going to be used in Somaliland; they were going to the Ogaden. The caravan's escort consisted of armed Somali tribesmen, belonging to the same tribe that half the members of the company belonged to. Neither side were prepared to fight each other.

They knew which track the caravan was coming up. There was a decoy caravan carrying twenty ancient Martini Henry single shot breechloaders and a few rounds of ammunition. This decoy caravan had no guards; it was supposed to contain about ten camels, in charge of an ancient old Somali, young women and boys. It had been specially arranged for us to find.

After the conference, pickets were set up at the end of all the tracks coming up from Berbera, except the one that the Somalis knew that the camel caravan was coming up. It was pointed out to us, quite sensibly, that they didn't intend to fight it, and there was no point us fighting it because Somaliland was going to be independent, looking after itself in a few years time.

Searching for arms, a rare *(a Somali portable home). The curved framework can be seen on the camels*

We all settled down - Somalis and English - to enjoy ourselves for three days. The Somalis, of course, expected us to behave like English officers, when out in the bush. As it became dusk, we all had a wash, put on our evening dress (white shirt, pressed white trousers, black shoes and cummerbund) and had our evening meal. A table was set out with white linen and the appropriate knives, forks etc., under an acacia tree, on which four Tilley lamps were hanging.

The four English officers, including myself, went through the rigmarole (we only had beer and whisky) of having a mess dinner. We toasted the Queen at the end of the meal, before we smoked, our Somali bearers, togged up to the nines, carrying out the duties of waiters. The rest of the Somali soldiers who'd already had their evening meal, sat round smoking, watching and criticizing. The Somalis seemed to know more about the protocol, and how a proper mess dinner should be conducted, than we did.

Nothing happened, the decoy caravan never turned up, we had no word of the other one, whether it only existed in the informant's imagination, we never found out. Everybody returned home highly satisfied with the three days. It was a strange place, Somaliland. You got the feeling that they weren't all that keen to be independent, as though it seemed a good idea to have these strange British people, spending money to run the health service, the hospitals, and paying for people to be soldiers. As far as I could make out, a British political officer ran the British Somaliland Independence Party. There were no demonstrations, riots or anything like that, that was normally found in independence parties elsewhere in the British Empire.

Lieutenant-Colonel William Fredrick Goldthorp. TA, RADC

When I got back from the gun smuggling trip, I found a telegram from my father. The telegram simply stated 'WIFE AND SON DOING VERY WELL'. William had put in an appearance on 28 September 1959. I can't understand it - there was I, trying my best to get out of the army as quickly as possible, and some sort of psychological virus must have transmitted itself in 1959, to my beloved elder son. William is now a Lieutenant Colonel in the Territorial Army. I bought him a State Patrol outfit when he was six years old and he is still wearing it.

The information was three days old, how do you congratulate your wife, three days later, as fast as possible? That turned out to be another problem! We didn't have telephones or telegrams; there was a radiotelegraph department, fifteen shillings a word. That was nearly a day's pay. It *was* a day's pay when income tax had been taken off it. Of course, I had the advantage that the Somali radio operator couldn't speak English very well. Mrs Margaret Goldthorp became one word, Brumby Wood Nursing Home became one word, Scunthorpe, Lincolnshire became one word, and United Kingdom became one word. The problem then was the message? It has intrigued my wife ever since. Message, eight words: 'BANG ON, FIRST TIME, GOOD SHOW, LOVE BILL'.

I have just been shouted at, AGAIN, by her who must be obeyed. She peeked over my shoulder. Apparently it was one word, BULL-SEYE, not BANG ON. I must have saved another 15 shillings.

I sent a message to Colonel Matheson, asking him if it was possible to arrange by telegram or other means, to get in touch with Interflora and have some flowers sent. Although he tried, that didn't come off. I sat down that night and wrote a long letter to Margaret, which took a week to get there.

A holiday souvenir

Young Somali soldiers have the same bad habits as British soldiers. Venereal disease did not seem to be much of a problem. Mainly because it was dealt with by the Colonial Medical Service. The officers at Boroma had invited me over for a couple of nights, because the Somali recruits were having a passing out parade. After which they had six weeks leave and went home with six months pay in their pockets. The sensible ones went home and used it to buy goats and other animals, which were added to the family flock, to increase over the years, so that eventually they would become an independent male. The flock would go towards the bride price when they married. The first day, I attended the passing out parade. The second day, Norman Rankin and I went and shot four auwl and brought them back to arrange a passing out party for the recruits. The first took three shots before we hit it.

Not all of them were sensible and went home. A third didn't get any further than the red light district of the town of Boroma. I was called, when the leave was over, six weeks later.

'We've got thirteen lads here, there's something wrong with their John Thomases', says the Major in charge. 'I think they've caught something they shouldn't have caught.'

Sure enough, they had. That was the only time I ever saw a

Major Norman Rankin, CO Boroma

Auwl for the Passing Out Party

primary chancre for syphilis. Syphilis had virtually disappeared from England, since the advent of penicillin. There are three stages to syphilis – primary, secondary and tertiary. The primary is a hard spot which appears on the penis. If you rub a glass on it, put it under the microscope, shine a light through it, you can see the little spirochetes wriggling about. On this day, I saw not one, but 13! We started treatment with large doses of intra-muscular penicillin and sorted it out.

Ration Allowance

In these out of the way places, the English officer was supposed to live a European lifestyle. He had an extra ration allowance, untaxed. I hadn't realized, when up in Dhala, because the officers' mess never asked for it, I just paid my routine mess bill. A couple of months later, I found an unexpected £60 in my bank account. I couldn't make out what it was and went to see Colonel Matheson to find out. It was my ration allowance, 20 shillings per day for the time I was in Dhala. In Somaliland, the ration allowance was 35 shillings per day, but the officers' mess only asked for 5 shillings.

How did that happen? All highly organized. We were in close contact with an Indian company known as Chattergee Somebody and Co. You could almost say they were part of the British Empire in East Africa and Arabia, because wherever we were, they were! It started when a couple of Indians started a trading company 80 or 90 years previously, they had married, had large families and spread all over the area. In any small town or city, you would find Chattergee Somebody & Co., the Senior Manager in some way related to the original partners. They provided almost anything and at reasonable prices. If you felt generous or stupid, you could contact Fortnum and Mason and have a fantastic, expensive hamper sent. But you could do just as well getting it from Chattergee, Somebody & Co. They supplied us with tinned and dried stuff, at very reasonable rates. Fresh meat – I provided that, except for the goats and sheep.

What about fresh vegetables and fruit? That should be very expensive. No it wasn't. 50 or 60 years ago, as usual, it was the sergeants that sorted it out. There were areas around Hargeisa where there was open water. It was as though underground rivers had come to the top for a little time. Some of these pools were quite deep and large, where we often went swimming. The sergeants had taken their bearers and started small market gardens growing their own crops – potatoes, peas, carrots, salads etc. The bearers started proper market gardens. Now their descendants were still running them and supplying us and the rest of the Europeans with fresh salad and vegetables, quite cheaply. We didn't do so well with apples and pears, but there was no shortage of oranges, lemons, limes, melons, bananas, mangoes, avocado pears etc.

My living costs in Somaliland weren't very high, just a few cigarettes and a not too excessive amount of Tennents lager. Tennents was the only lager we had. By the time I had been trundling along for 3-4 hours in my one ton truck, feeling hot, thirsty and dusty, I could see the image of a bottle of Tennents sitting on the bonnet of my truck. The mess orderlies at Buroa got quite used to me. As soon as they saw my one-ton truck turn into the mess compound, one of them would be pouring out a cold bottle of Tennents lager. By the time my six months was up in Somaliland, I was building up a nice nest egg at the rate of £2 per day.

Dracula

We had, of course, wherever the Army was, our own cinema, just outside the fort in Hargeisa. As usual, it didn't have a roof, which could be a bit of a problem in the rainy season. In the middle of a very interesting film, the heavens would open, you couldn't stay and watch the rest of the film because you'd have to swim to get home. It came to a rapid end, we had to organize another showing. The shows were free. The Somali soldiers sat on the floor in the main part of the cinema. We had a few rickety chairs on a little platform at the back.

I probably saw *What Lola Wants, Lola Gets* which was a film about Faust, only this time Faust was a fat middle aged American who wanted to play baseball, the devil was a she-devil called Lola. I had seen the film in England, seen it on board ship, in Aden, in Dhala, and now in Somaliland. I would see it again in the Trucial Oman Scouts. The one I remember was the Hammer Horror Production released two to three years earlier, in full colour, with bright red dripping all over the place, *Dracula*.

That was an interesting evening, when the film was over. We found out subsequently that the Somalis had a legend about a blood-sucking woman. We had a little problem at the end of the film. The lights went out in the cinema, and there was a large gang of Somali soldiers who needed to walk through the black, midnight air, to their barracks. This again was when the old witchdoctor – the Hakim Sahib – came back into his own.

As my fellow officers waited to give me a lift back to the mess, I walked back with two large Somali sergeants, one holding each hand, and two or three Somali soldiers holding theirs, a large bunch of soldiers in front of me and a large bunch of soldiers behind as they jostled, moving around, touching me to make sure I was there. The Somalis were great gossips about what English officers got up to. We had gone skinny dipping at the swimming hole a few times. They noticed that I always wore, under my top uniform, a little gold chain with a gold cross that Margaret had given me just before I left for Aden. They'd also noticed that a cross was very useful to chase off vampires. They felt very safe walking back without lights, just a bit of starlight, with the Hakim Sahib with them. They knew that all Englishmen were Christians and not proper religious people like themselves, who were Muslims, and that crosses had something to do with Christianity. They had never come across one before that actually wore a cross and it was worn discreetly under my uniform so nobody ever saw it unless I as swimming.

I think they thought I had some extra kind of status, in addition to being an officer, doctor, teacher, wizard and wise man etc., I must be from a family that was specially religious and produced priests, like their mullahs, who also ran in families. I didn't mind escorting this large group of Somali soldiers back to the fort, I was right in the middle, if Dracula had been there, he'd have gone for one of those on the outside!

The Wedding

Around September/October of that year, we had a proper English wedding in the little Anglican Church in Hargeisa, the groom an officer, about 30 years old, and his bride (whom I'd never seen before until the wedding) in her late twenties. They had met in Somaliland. I wasn't a guest, but like a lot of non-guests, I went to have a look and took several photographs outside the church. There is one of all his officer friends lined up with swords out of their scabbards, pointed downwards before making an arch, another with the bride and groom coming through the arch, and a final one at the church gate with their attendants - a little boy about four in white shirt and dark red velvet trousers, and two little girls of five or six, in pink velvet dresses.

It's strange to think, when looking at that photograph, that those children will now be nearly fifty years old. I would have liked to include one those photographs in this book, but because of the

The Wedding Arch

story I am going to tell, I thought it best to leave the photograph out. I don't want them to be identified.

About a week before the wedding, the groom came into my office and said, 'Doc, can I have a quiet word with you?'

'Yes, of course. Sergeant, would you go outside and close the door.'

Then, he made the strangest request, which I had to ask him to repeat.

'Doc, I'm getting married next week. Could you let me have a supply of those Durex that I believe all doctors carry?'

I had to say 'Pardon?', because it was a bit of a shock. It was the first and only time in two years National Service that anybody came and asked me for a supply of army Durex. The squaddies were supposed to come and take a supply before they went on leave. They weren't for contraceptive purposes, but to prevent nasty diseases. The other married officers must have been practising some sort of contraception, because they only had small families. It was probably the super thin gossamer lubricated supplied by Durex all over the world in gross boxes! In my early years, I was a regular customer of Durex gross boxes, which I could get at 50% discount. I supplied most of my married pals that I'd grown up with at Crowle, or gone to the grammar school with. A non-profit organization, I let my friends have the 50% discount.

My answer was 'I don't know where they are, we'll have to look for them'. I looked through the desk drawers, nothing could be found. Then, I pulled at the top drawer just above the place where your knees go; it stuck, I gave a big heave, it opened, and sure enough there was a box of Durex. I opened it, took a big handful and gave them to the groom. I put the lid on, closed the drawer and forget all about them.

There is, of course, a marked difference between super, gossamer thin lubricated in hermetically sealed packets and army issue condoms. Being the army, they're as cheap as possible! They were in little yellow envelopes, certainly not gossamer thin, and the lubrication was talcum powder. Perhaps that's why the squaddies wouldn't use them!

The wedding came and went; he went off on his honeymoon and life continued. Three weeks later, I was looking for something else in that top, stuck drawer. It was difficult to open, I gave it a great heave; it suddenly came unstuck. The packet of Durex came flying out, crashed on the end of the drawer, flew open, Durex flew everywhere. I said something like 'SHIT' and proceeded to gather them up to put back in the box.

The box was almost empty, and suddenly, a little white wiggly thing caught my eye. On closer examination, there were three or four tiny white grubs. Strange, thinks I. I opened one of the Durex packets, looked at it, didn't have to unroll it, it was the teat, there were three or four tiny holes in it. I took another one, unrolled it, three or four more tiny holes. Took another one, there were so many holes in it, it looked like a fishing net!

'Sergeant, do you know where they keep the rest of these boxes of preventatives that Europeans use?'

'I think there's four boxes in that cupboard, Sahib.'

We opened the cupboard and there were four boxes. The boxes weren't sealed, we opened them, turned them over and sure enough, at the bottom of each box, little white grubs. An investigation ensued; inspected several samples; all full of holes!

I sat down, elbows on the table, head in my hands, and thought 'Oh, God. Those were not the sort of things that you would inspect carefully before use - in bed, at night, when it's dark.'

I rushed round to the adjutant's office, burst in and said,

'Do you know where Captain so and so has gone for his honeymoon?'

'I haven't a clue, Doc. Made a special purpose of not telling us. I know he hasn't gone back to England. Why do you want to know?'

'Well, there's something I'd like to get in contact with him about'.

'He'll be on leave for several months, but he's coming back in the New Year, and he'll be joining the King's African Rifles in Kenya. If it's that serious, you could always send a letter to the adjutant of the KAR and he'll keep it until he gets there.'

Thinks – five or six months will be too damn late! Her interesting condition is going to be quite obvious by then. Best keep my mouth shut! I've spent the rest of my life firmly convinced that that married couple would start their family ten or eleven months after the wedding, much earlier than they expected. Somewhere, probably in England, is a respectable professional man of 42, hopefully happily married, with a family. Or, it could be an equally 42-year-old respectable, married lady who by the look of her mother would be quite attractive and very charming. She will also have a family. Who's to blame? The army or me?

The army just said 'We send you boxes of Durex so that you can hand them out to the soldiers when they go on leave, so they won't get VD Of course, nobody will come and get them. They get VD in any case.'

I had no idea how long those packets of Durex had been there; I'd never asked for any new ones. Nobody told us how to maintain and look after the supplies of Durex.

Nobody told us that there was something in Africa that liked to eat Durex! I have realized, subsequently, in Africa, there is something that eats everything. I reckon if you look round in Africa, you could find something that eats granite. Of course, one shouldn't be surprised, rubber is vegetable matter. It's made from the latex sap of rubber trees. Rubber trees evolved in Brazil and are grown in Malaya, Burma and South East Asia. So, why the H–ll is there a weevil in Africa that eats them?

The Parade

The information went round that the Colonel had decided to hold a full parade of the Scouts the following week, when he wanted to make an important statement. It was partly about discipline, but I think there was something about the future. What was going to happen when independence came. Shortly afterwards, I bumped into the adjutant, asked him and he confirmed it. I told him my knowledge of drill was non-existent and would I be required to be present. At lunch, unfortunately, the adjutant said he had had a word with the Colonel and yes, I was expected to be present.

'Oh, God,' I said, 'my drills hopeless. All I'll do is make a fool of myself and a laughing stock of the rest of the Officers. Can't you get me out of it?'

'Doesn't seem like it, Doc.'

'You know, he doesn't even let me salute him.'

The adjutant said, 'Leave it to me, Doc, we'll get something sorted out'.

It was arranged that my senior sergeant would get all the orderlies together; they'd march out and do all the stamping and shouting that usually happens when soldiers march about. Then line up in two rows, in front of the MI section. Then when the Sergeant moved off towards the right hand side and stood at attention, I was to march out. I can still remember it. Six paces forwards, right turn, seven paces forwards, left turn, two paces forwards, stand at attention, stamp your feet a lot and stand easy. When it was all over, I had to turn round, I think it's called about turn, which is also accompanied by a lot of feet stamping. Then, I had to march forwards two paces, stand at attention and shout 'Squad dismissed', which meant we could all bugger off.

The great day came. Every available Somali soldier and every available English officer and sergeant was present. I marched out as instructed and stood in front of the group of medical orderlies. The Colonel came mounted on a horse. None of us had seen a horse for ages; we didn't know there was a horse in Somaliland. Ponies, yes, but never a horse! He didn't look comfortable. He rode his horse to the front of the parade. I think he was on the horse because it made him high up and he thought his voice would carry. He proceeded to give a dissertation. I hadn't a clue what he was on about I don't think my Somali medical orderlies had a clue either. I can't even remember if it was in English or Somali. It was probably in English, because an interpreter didn't accompany him. When it was all over, he turned his horse round and rode out through the gate with a look of relief on his face.

Prior to the parade, for a few days, there had been a new game in the officers' mess. It was known as 'training Doc', where I would be put through my paces by several officers giving advice. This was usually in the evening, after the evening meal. The officers' comments were accompanied by about 2-3 bottles of lager. I as the victim wasn't allowed any, otherwise I wouldn't remember what I was supposed to do.

The night of the parade, matters were discussed in the officers' mess. At that time, if you learned the language of the place you were in, you got 7s. 6d. per day extra. It was quite useful I suppose if you were in Germany because you learned a useful language and whilst you were in Germany, you got 7s. 6d. per day. It wasn't too bad in Aden because Arabic was spoken over a fair amount of the Middle East, so that's a useful language. Not quite so useful, unless you're going to spend your life in East Africa, is Swahili, but God Almighty, what the use of Somali is, I don't know, as soon as you left the place, you lost your 7s. 6d. a day. Several of the majors and captains had tried to learn Somali. It was a very hard language and I gathered the Colonel had been learning it for three years! It was considered that if the Colonel had given his speech in Somali, he would have had to learn it off by heart, and then the sergeant major, who was a Somali, would have had to be present, so that he could speak the words in the correct, proper manner, after the colonel said each sentence. The Colonel would give his version, and the interpreter would translate it into proper Somali.

There was also a discussion as to where the horse came from and it was noticed how quiet the horse was. The horse was almost completely white, it was decided that the white wasn't its proper colour. They'd found a horse so ancient and quiet that it had turned white with age! I was informed by some of the other younger officers that the riding ability of the Colonel, a first-class infantry-man, was such that he was likely to fall off a horse that was standing still.

Locum

At the end of November, my replacement finally arrived. At the beginning of December, the Italian doctor who ran the hospital at Berbera had to return home urgently. It would be a couple of weeks before they could get a replacement. The Colonial Service asked if I could help out. The Colonel said that - in view of the fact that our regular MO has arrived, we'll let you borrow Bill. This probably impressed the Colonial Service and made the Colonel in Command of the Somaliland Scouts feel very good. It did have an effect on Colonel Matheson; however, who was to say later on, when I'd relieved somebody and they were returning 'Put Bill Goldthorp on the next plane back. He doesn't mind going where I send him. He's alright when he's there, but I can never get him to come back!'

Before I left for Berbera, I was called to the CO's office.

'Bill,' he said, 'you know they hang people in Somaliland?'

I didn't but said, 'They do at home, Sir.'

'Yes but they expect a doctor to be there. If they ask you to attend, you can if you like. My advice is don't. We are soldiers not murderers. If they ask you tell 'em to piss off. If they insist get into that jeep and come straight back here. Their hospital can go to pot if they try that on, for all I care. If they try to foist that on you, I'll be straight round at the Governor's giving him an earful.'

Perhaps the CO knew something I did not, the subject never cropped up, The Colonel had probably made his point clear.

Coffee Shops

I've mentioned the rough tracks that were called roads in Somaliland. Like all good main roads, motorways in England, and their service stations, the tracks in Somaliland weren't any different and had their 'coffee shops'. These coffee shops would be found all over the place. Although called coffee shops, they didn't sell coffee, only tea and the odd bit of unleavened bread, like a chapatti. They were always in the back of beyond, one looked round and wondered where their water came from.

We would stop and have a cup of tea at these places. A rather scruffy mug - enamel and cracked - it didn't seem to do my driver, or Mohamed the bearer, any harm, so I assumed it wouldn't do me any harm. I did wonder in the rainy season when the large ruts in the road outside the coffee shop were full of water, just how far they went to get the water! Whenever we stopped, we were always

Coffee shop and proprietor

welcome. They'd be squatting on the ground. I'd be sitting on a piece of wood, drinking my tea, surrounded by Somalis of all descriptions, some wearing nice, clean clothes others scruffy dirty old ones. There was always somebody who could speak English.

Another way Somaliland differed from Aden, the Arabs were keen to get you to know a bit of the language and helped you. I still know some Arabic words. I do not know one Somali word, try as I might, nobody would teach me anything in Somali. I mentioned it to my Somali sergeant Abdulla. He told me it was a waste of time me learning Somali, nobody spoke Somali except Somalis. I had the great advantage of speaking English, and that's what I should speak. They wanted to practise their English on me and I should help them.

The Economy

They were nomadic tribes, the economy grazing and producing large quantities of young camels and sheep, which were exported live from Berbera. I was able to see a lot of that when I did the locum at the hospital there. The sheep were funny, scraggy things; whether there was much wool on them, I couldn't tell; they didn't have a woollen industry.

The animal rights people would have had a ball about the sheep and camels. Their main market was Saudi Arabia, they were all Muslims, therefore the meat must be eaten the day it is killed, everything had to be exported live. The animals were killed by having their throats cut. The blood went to waste, just soaked into the ground. It might seem cruel, but you have to remember, this is very hot territory and these rules were developed before there were any means of preserving meat - in fact, a very sensible rule. Flies surrounded the places where they killed the animals, millions of flies landing on the meat as soon as it was produced. Modern abattoirs, deep freezing and exporting refrigeration ships did not exist when these rules were first made.

The young men of the village would accompany the camel herds and go wandering through the bush from one of area of feed to another, their source of food being the camel milk and any game they could catch. On the eastern side of the protectorate, where it was almost desert, they had to cover a large area in order to find forage for the camels. These young Somalis were all tall and slim, they didn't have the bulging muscles of an Irish navvy, but they were pretty fit.

The western side of the protectorate, from Hargesia towards Borama and beyond, was greener. There were areas where there was enough rain each year for them grow crops. On the road to Borama, you would pass large fields of millet and sorghum. In each field, over the top of the millet, you could see platforms with little roofs on which small boys sat with rattles and sling-stones, trying to scare off the birds that came for a meal as well. Some had nets, so that they could catch them. They might have been small but when you'd put them all together, there was a nice meal.

The place had been fully surveyed by the British; there was no oil; no minerals of any sort; just scrub desert and considered valueless. What real good we'd done the Somalis, I don't really know. We had started a rudimentary health service; we'd blasted tracks that could be used as roads. There were no Somali doctors, lawyers, schoolteachers, or anything. There were no Somali schools except the ones run by the local mullahs. We had only gone in, in the first place, to keep the French out, so we could protect our sea route to India. Now there was no Indian empire, there were aeroplanes flying all over the place, Somaliland had no value to us. I got the feeling that as soon as Harold Macmillan had done his wind of change speech, the authorities in England bailed out as quick as possible. Somaliland, which had no resources whatsoever, was one of the first of the East African countries to be fully independent.

Bits and Pieces

Geckoes

Little lizards, three inches long, with sucker pads to the feet, that came out at night, and ran about the ceilings of our rooms and balconies, catching flies. We had electricity in the officers' mess in Hargeisa, also in Buroa and Berbera. They was a large diesel generator at each place. The geckoes liked our electricity supply, particularly on the balcony, an electric light was attached to the ceiling. This attracted lots of flies. We always had four or five geckoes running about trying to catch flies. When sitting on the balcony talking at night, we would watch them. We arranged bets and races. Which gecko will get to that fly first or how long it would take it to catch two flies. The bets were never heavy - 3d. or 6d. We got mixed up about what we'd done, eventually we kept a book.

Stink ants

These were large ants, black and about 3 cms long. They were harmless, but when you trod on one, particularly in your room, they STANK! They'd stink for a couple of days. If you were wearing shoes, you'd be scrubbing the soles trying to get the stink off. One tried to put the light on before entering a room, if there was a stink ant there, you'd get a brush and shovel, sweep it onto the shovel and throw it out of the door.

Mud wasps

These were massive insects, large wings, big thorax, and a skinny abdomen with a big round bump at the end. They didn't live in nests, but lived singly. They collected up sand, found a source of water, mixed up a ball of mud, and made little nests the size of walnuts on cliff sides and similar places. The officers' mess made a very good cliff. They were always busy building walnut size lumps on the whitewashed wall. It was our sweeper's job, twice a week, to go round knocking all the nests off and clean everything up. Unfortunately, the sand wasps were extremely industrious, and before you knew what had happened, the wall would be covered with lumps again!

Birds

There were a fair number, but I can't remember a lot. One was the weaverbird, which made a nest the size of a coconut by weaving grass together and dangling it from the end of a branch. Weaverbirds lived in flocks of about 500, a tree would be covered with little nests, with numerous noisy weaverbirds twittering round it. They were the size of sparrows, but prettier and had little golden highlights in their feathers.

Ostrich

We did see ostrich; not great flocks, you saw them as you drove along, in groups of two or three, in the drier parts to the East. We didn't bother with them usually. Once we decided to find how many omelettes we could make out of an ostrich egg. We asked the sweeper to get us one. Sure enough, he provided the ostrich egg. We had to use a hammer to break it. Unfortunately, we couldn't make omelettes because the egg wasn't fresh; it contained a half grown chick, so that experiment failed. We never managed to get another egg, we were unable to continue with the experiment.

Red eyes

These were pigeons, same size and colour as our racing pigeons but with bright scarlet eyes. Not easy to catch but we would occasionally get some with a shotgun. Pigeon pie made a nice change, but there was a problem, we had to get one of the wives to show our cooks how to make the pastry.

Tick birds

Blue-grey with a red beak, found riding on all large animals. They were actively hunting for irritant ticks. The animals welcomed them. They restricted themselves to the ticks and did not damage the animal and draw blood to drink like some tick birds.

Locusts

Plagues of locusts were a curse, I saw several smaller ones that had escaped the attention of the East African Locust Destruction Unit, I cannot remember its official name. Massive winged grasshoppers the size of your forefinger. Driving through a swarm was as bad as driving through a fog. The radiator on the front of my one-ton truck would be jam packed with dead locusts.

The locust unit, British organized and financed, moved, as necessary, from the Sudan to Ethiopia, Somaliland, Kenya, Tanganyika and Uganda, wherever its monitoring services were needed. Locusts are just grasshoppers, present all over that area, living solitary lives. Climatic conditions have to be correct for swarms to develop – heavy rainfall and greenery. Grasshoppers congregate and have a high old time from the copulatory point of view. They lay eggs in billions, when hatched they cannot fly, are called hoppers, and can only move by walking. They walk, eat, grow and go through several stages of shedding their outer shell as they grow, until they can fly, and that's when they swarm. Flying together, they eat every bit of greenery and destroy all the crops in their path.

The locust unit tried to discover where the adults have congregated. It is easiest to prevent a plague if the locusts are found in their hopper stage, when poisoned foodstuff is scattered from the air. Trying to control locusts by spraying DDT from the air was too late. Once the unit camped on the airfield at Hargeisia, it was like a small town. Caravans, petrol and water bowsers, six bi-planes, maintenance unit, signals and radio, like a regiment. Which it was, a regiment at war against the locust.

Uniform

That became a problem because all these little outfits had different uniforms. The APL was different from the Somaliland Scouts, which was different from the Trucial Oman Scouts. I'd only had one allowance for tropical kit. I liked the Somaliland Scout outfit. I didn't need a new pair of shorts. Instead of a shirt, a jacket was made out of khaki linen with a belt and brass buckle. The jacket was worn over your shorts. There were also the socks - woollen khaki, quite big. Pulled up to your knee, turned over so it was double below the knee. They were large socks. I made the mistake of taking a pair home. They're much bigger than ordinary socks and hold a lot. Every Christmas Eve, there was a fight between my children to decide who was going to hang one of Dad's Somaliland Scout socks up for Father Christmas.

Boots

Nice sturdy, leather brown boots, with a good leather soles, made in Kenya. They weren't big, heavy boots - rather classy. I bought a pair, in fact, I've still got them and I wear them occasionally. Usually, they can be found in the cellar. My wife often says 'What on earth do you need to keep those for? They're old, throw them away'. This, I might add, from a lady who has seven double wardrobes full of clothes and six top wardrobes full of shoes, and often encroaches into my one wardrobe.

Tougs

Dry watercourses, like the wadies in Arabia, but the surrounding area was not mountainous. Often, the toug went for miles and you came across them a long way from the mountains. The roads crossed the tougs, in places stones had been thrown down to make sure that the lorries wouldn't sink in the mud when it was wet. In the dry season, they were no bother. In the rainy season you could run into trouble.

A spate, a flash flood, could wash a road bed away. It would be raining in the mountains miles away and when you came to a toug, you'd find it in spate - a heavy, torrent of rough brown water. There was no way anybody could cross it. There was no option but to stop, get out, if you had the wherewithal make a cup of tea and pass the time by talking to anybody else who was waiting, Arab, Somali, Pakistani or Indian. Fortunately, all of them spoke English. I always had my MO's bag with me, at such times I would end up doing a GP surgery.

Mohamed and the Red Toug in spate

Mess Dinners

These occurred every month. They were rather boisterous affairs, not because the younger officers got drunk, but because some had been stuck in an outstation miles away for a month, since the previous mess dinner. The colonel and majors would turn out in their tropical mess kit. The Somaliland Scouts didn't have their own mess kit. These chaps turned out in the tropical mess kit of their parent regiments. The rest of us wore the usual whites with black cummerbund. It started in the usual way, a few beers beforehand and some not very nice wine from somewhere, probably Chattergee, Something & Co. The orderlies had prepared the room and all the mess silver was out.

The centrepiece was a two-foot high solid silver statue of a Somali soldier on a camel from the Somali Camel Corps. There was a lot of silver. The officers in the past had been very proud serving there and had bought a lot of silver. There was argument at time about what was going to happen to it – whether it was going to be sent to a museum in England, or whether it would be handed on to the Somalis when they took over the Regiment. I believe the eventual decision was to hand it over to the Somalis. By now, no doubt, it's been pinched by one of their robber barons.

After the loyal toast, we were allowed to smoke and relax. We had a kind Colonel, whose bladder was as bad as mine, so we didn't have to hang around with bladders up to our eyebrows, waiting for him to go for a pee. As soon as the loyal toast was carried out, the Somali bearers came in and discreetly removed everything that was breakable. The armchairs were shoved onto the veranda. The Colonel and older majors retreated to the veranda and opened a bottle of Bells or something similar. Then the younger lads started playing their games. Indoor rugby with a watermelon; knights on horseback - a piggy back game where one officer is the horse and another the knight. They proceed to charge and try to dismount each other. People were bumping off tables, bouncing off walls and general mayhem ensued. This lasted until 2.30 a.m. - 3.00 a.m. It wasn't fuelled by booze either; once it got going, nobody had time to think about another glass of anything. I tended to get fed up round about 1.00 a.m. and go to bed. I knew my services would be required the following morning.

One of my duties in the early part of the evening after dinner was choirmaster. I had studied choral singing at university - on Saturday nights in the bar at the Men Students Union, as a regular member of the Manchester University Rugby Club's Choral Society. In Somaliland I led the four part harmony of such erudite numbers as The Ball of Kerrymuir, These Foolish Things and others. Occasionally my memory was stretched, I was expected to get through Eskimo Nell. Tony Thorne describes his friend Captain Geoff Strong's ability to recite all 28 verses. Tony Thorne had yet to go to university, he would be unaware that he was listening to the abridged version. I have just removed my copy from where I have hidden it from my wife for forty years. My version has 53 verses, a certain amount of prompting was required. It is not the sort of thing that a Consultant Gynaecologist is called upon to do.

The following morning, breakfast was served on the veranda. In the dining room sometimes you'd find one of the Somali bearers with a large tin of white paint, re-painting the walls. I'd get there for breakfast about 10 o'clock; the others would arrive shortly after. It wasn't an 'all fried' morning - it tended to be large amounts of coffee and the odd bit of toast. I would examine sprains and bruises, apply the appropriate treatment and dish out a few aspirins.

During the dinner weekends the mess would fill up. All the rooms would be occupied. Those from Buroa had a long way to come. They turned up on Friday night, so on Saturday morning a large number of officers were present for breakfast, which was rather hilarious. After lunch on Sunday, all the outlying chaps would be getting into their transport to go home, probably not to return for another month.

Sweepers

There was no caste system in Southern Arabia or Somaliland, but there was a group that was almost like the Hindu untouchables. This was the sweeper class, the ones who kept everything clean, sweeping the streets and the houses. They removed the rubbish, built and emptied latrines. They were the lowest of the low, but they did not do too badly. I never met an undernourished one; their children were all fit, chubby and active. They were never unemployed. Some could be a bit crafty. The sweeper at the officers' mess in Hargeisa promised to get me leopard skin. I had one hell of a row with him, but even I was not daft enough to pay for a leopard skin that had come off a spotted hyena.

Shopping

We were living in the capital of Somaliland - Hargeisa - so one would assume, like all capital cities, the wives of the officers would come on shopping trips - they didn't! There were no shops. I wish all capital cities were like that! In fact, there were no hotels for them to stay at even if they did come. Any wife who wanted to spend a few days in Hargeisa had to stay with one of the other wives in her bungalow. Wives socialized in the area where their husbands worked. They formed tightknit, little gossipy clubs. On special occasions, such as the wedding, all the wives came in. Husbands were put up in the officers' mess and the wives and families were spread out amongst the married families in Hargeisa itself.

Chapter Ten

Berbera

I was lent a land rover to go to Berbera and went with Mohamed. The road, unsealed, descended slowly. The surrounding flora was green - large trees and bushes, not much grass but plenty of leaves. The reason, the road followed a dry watercourse. Although it appeared to be dry, periodically you'd pass an open patch of water. I can't say underground river; because unlike the underground rivers in England, where you have a cave with a river running through it, here was a flow of water to the sea, through the sand and soil underneath.

We eventually reached the coastal plain. It was all sand. We drove to Berbera, a patch of sand with buildings on it. The hospital was 500 yards from and faced the sea. To the south, the mental hospital, known by the locals as 'The Mad Jail'. Buildings were scattered haphazardly; a Courthouse, a Police Station, and a European Club. Along the beach, to the north of the hospital, was a row of about twenty European bungalows, the majority empty, only 6 or 7 being used. Some, by the appearance of the gardens, once well tended, had been empty for a long time. I got the feeling that they were running things down as independence approached. I never found where the prison was. I didn't look for it. I had one trip into the bush. I came across the Chief Magistrate's bungalow, a very grand affair with a beautiful acre of garden round it, lovely green lawns and thick hedge through which nothing could get.

There was no water shortage in Berbera. The underground rivers had been tapped and there was an ample supply of water, fresh and pleasant to drink. The port wasn't what we would expect a port to be - there were no cranes, jetties, or docks. Just ships, out at sea at anchor, the cargoes being taken off or loaded by lighter. The main cargo was live sheep and camels. The sheep were put in the holds and the ships decks packed camels. They went up the Red Sea. The Yemen occupies a fifth of the eastern side of the Red Sea. The ships did not have far to go before they reached an Arabian port. Three or four days would be bad enough, I don't think the conditions were brilliant.

Hospital

There was a flat on top of the hospital, an attempt had been made to tidy it up, but Mohamed and I had to finish the job. It was fully furnished, the kitchen fully equipped, a bathroom and toilet, dining room, nice big lounge, and a couple of bedrooms.

Mohamed did the cooking. I gave him twenty shillings every four or five days. He went to the market and produced good European style meals. I ate on the balcony at night, looking out to sea. At first, in the evening after eating, I wandered round to see what the nightlife was. I visited the European club on a couple of occasions. Apart from a bored Somali waiter, it was empty. The only place you could get a cup of coffee was Chattergee Somebody & Co. The manager was too busy to talk. My eventual routine was to eat at 7.00 p.m., sit down with a book, pour myself a whisky and fall asleep, to be woken by Mohamed at 9 when he came to clear the table. Then I went to bed and woke up at the crack of dawn - 6 o'clock.

The days were full and busy. There were six wards - two large wards for male and female tuberculosis patients, two surgical wards

Berbera Hospital

and two general wards. There was a decent sized operating theatre, and a fair amount of equipment, which didn't seem to be used very much. I did four operations in it; the anaesthetist being what I describe as a sergeant nurse, or a three-stripe nurse.

Nursing Organization

There were no female Somali nurses, all were male. There were some female nurses in the protectorate, all were British, SRN and SCM. The nursing organization followed the British Army pattern - the recruits were nursing privates, no stripes. They had a training period during which they learned to read and write English and basic nursing principles. When they qualified, they became one-stripers, like a lance corporal, known as dressers. A two-striper was the equivalent of our staff nurse or a corporal in the army. A three-striper, the equivalent of a sister, or sergeant, and then there were super specialist nurses that were the equivalent of a staff sergeant. A three-striper was in charge of the wards. The staff sergeant nurses were specially trained. There were a couple in charge of the mental hospital. They had been trained to look after mental cases and gave ECT (electro-convulsive therapy). There was a staff sergeant pharmacist, and a Staff Sergeant medical laboratory officer who carried out simple blood tests and bacteriology. There was no blood or blood transfusions or anything like that.

One was the specialist hernia repairer. This man's full time job was examining patients with hernias in the groin, inguinal hernias, femoral hernias, direct and indirect. He had been taught to repair them under local anaesthetic. I never saw him work, because for the fortnight I was there, he'd gone elsewhere.

There were other staff sergeant nurses throughout Somaliland, in charge of little medical centres, with one or two one-stripers to help him. The staff sergeant nurse was responsible for diagnosis and treatment, and giving out drugs. In tuberculosis cases, he maintained their drug supply.

My experience of tuberculosis was nil. When I went round the two wards with the sergeant nurse in charge, I listened to what he suggested, then recommended it myself. What I did notice, was that the ward would be full at night time and going round the ward the next day, there would be three or four empty beds. On enquiry, the answer was always the same - 'They died during the night, Sahib'. That's one thing I could never fathom. In all branches of medicine I had worked in up to then, I knew how to spot a person who was going to die in the near future. I just hadn't a clue about Somalis with tuberculosis. Young men or women who seemed to be reasonably well when I did a ward round one morning would be dead the next morning.

They had tuberculosis pretty well taped - treatment: the patients were in for 3 months, using the antibiotic Streptomycin, PAS (Para-amino-salicylic acid) and Isoniazid. When they were better and their sputum no longer TB positive, they went home. They then went on treatment for two years, with PAS and Isoniazid. The importance of keeping on with drugs had been drilled into them. They were well aware of the danger of tuberculosis and what a killer it was, so there was no danger of them selling their drugs in the local Souk. They could be days away from replenishing their supply. A herdsman may have to walk a week to get his follow-up treatment and if he had to collect his drugs too often, then he'd tend not to bother. All the TB patients were given six months supply at a time. If they could come back to be seen by a doctor, they did, mostly they went to the scattered medical centres run by the staff sergeant nurses. The results, all in all, were pretty good.

Mental Hospital

I visited the mental hospital (Mad Jail) twice. The Mad Jail consisted of two enclosed blocks with 12 foot high walls of sixty yards in a square - one male, one female. In between was the administrative area where the odd drugs were kept, clothes were made, food prepared, and the general administration of the unit carried out. One entered through a gate that was always locked. That section was open to the elements. There was another gate, also locked on each side, which entered the male or the female ward. In the centre of each compound was a raised platform, 2 foot high, 30 yards long and 20 yards wide, with a thatched roof and open sides. Piled along the far wall were the charpoys they slept on. There seemed to be millions of people wandering around the compound, or sitting talking in the shade of the platform area.

Along the side of the wall, adjacent to the administrative block, was a series of showers, taps and other water points. It never occurred to me to inspect them at the time, and I cannot remember, but I am sure that they had a proper flush toilet block - probably Asian type. There were too many people for them to be able to manage with a latrine and they had an ample water supply. They didn't need a sewage farm, they were only 500 yards from the sea, a pipe could have been taken out to sea to discharge the sewage. However, this is only surmising, but it couldn't possibly be any other way considering the number of people.

On the north and south wall of the each compound were a series of what I can only describe as cages, 10 feet square. In these, were the wild, unruly, violent patients that they couldn't control. One, on the female ward, has stuck in my mind every since. She was a wild woman of about 40, staring eyes. If you approached the front of the cage, she attacked the bars, spat and tried to scratch you. She wore an old brown dress, split at the front down to the waist. She must have had children. Her breasts were pendulous. She would approach the front of the cage, bent forward in a crouch, like a chimpanzee, moving from side to side, with her dress hanging down, and her breasts swinging from side to side. When they fed her, or gave her water, the food was pushed through a small space under the door, while another orderly stood by with a pole to push her away. She defecated and urinated in the cage.

Nobody would go in there. Every morning, the cage was cleaned, two orderlies with a hose the size that firemen use, hosed the cage down. Then, they hosed the woman down, who resented it. She charged, screeching and tried to attack them through the bars. I watched, and there was no doubt by looking at the faces of those male orderlies they were taking sadistic pleasure in hosing that woman down. I grabbed the hose, called the staff sergeant nurse and was about to arrange their dismissal. The staff sergeant pointed out that there was great difficulty in staffing the place. He assured me that he would discipline them and such action would not occur again.

Apart from that case, they were doing the best they could with extremely limited sources. There were two treatments – Phenobarbitone and ECT. There was no attempt to make a real diagnosis. If the patient was overactive, he was sedated with Phenobarbitone to keep him quiet. If he seemed depressed, he was given ECT. The ECT was a real eye opener when compared to the careful anaesthetizing drugs to relax muscles and all the rigmarole of giving ECT in England.

ECT was given in a dry watercourse, under a large acacia tree, outside the hospital. A large cast iron bed that had been wrapped up with old blankets and bags was used. The ECT sessions occurred twice a week. Any interested person came along to watch. The outpatients came, sat down, watched and formed a queue. The inpatients came from the mental hospital with ankle irons, and joined the queue.

ECT was given as follows:

The patient lay on the bed.

The staff sergeant nurse in charge placed the electrodes on either side of the head. Four massive Somali mental orderlies, the size of Henry Cooper, held one limb each. The staff sergeant nurse then placed a wooden gag with some old rag round it in the patient's mouth, and switched on the machine. The patient had something like an epileptic fit with everybody sitting round watching, assuming it was the normal run of things. At the end of treatment, the man would be unconscious. The four Somali heavyweights would lift him off the bed, and place him on the sand at the side of the dry watercourse. Eventually, he came round, got up and went home, or in the case of inpatients, went back to the mental hospital, where his ankle chains were be taken off and he went back into the main compound.

Quatt Mania

The victim was a young man of about 25, well educated; half Somali and half Indian. One day, he went out with his pals, rather like a similar young man in England would go out. Instead of going to the pub and getting plastered, he went to the local quatt market, bought some quatt, started chewing, overdid it and went into a manic state. All over Somaliland, were two or three tribal elders who had been picked as local magistrates. One of their duties was to assess a person accused of being insane - mad, as they would call it.

This young man was taken before the magistrate, assumed to be insane and incarcerated in the Mad Jail. Anyone put into the Mad Jail was reassessed by the doctor at the end of a week. So, we had a healthy, young, intelligent man, put into a mental institution of the type described with Quatt Mania. This lasted for 48, maybe 72 hours. Then he comes round, realizes where he is and for the next four or five days, stays in the Mad Jail. By which time, he is in a state of abject terror in case he has to spend the rest of his life there.

I held court in the doctor's office in the main hospital, where I had things to sign and agree to, which the staff sergeant nurses put to me. Mostly, I just looked and said 'What's the usual routine? Is this it?' and then signed. I also saw a number of patients. The week was up and the young man was brought in. As soon as he came through the door, he fell to his knees, put his forehead on the floor, hands in the air and salaamed.

'Doctor Sahib, Doctor Sahib, I am not mad, Doctor Sahib, Doctor Sahib, I am not mad, please do not let me stay in that place any longer.'

He got up, walked three steps, but instead of sitting in front of my desk, walked round the side, knelt down picked my boot up and kissed the tip of it.

'Release me, Sahib, release me.'

Not the sort of behaviour that I am used to from the average NHS patient! I was annoyed, snapped at him, told him to stand up, behave like man, and sit in the chair so that we could discuss matters. I was given the history; it was obvious that he was back to normal. He was quite sane, but, I thought I'd better twist the knife in a bit.

'You are a Muslim.'

'Yes, Sahib.'

'As a Muslim, you do not drink alcohol?'

'No, Sahib.'

'You would consider it foolish for a man to drink alcohol?'

'Yes, Sahib.'

'You are aware that English men like myself, do drink alcohol and when they drink a lot, they can get very drunk, just like your Quatt Mania? In England, a man who gets drunk would be taken to the magistrate and put in jail for at least a month. Would it not be sensible for me to keep you in jail for a month?'

'No, no, Sahib, not the Mad Jail, not the Mad Jail!'

'Will you promise me to be careful about chewing Quatt again? I am not saying you must not chew Quatt, but under no circumstances do we wish you to develop Quatt Mania again. If you do, there will be severe consequences.'

Well, words to that effect, because some of the big words like consequences he probably couldn't understand.

I then said, 'Release him'.

He backed out of the office saying 'Thank you, Sahib, thank you, Sahib', salaaming as he went.

After he left there were a few wry smiles.

In the office was a massive fridge, run on kerosene. All the drugs, particularly vaccines, were kept in it. This was another fridge like the one in Dahlia that had conked out. We'd kept it shut and covered with blankets, but all the ice had melted. The water was still cold, but you could put your finger in without having to pull it out because the water was at freezing point.

A middle aged Indian lady - a trader's wife - came in; she had arranged to take a boat that was going to Tanganyika. It was essential that her cholera and yellow fever were up to date, and she wanted injections for both. I told her she couldn't have them because the fridge had conked out and the vaccines weren't any good. She was desperate to go. I told her what had happened, she put her own finger in and said the water was still cold, it's not too bad. She decided to accept any consequences and I injected her with cholera and yellow fever vaccine and signed the certificates.

Surgery

I did four operations whilst I was at Berbera. One was a case of chronic osteomyelitis. There was a lot on the surgical ward, all with sinuses from the bone that were leaking out through the skin. The doctor who took me round just before he left showed me several cases.

He said, 'This case is getting ready for dealing with. You will be able to feel when the dead bone becomes powdery and it can be removed. We use a curette.'

He demonstrated the curette, which was the same as that used for curetting a uterus. 'We stick it down the sinus to where the dead bone is and scrape the dead bone out.' A few days later, examining the affected leg and discussing it with the sergeant nurse in charge of the ward, I thought, 'The change is there, which he described'.

I took the patient to theatre. Stuffed the curette down the sinus a couple of times and removed normal red bone marrow. I looked at it and thought it would be better to take the thick sides of the sinus out, cut through to the dead bone, chisel it out until you got to healthy bone and then close the wound round a drain. I wasn't sure what to do. I thought it best to take no action until I knew exactly what to do. I browsed through the hospital library; there were a few textbooks there from 1940. It wasn't until I got back to England that Christmas when I got out my Bailey & Loves *Short Textbook of Surgery* that I found that would have been a reasonable action to take.

Female circumcision

In all the time I had been in Somaliland, I had not seen many women and never carried out a vaginal examination. What happened now was a serious shock! I had heard that women in that part of the world were circumcised, and assumed it was something like removing the clitoris. The sergeant nurse in charge of the female surgical ward told me that this lady had a 'swelling on her privates'. He hadn't examined her, but his wife had and said it was a 'dangly, round thing'. The woman did not want to be examined before I operated. The sergeant nurse gave the anaesthetic. I examined the 'vulva'. There wasn't one. The perineum was just flat with a hole in the middle (the perineum is the area between the pubic bone at the front and the back passage, between the tops of the two thighs). There was a pedunculated dangly cyst, which I removed quite easily. I then looked to see what had been done.

This procedure is done on girls of 10–11 years of age, without anaesthetic. It is done, not at the insistence of the men, but the older women of the tribe – grandmother, mother and elderly aunts. They find a woman who claims to be an expert at the procedure. The girl is held down, with her legs up; one of them places a hand over her mouth to muffle her screams, and then either using a razor blade or one of their own rusty, blunt, home-made knives, the 'expert' carries out the operation.

There was no hair-bearing tissue on the vulva at all. The operator had started on the outer aspect of the labia majora, which are the thick outer lips of the vulva, right at the bottom, close to the top of the thigh, and had cut through to the other side. In the process, removing the labia majora, the small lips (labia minora), and the clitoris. At the back, under the labia majora, there are two glands called Bartholin's glands, which provide lubrication during intercourse; they had been removed, It was just flat, with a hole in the centre.

In front of the vagina is the vestibule, a triangular shaped area, 2.5 centimetres long, stretching from the base of the clitoris to the front of the vagina. In this lady's case, the vestibule was about 1 cm long.

The edges of the vaginal opening were firm, where scar tissue had formed when the skin and vaginal mucosa came together. The colour was a light brown, lighter than the rest of the lady's body. The area had been left raw. Skin had to grow back from the edges, and the melanophores, which produce black pigment, were less concentrated than usual. Underneath the skin, the tissue was thick and hard, the skin was like parchment.

To say I was shocked and upset was an understatement. This woman had had children. When the procedure is carried out the sides are stitched together. The reason for the operation is to maintain purity until the day of marriage. It is still a problem in Somaliland and stretches through the Sudan, even as far as parts of

Nigeria. Only some time this year, 2002, has the Nigerian parliament made the procedure illegal.

What the layperson does not know is that the procedure in England has had to be made illegal. A special law has been passed to prevent it being carried out in England. That is thanks to our surgical specialists in Harley Street, who instead of having brain cells in their skull have pound coins! The argument they put forward was 'If I don't do this, they'll take the girl back to Somaliland, it will be carried out by some old woman in a dirty manner; there will be no control over the bleeding and no control of infection. There is no way you can avoid this girl having a female circumcision. Therefore, it is far better that I carry out the procedure in an operating theatre, where bleeding can be controlled and there is no infection. That will be £1,000 please'.

I have never seen a female circumcision since. In my part of England we did not have immigrants from Somaliland, but there are a fair number in London and South East. The gynaecologists there will be much more aware of the complications that occur.

A lay reader may find this little section hard to read, and feel that it shouldn't have been included in this book. To my mind, it is such a serious problem that the more people know about it, the better. Then more pressure can be applied to stop the older women in these areas from continually forcing this mutilation on young girls.

I am not one for mutilating little boys either! But, you can find an odd medical reason for that. For instance, a circumcised man is less likely to acquire HIV (human immuno-deficiency virus), which causes AIDS, and the wife or partner of a circumcised man is less likely to have cancer of the cervix than the partner of an un-circumcised man.

Here is the place to comment on the older male Somali's attitude to virtue in women. While I was in Hargeisa, word came through on the grapevine that a young British soldier had been arrested for attempting to rape and murdering a young Somali woman in Aden. Abdullah Hersi, my senior sergeant, was with a friend of the same age, in the MI Room with me when the news came through. I said how sorry I was and that was not acceptable behaviour for an Englishman, thinking of the many young Somali women working in Aden as ayers (nannies), all highly respectable as far as the British families and soldiers were concerned.

'Doesn't matter Sahib, she was a fool. All Somali women who work abroad are no good. Her virtue had gone, she should have let him do it then blackmailed him.'

'They are not like that,' I said. 'They are respectable.'

'Any woman who goes to Aden Sahib, is no good.'

'But they are sergeant, and they earn money that they cannot do here. That will help when they get married.'

'No! Sahib, no proper man, from a good family will have them. They may have money, but only men of no status will have them.'

Abdullah Hersi was not a wealthy man, but he had position and status, which he valued above wealth. He was saying in his own way, that only men that most Somalis regarded as the dregs of society would be prepared to marry a Somali woman who had been abroad.

At the end of a fortnight, my sojourn into civilian colonial medical practice came to an end. The regular doctor came back. My one comment – that hospital required three or four doctors to run it and should have had three or four doctors. Mohamed and I got in our jeep and took a leisurely drive back to Hargeisa. I stayed a couple of nights in the officers' mess. An Aden Airways plane took me back to Aden. So ended my Somaliland venture, apart from a pleasant surprise awaiting me when I returned to Aden after my Christmas leave.

This was a letter dated 22 December 1959, signed Maurice Mac-William (see p.204). It brought a little tear to my eye. I never managed to arrange the visit. I had forgotten about the other one I found with it. In case it cannot be easily read:

> I am sorry I did not see you on your way through Hargeisa to Aden, to thank you in person for your great help in taking over Berbera.
>
> I am most grateful for your help and on behalf of the department and myself send you our sincere thanks.
>
> Best wishes for a Happy Christmas with your family.
>
> Yours very sincerely
>
> W. Thomas.

My memories are of having a great time, up to every skive, trick and wangle imaginable and yet I have those letters. The one from the Health Department is understandable, it is just a thank you letter. The one from Colonel MacWilliam, what had I done to deserve it? I just enjoyed myself for six months.

I nearly fell in love with Somaliland. I tried to get my transfer made permanent. Somaliland was beautiful, magnificent, and fan-

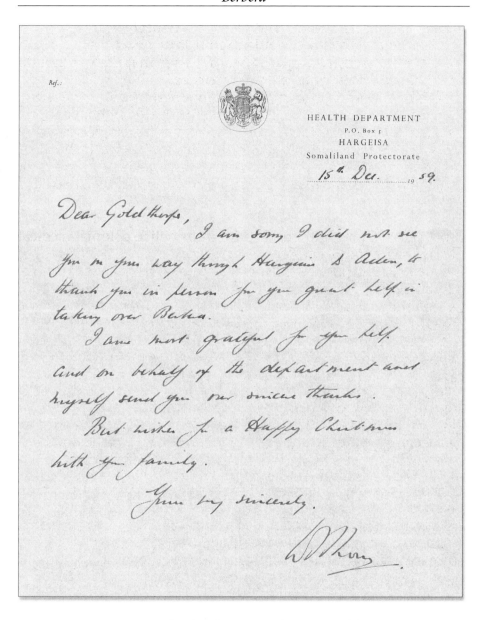

Ref.:

HEALTH DEPARTMENT
P.O. Box 5
HARGEISA
Somaliland Protectorate

15th Dec. 19 59.

Dear Goldthorpe,
I am sorry I did not see you on your way through Hargeisa & Aden, to thank you in person for your great help in taking over Berbera.
I am most grateful for your help. And on behalf of the department and myself send you our sincere thanks.
Best wishes for a Happy Christmas with your family.

Yours very sincerely.

tastic, I got out into the bush as much as possible. A trip east to Buroa, one week, west to Boroma the next. Buroa was about 120 miles away. Trundling along in my old one-ton Morris at thirty miles an hour on a rough unpaved road, may have seemed a chore to some. But to me it was marvellous, there was something different each trip. Khaki coloured, smelling of oil and petrol, the trundling old Morris did not disturb the game. They must have thought it was a new kind of elephant or rhinoceros.

From:- Lieutenant Colonel MEM MacWILLIAM, DSO, MC, TD.,

SOMALILAND SCOUTS,

SOMALILAND PROTECTORATE.

DO/191/1   22ⁿᵈ December, 1959.

My dear Bill,

    I was hoping to see you in ADEN before you left
on your Comet, but Colonel MATHESON told me you had
made an early start. I hope you had a really splendid
Christmas leave, which you fully deserved and that you
found your family in good shape, especially your first
born.

    We would all like you to know how much we
valued your work and the energy you put into it during
your stay with us. Both the soldiers and the families,
both BRITISH and SOMALIS, have good reason to be most
grateful for all your help and attention. I personally
feel that the test of your success was on the issue of
the SOMALIS faith and confidence in you and it was
patently clear to us all that you gained this very
quickly and that the issue was never in doubt.

    I would myself have liked your stay to have been
longer but my hands were tied on this score. Neverthe-
less, I hope you will be able to find time to make at
least one visit to us before your tour in ADEN finishes,
and you will be most welcome.

    Let me wish you a most successful career in
medicine and, having seen you in your early days, I am
completely confident that you will do very well indeed.

    With salaams and every good wish for 1960 and
the future from us all.

                         Yours ever,

Lieutenant W.R. GOLDTHORP, RAMC.
                          Maurice MacWilliam

Admittedly I shot a gazelle each trip, but after that I would often
just stop, stand and stare, or walk a mile or two to a new viewing
point.

A mountain, the Gan Leaban, towering over the Mandera plain,
like a lion's paw, which is what the name meant.

Leopard's tooth rock, the Jubu Mia Dere, a massive canine tooth

Douberaine Pass, a main road

rising from one of the large jumble of rocks rising out of the plain. These high rock piles with intertwining caves and tunnels were said to be the haunt of leopards and other predators.

Passes down onto the sandy desert seacoast plain, the Benan Gama pass with sulphur springs at its head. The Elambidol pass from the Gubato plain going down to the coast. The Gerato pass built by the Somaliland Scouts.

On the map the 'city' of Las Dureh, a flat sandy expanse, plenty of wells, a few of the Kraal-like huts the Somalis used. A white painted police post, single storey, crenellated walls for decoration, a flag pole, but no radio mast. A carefully tended green shrub at one corner, the only one in an area of over 500 acres.

I suppose it was the side effects of my trips. I visited all the out stations every fortnight, as a result I, without planning it, was on top of everything. The Staff sergeants in charge of the MI rooms knew when I was coming, anyone they were puzzled about was kept for me to look at. Requests for drugs or new equipment were given to me and I brought them with me on my next trip a fortnight later. An MO could have remained at headquarters in Hargeisa and have people and requests brought to him, most would have found that acceptable. Officers and families in particular could feel isolated in the out stations, my visits must have helped to alleviate that.

Then there were my impromptu civilian surgeries.

If a toug was in spate we could be held up for three or four hours. When a Mammy wagon drew up with a load of Somalis of all ages, Mohamed my driver and Mohamed my bearer went over to talk. I was not prepared to sit there like the Great White Man, on my own, bored to death. I went with them. The driver, a trader could always speak English, and often some of the others could to. Inevitably it would be asked 'Who is the officer?'

Mohamed would answer 'The Hakim Sahib.'

One Somali would make a tentative approach and when I did not object I was surrounded by a group of them. Confidentiality not being on their agenda I took histories and examined people in full view of a cheerful chattering gang of locals. That was not work, that was fun.

Christmas at Home

Oh dear! This is going to be a bit difficult. The male chauvinistic pig is speaking. I've been criticized by her who must be obeyed for years about that home leave. Now numerous other wives are going to follow suit.

As soon as I returned to the airport at Khormaksar, I scrounged a lift from one of the RAF officers. He took me to Colonel Matheson's office, I knocked, entered and reported in. He asked me to sit and a discussion went on for about 10-15 minutes, about how I'd got on etc. Then I dropped a large hint - I just mentioned that Margaret had had a little boy and I hadn't seen him yet. I didn't actually ask for a 'Casivac' escort duty, but I certainly implied it.

Two days later, I was notified that I was to act as a 'Casivac' escort for a sergeant. He'd come out to Aden, the cheap booze had been too much for him, and he'd almost become a chronic alcohol in about six weeks! We flew back by Comet, via Libya, where I changed from tropical gear into British winter civilian clothes. We sat and chatted together. He was incensed when I told him I was his escort. He thought it was just a con trick to get me home for Christmas. Maybe it was! We landed somewhere in the south of England. I got a rail pass and went to Doncaster, where Margaret and my father picked me up.

It's surprising how shy and reticent you become when you've been apart for that length of time. Margaret, of course, had converted from 'glamour pants' to a mother and, like many ladies when they have their first baby, had put a bit of weight on. That's where

I made my first mistake! 'How do I look?' she says, looking bright and chirpy, bit of make-up on. Well, it was obvious she'd put on a stone or so. I didn't want to say that she looked overweight; I tried to be tactful in my usual manner and said, 'You look a bit square'. That phrase has been thrown at me periodically for the last 42 years!

The whole of Crowle, particularly Crowle Fieldside Methodist Church, were firmly of the opinion that once Bill Goldthorp got home for a month, he'd leave his wife in another interesting condition! They hadn't counted on the most reliable contraceptive that has been ever been invented - the future Lieutenant Colonel William Goldthorp.

There were lots of discussions at that time about whether one should have demand feeding or regular feeding every four hours. There was no problem with William - it was demand feeding. Every 1½-2 hours. All night. He only slept during the day. That is my abiding memory of that leave. I don't know whether, if I had been at home permanently, I would have been able to go to work. I'd have had to be unemployed for about 6 months. He was onto full cream milk by the time he was four weeks old and that didn't satisfy him. In order to thicken it up, instead of water, we moved on to barley water and made a sort of gruel with full cream milk. This, of course, wouldn't go through the teat in the feeding bottle.

One of my abiding memories of that leave is staggering downstairs in the middle of the night, in December/January when it was freezing (nobody in those days had central heating), into the kitchen, opening the Rayburn door. With a large darning needle held in a pair of pliers, stuffing it into fire until it turned red-hot, using that to increase the size of the hole in the teat, so that he could drink it as fast as possible! He should have been fed on elephant's milk. As I said, we'd get him settled down, he'd be fast asleep and an hour and a half later, would come the next demand - with a fog horn voice that could be heard about 10 miles away. Yet he slept all through the day, so that when I went to visit my relatives, there was the usual statement 'Oh, what a lovely little baby'.

Eventually, the four-week leave came to an end. I had to return to Aden. I can't really say I was distraught to get back on the train in Doncaster and think 'Thank God, when I finally come out in November, he'll be weaned and eating proper stuff - hopefully in the day'.

Chapter Eleven

10 Brigade Group Medical Company

When I returned to Aden, I had been moved from Khormaksar and now I became a proper army MO I moved my things to one of the hotels in the Crescent in Steamer Point. I can't remember much about it – the room was air-conditioned, the food was awful. What I remember, particularly, is 'egg soup'. How on earth can you have 'egg soup'? Put an egg in water, it coagulates, goes hard and yet some Arab, so-called Chef, dreamed up this concoction of 'egg soup', ground up boiled egg floating in hot water!

I now hit a rather bad patch. I was attached to Ten Brigade Group Medical Company. Here, we had the other Lieutenant Colonel of the RAMC in Command. I have described him previously as a

The Crescent, Steamer Point

Number 1 Street, Aden

pillock; I can't remember his name, so from now on he'll become known as Colonel Pillock. I've got the usual pile of photographs – lots of lads lined up in rows, typical of the army, boring photographs. There's not really much to say about Ten Brigade Group Medical Company. I was horrified to find that Ian Stewart, who had signed on, was part of it and seemed to be enjoying it. There was also a chap – Captain Griff Edwards – who'd come up from the ranks. He's been in the army and the medical corps all his life. He was a good bloke and a good organizer. Then, there was this excuse for a doctor. Well, he wasn't a doctor, he was a soldier. Instead of going to Medical School, and using up a place that a dedicated man could have occupied, he should have gone to Sandhurst as an officer cadet.

He was all Brasso, Blanco and Bullshit. What upset me was that Ian Stewart seemed to be enjoying himself. 27 years old, three years qualified and not doing medicine, wasting time playing at soldiers. Doctors should be in charge of medical units and their organization, but the soldiering bits and all that crap should be left to those who know how to do it properly.

Although I must admit if you considered who was more likely to become a Staff Officer, it was more likely to be Colonel Pillock than Colonel Matheson; Colonel Matheson had the disadvantage of still being interested in medicine. In the army, like the civil service, if you want to get into the top grades, you have to give up any career ability, and become a pure administrator. The most brilliant brain surgeon would never become a Major General unless he discarded his talents and became a desk bound useless walla.

This has always puzzled civil service administrators, why cannot they recruit administrators from the top echelons of the medical profession. The answer is simple; as soon as a doctor of any specialty becomes an administrator he drops to the bottom of the professional hierarchy. Start telling a Senior Surgeon or Physician what to do, you soon get the answer, where the F—ing h-ll were you at 0230 on Saturday morning when that train crashed, snoring you head off I suppose.

'Right Captain', I'd been in for a year, promoted. 'I want you to take the parade this morning.'

'Are you sure Sir? I am hopeless at it. It will make the officers look a laughing stock.'

'Do as you are ordered.'

Shrug shoulders, 'So be it.'

'Don't be insolent to a senior officer.'

Fortunately the squaddies detested him more than I did. 'Corporal march alongside me and whisper the commands.'

'Lads we are going to march along three sides of the square, then back again. I'll position myself, so that you lot are between me and the window in the old b-st-rds office, so he can't see me.' Big grins all round; they were all National Service, conspirators already.

Later he came to watch us and he spotted the corporal trick. I was ordered to do it on my own; the lads marched with precision doing the correct thing at the correct moment, no matter what I said.

The parade was dismissed with the usual stamping of feet, saluting Yes siring and No siring. I was standing behind the pillock, no one within earshot, and I softly said 'Yes Sir. No Sir. Three bags full Sir.' The back of his neck turned red, I knew he had heard me. Colonel Pillock called me to his office the next day. I was reprimanded for being uncooperative and having an unmilitary attitude. If I was not careful I might end up on the Jebel Akhdar, Matthew was due some leave. Matthew, not having much medical work to do had taken over the administration and reconstruction of the bomb damage to the Jebel and it's ancient irrigation systems. He had done it for a year, the military authorities had acknowledged his efforts by awarding him a military MBE. He had only been in the army just over a year, the Pillock must have been in nearly twenty years and not got one. This was an opportunity not to be missed.

Fellow conspirators

'Thank you Sir. What a good idea. Matthew came out with me, he's just been awarded the MBE, published in the New Years Honours I believe Sir.'

Silence, then 'Dismissed.'

Actually being with the 10 Brigade Group Medical Company was not too bad if you could get away from the Pillock. I was able to get away for almost five whole days on one occasion. I joined No. 1 Ambulance Section on a five day exercise in setting up an ambulance station. The Pillock accompanied us, took one look at the campsite selected and promptly boggared off home to snuggle up to his wife in a nice air conditioned bed.

We followed the road through Sheikh Othman, round to Little Aden and beyond. To a large bay with a truly magnificent name, after the two things soldiers like the most. BIR FUKUM. There we set up camp where the sand dunes came down to the sea. We tried to practice casualty evacuation. With four lads trying to carry another of their number, a non volunteer, the result was hilarious. Soft sand doesn't give much grip for the stretcher bearers, stretchers and contents sliding and falling in all directions.

We tried valiantly for a couple of days, then it dawned on us that the Pillock wasn't coming back, after that we enjoyed ourselves sunbathing, swimming and fishing. The Royal Dragoons were

Seashore, Bir Fukum
Jebel Shamsham on the horizon

stationed in Little Aden. A couple of sergeants and an ambulance disappeared late one afternoon and returned with a supply of an appropriate beverage enough for all ranks. Where would the British Army be without its sergeants.

I believe I now know the identity of Lieutenant Colonel Pillock MC. I wonder if I would have behaved differently had I known about the MC, I doubt it. My assessment of his future, mentioned above, was correct. If my information is correct he progressed to the top of the medical military hierarchy. My information also states 'respected and liked by all who knew him'.

Oh Dear! Obviously the fault must be mine. Tact has never been one of my strong points. Indeed a few years later when I was registrar, one of my senior registrars was to tell my wife:

'The trouble with Bill is that he never knows when to keep his mouth shut.'

At least my friends had my welfare at heart.

Perhaps a reappraisal of my National Service is required. I always thought it was because I was considered reliable that I was sent to all those back of beyond places. Did the army medical hierarchy regard me in the same way the RAF regarded Piss Head P—ce? The difference being that while Piss Head upset the Top Brass while

Bir Fukum 1960
No.1 Section Camp 10 Brigade Group Medical Company

'three sheets to the wind', my ability was to do it when I was stone cold sober. The services were always prepared to forgive misdemeanours when under the influence, after all it might be them next time, but stone cold sober!

A substantial proportion of National Service MOs regarded it as a total waste of time and misuse of manpower. I would estimate well over 30%. If I had not been sent to Aden I would have been among that number. Unimportant repetitive things to do, little medical experience and annoying army rules and regulations, which often seemed pointless.

My next section starts with a letter from the chap I was relieving, Graeme Matthew, he describes the two places that I might be sent to. He also included a two-word phrase which as soon as I read it, I knew I would enjoy my next six months. 'No bullshit.' In 10 Brgd Gp Med. Co. there was too much BULLSHIT.

Eventually, I had to go and see Colonel Matheson, from the drift of the conversation I gathered the Pillock had been complaining.

'You're not very happy at the moment Bill?'

'You could say that again Sir. Just wasting my time at the moment, playing at soldiers. It's OK for Stewart he wants to be one.'

'What about you?'

'No way, Sir. I wouldn't have come near the army if I hadn't had to. You only want us because we're Medics, we should be used as Medics.'

'Would it help if we arranged a few sessions for you? Then you won't be making it obvious that you detest everything you are doing'.

'It's sheer boredom at the moment Sir.'

'You can help out at Singapore lines, the MO there has other things to do, he's a regular. Two mornings a week and Tuesday and Thursday afternoons.'

A favour with punishment – I was supposed to be off duty in the afternoons.

I believe the South Warwicks were there at first, but then we had the pleasure of the Highland Light Infantry. Highland! My backside. That lot had never seen a Scottish mountain, they wouldn't know what a molehill was. Glasgow, the Gorbals and surrounding area. They were doing a year in Aden after two in Singapore. What a difference for that lot, in Aden a VD rate of nil, whereas according to their MO in Singapore it was 190% per annum. The mind boggles at that.

What were they like, small untidy and scruffy, 5 foot six or seven, scraggy, like Charles Atlas's seven stone weaklings. What a contrast to the No. 20 Marine Commando unit at Little Aden. (I think it was No. 20) Five foot ten to six foot, twelve stone of solid muscle, highly trained particularly in unarmed combat. The HLI hated their guts, whenever the two groups met on a Friday or Saturday night in Steamer Point there was a riot, an extremely vicious punch-up. The Marine Commando casualties in hospital began to mount so that it was in danger of becoming an ineffective fighting unit. HLI casualties were minimal. The unarmed combat taught to the Commandos was less effective than what the HLI had been learning in the back streets of the Gorbals since they were about eight years old. Eventually both units were confined to barracks on alternate nights, if not Steamer Point would have been razed to the ground and the hospital packed full of commandos.

A platoon of each was very effective working together after trouble from a group of dissidents. It was like running a well-developed foxhound with his sidekick the Jack Russell, but these Jack Russells were a damn sight more vicious than usual.

I usually ran my afternoon sessions at Singapore lines on my own. This absence of witnesses was useful for one HLI sergeant who came to see me. I have never seen anyone in such a mess, his face looked like a piece of liver. Someone had given him a good going over, his face and upper torso covered in bruises, abrasions and cuts. It took almost an hour to clean him up, stitch cuts, tetanus injection, antibiotics etc.

'I'd better sign you off for a week, Sergeant.'

'No thanks I'll be alright Sir, I've just to keep out of the way for a week and I'll be OK.'

'Don't you want the blokes who did this to be caught?'

'No Sir. If the CO sees me like this I'll loose me stripes. Me mates know who they are. They'll sort it out, it won't show on their faces, but they won't find it easy to move. It's an other ranks problem Sir. Discipline, but nothing to do with officers, the sergeants will sort it.'

'But they have used more than fists on your head.'

'Yes, Sir.'

'Suppose you get concussion, or there's a delayed bleed in your head, it could be serious.'

'Oh! Not to worry Sir.'

'I should report it.'

'I've not been here, no one saw me.'

"If they come looking for you, they'll see what you are like. Let's have an agreement, I say nothing, but if you have any headaches, start vomiting, get double vision contact me, also tell your mates if you get drowsy or can't wake up to get in touch with me. I've two RAF pals at Khormaksar, we can take you there for observation, but if it's serious it will be Steamer Point regardless.'

'Thanks Doc, we know we can get a good deal from you National Service Docs.'

He must have been all right because he didn't contact me again.

It was at Singapore lines that one orderly and I immunized a company of Jocks, Somali style as described above.

Dripping Donks

Donk, yet another nickname for a certain part of a gentleman's anatomy. Dripping! Let's talk about that.

I am going to be politically incorrect again, but I am merely recording a common adaptation of 'Absence makes the heart grow fonder' made by soldiers in tropical areas - 'Absence makes the blacks grow blonder.' It certainly did when our National Service lads went to Kenya.

National Service other ranks were allowed two weeks leave in Kenya, they could tour Kenya if they wished, but most stayed in Mombasa where they landed. At dawn on Thursday a plane load of about 100 young men left Khormaksar for Mombasa, picking up an equal number to bring back landing around 1300 hours. My session at Singapore lines started at 1400 hours. 10 to 20 returnees would visit me that afternoon. Another 30 finding it necessary to visit the MO in the following week. We estimated that on average 50% of the lads that had been on leave to Mombasa visited us. They certainly had not bothered to collect any prophylactics before they went. Not that it would have mattered because the ladies who entertained them would not allow them to use them.

Was it prostitution? It was different from what we understood as prostitution. Once with an ordinary prostitute and the lad may have got away with it. As medics we did not like the system, it almost guaranteed our lads would be infected, but it seemed to be preferred by the young ladies and certainly by our young men.

A young lady wishing to entertain a young soldier would attend the bars and clubs they frequented on the Thursday and Friday when they arrived. When a suitable arrangement had been arrived at the young lady took the young soldier home for the fortnight. Seven or eight times a week with the same young man being preferable to seven or eight times a night with seven or eight men. The young soldiers appreciated it, what's more if they had had a rare old time and the young man was running out of cash they lived quietly together until it was time for him to fly back to Aden. Our National Servicemen were not paid much, there was hardly anything to spend it on in Aden, to a young African woman they must have seemed very wealthy. As for the refusal to use condoms, VD must have made the girls sterile, otherwise there would be a massive tribe of Anglo-Africans around Mombasa.

Thank God AIDS did not appear until over twenty years later, we would have had a terrible problem. Gonorrhoea (the clap) and Non-Specific Urethritis, the first sensitive to penicillin, streptomycin, tetracycline and others, the second although we did not know the cause, sensitive to tetracycline and related drugs. The latter we now know to be due to Chlamydia, which is now, following the so-called post pill sexual revolution, probably more common amongst our own young women than it ever was amongst those young ladies in Mombasa.

Death

Basically our lads were a healthy lot, not much illness, but something serious could strike quickly. Not bacteria, but viruses. The patient was twenty-year-old young man on his way home from Singapore after completing his National Service. He had flown from Singapore and was spending a few days in Aden waiting for a flight home. I was asked to see him, he had had flu for a couple of days and was suddenly getting worse. I saw him early one afternoon, and sent him to the hospital at Steamer Point. Next morning when I went to the MI room at Singapore lines, I found a sergeant and platoon with gun carriage and coffin going through the burial drill for a soldier. On enquiry the sergeant told me it was for the young man I had sent into hospital the previous day.

'He's in a bad way Sir, won't last the day out. They go off quickly in this heat, we have arranged a full military funeral for this evening.'

I was a bit shattered, funeral drill before the boy had died. I was going to write man, but he was little more than a boy, on his way home after serving his country, about to start his proper life. Destroyed before it began. I know it happened to tens of thousands of young men in two world wars, but this was peace time. If he hadn't had to do National Service, he would have stayed at home and be like me, a grandfather!

It seems strange that at that time in Aden there were three future

Consultant Gynaecologists. Ian Manson, another Manchester graduate, a year older than me, was the Obstetric Specialist at Steamer Point. In actual fact I cannot remember us meeting all the time we were there. We have known each other all our adult lives, and he only lives at Chorley, about 30 miles away. At least he deserves a mention.

Chapter Twelve

The Jebel Akhdar

You are now going to visit these modern tourist areas in 1960 just after the British had helped the Sultan of Oman to disperse the Saudi backed rebels, from a time when the United States and the British were at war. American backed oil companies assisting the Saudies and British oil companies and government backing the Sultan of Oman.

My next adventure started towards the end of March 1960.

I can't remember how the instructions came, but as you can see from the letter, I was in the area of the Jebel Akhdar by the 29 March. I left Khormaksar by twin pioneer and landed on the RAF strip near Nizwa. I say airstrip, because that's all it was. The general area was one of stone desert with scattered bushes. Nearby was the town Nizwa.

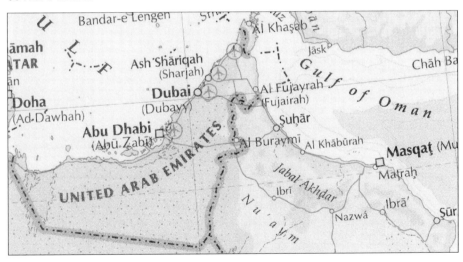

Muscat and the Trucial Oman, now the United Arab Emirates. In 1960 the borders were still fluid and disputed, especially in the unusable desert, oil had yet to be found. • Collins-Bartholomew 1997.
(Reproduced by kind permission of Harper-Collins)

Al'Jebel Al'Akhdar
(The Green Mountain)

Rising to nearly 10,000 feet, the Jebel Akhdar (or Green Mountains) form the central section of the Hajar Range that stretches over 400 miles from the Musandam peninsula in the west to the coastal town of Sur in the east. Jebel Akhdar's towering peaks, plunging valleys, date palm groves and hidden terraced villages offer a stark contrast to the flat plains of the fertile Batinah coast to the north and the great desert plateau of southern Arabia to the south.

This mountainous region is divided into two distinct zones, the northern slope sheltering the towns of Rustaq and Nakhl, and the southern slope of the interior. We begin to the south at the oasis town of Nizwa.

NIZWA was once the capital of Oman. Today it is best known for its large fort and silver souq. Dominated by a huge circular tower, the fort stands in the center of town, surrounded by a mix of local markets and ancient mud-brick homes. The Silver Souq is the best in Oman, an excellent place to buy a tradition Omani Khunjar (ceremonial dagger), made locally by Omani craftsmen. Nizwa has also long been an important agricultural center thanks to farms fed by Oman's largest falaj (aqueduct) called the Falaj Daris, built in 1680 by the Imam, Sultan Saif.

The road to Nizwa from Muscat takes us through the Sumail Gap. Here the Wadi Sumail cuts a deep cleft through the Hajar range permitting access to the interior from the Batinah coast and the Capital Area. Winter storms often fill this usually dry riverbed sometimes making transit difficult. Even today the modern highway from Muscat to Nizwa and Salalah is occasionally cut by rising water. The photograph (left) shows the wadi in flood close to the village of Fanja.

This page, and Opposite: Information taken from the internet – http://www.oldera.com /oman/jabal.htm

As we emerge at the southern end of the Sumail Gap we pass the wayside oasis of Birkat Al Mawrs. Here ancient date groves are fed year-round by a falaj (aqueduct) emanating from the foot of the nearby 7000 foot Jebel Saiq. In addition to her picturesque date groves Birkat also possesses a fine fort dating from the days of the Imams.

High above Birkat, 6000 feet up on the Jebel Akhdar plateau, lie the terraced villages of Bani Habib and Sharijah. Here, above the heat of the desert and in ancient terraced fields, Omani farmers grow vines, limes, pomegranates, onions and other vegetables for market in nearby Nizwa and the capital area.

BAHLA: The historic fort and walled town of Bahla lie in the shadow of the jebel, 20 miles west of Nizwa. Dating back to the 3rd millennium BCE the entire complex of fort and town are recognized as a World Heritage Site. The town stands amid acres of date palms which are in turn surrounded by 7 miles of ancient defensive wall

MISFAT is without doubt one of the most picturesque villages in Oman. Resting high on the side of a deep wadi on the southern slope of the Jebel Akhdar, Misfat is built entirely of stone and mud-brick. Immediately below the village a system of terraced fields, fed by a tumbling central falaj (aqueduct), plunges straight down the side of the wadi in spectacular fashion. Approached along a single dirt track, even today cars are not permitted in the village which continues to maintain its traditional agricultural way of life.

JABRIN: Ten miles west of Bahla, following the foot of the jebel, and a short distance out onto the desert plain, lies the historic oasis and 17th century fortress of Jabrin. The fort's maze of rooms were once an Islamic college and today boast many unique design features and finely painted ceilings.

RUSTAQ: We will also see some of the northern rim of the Jebel Akhdar in particular visiting the town and fort of Rustaq. Rustaq Fort was first established in pre-Islamic times and for a while, during the 18th century, served as the capital of Oman. Today the fort holds tombs of some of Oman's early rules, including the founder of the present Albusaidi dynasty.

AL HAMRA (the Red Town): The traditional mud-brick town of Al Hamra (left) stands at the southern foot of the Oman's highest peak, the 10,000 ft Jebel Shams. Amid this breathtaking scenery the ancient town seems to spring from the very bedrock.

From:- Lieut Colone D MATHESON, M.B., RAMC

Headquarters
British Forces Arabian Peninsula
British Forces Post Office 69

BFAP/2247/2/A/MED

8 Apr 60

Dear Bill

     I got your letter of the 29th a couple of days ago and am arranging publication of the necessary Part III Orders.

     Matthews turned up here last night on the casevac Comet from Bahrein and I ran into him at the RAF Hospital whilst I was boarding Lt Keightley home. He gave me a good picture of the form and at the moment is running round seeing if he can get on to a BOAC plane tonight, there being no hope of a RAF indulgence seat just now. When he gets back in about 6 weeks he will return to Saiq and relieve you. You will then go down to Bait Al Falag and relieve Hind who comes here for a 2 month spell among the flesh pots of Aden. He will then return and you will come back here. I am thinking again about how to cope with Hinds subsequent reliefs at Bait but there is plenty time for deciding on that.

     I hope you enjoy your time at Saiq and find the work interesting.

Yours sincerely

Donald Matheson

Capt W.O. GOLDTHORPE RAMC
c/o Northern Frontier Regt
British Forces Post Office 63 Group 'B'

I relieved Matthew, who had been Medical Officer on top of the Jebel Akhdar for over a year. The Jebel Akhdar, a massive mountain range, towers over the whole plain. In parts, it reaches 10,000 feet. I note on the map, the highest point is 3,018 metres. Saig, where I was based, is 8,000 feet, which was why I suffered altitude sickness when I first arrived. It rained a lot on the Jebel, on the north east side, where there were wadies and riverbeds that ran down to the sea. On the south west, where Nizwa and other towns and villages were, the wadies ran out into the desert, eventually on occasion, reaching Saudi Arabia. It was mainly desert, but there was the odd oasis.

Jebel Sham, north end of Jebel Akhdar

Nizwa and Bahlah were large oases, as was Ibri. These oases were round what were often dry wadi beds, although when I was in Nizwa, there was some open water. Nizwa, in addition to being close to the Jebel, was a point were several major roads (tracks) joined: the main road to the capital Muscat, a road to the south, the Oman proper, and another going north west to the Trucial Oman States, now United Arab Emirates. Near the airfield was a small hospital, consisting of two or three MI rooms, a small surgery and a ward with about twenty beds. As in most of parts of Arabia only men got ill, only male patients were ever in it. It did have an interesting side, however, as I was told by one of the MOs. The local people hadn't quite got round to trusting the British doctors, some days he would go into his ward, that had been packed full the night before, to find it empty. One of his patient had died; the others had got a little anxious, packed their bags and gone home!

Close to Nizwa was the camp of the Northern Frontier Regiment of the Sultan of Muscat's Armed Forces, a regiment of Baluchi soldiers recruited in Pakistan. They had their own fort, the Nizwa fort, newly built, two storeys, not very big, the administrative centre. It wasn't fortified, one shell from a fifteen pounder would have blown it up. Nearby was a camp of English sergeants who were the specialists in various departments, i.e. arms, REME, signals etc. I spent three days at that Medical Centre, waiting for a plane; during that time, I was shown round the area.

```
                                    c/o NFR,
                                    BFPO 63  Gp B
                                    March 9th

Dear Bill,

    I hear you are coming out here while I am on leave but that (this
from Wing Commander Ferguson, SMOPG) you may go to Bait al Falaj
while Ian Hind comes up here - or half in one place, half in the
other.        In any case you would probably like to hear a
little about the places and jobs.
    Bait al Falaj.  Officially MO to small British detachment but
the MO of HQ SAF will be on leave and so there will be quite a
lot to do at this time.    All told about 25 BORs, 25 Officers
4 beds in British MI room,  about eight beds in native MI room
with a daily sick parade of up to forty.    You have a British corporal
with detachment but the native orderlies have very little knowledge
and the standard is not a high one to maintain.    Comfortable
air conditioned room but probably shared   (new house may be ready
in time to avoid that).    Good food.    Mess of odd characters but
including some young air force officers.    Daily routine up
to oneself.    No bullshit.    Temperatures may reach the 100s.
Recreations; swimming, tennis, good sea fishing, some shooting.
Occasional films arrive.    American Mission Hospital in
nearby Muttrah, takes native cases.    British Casevac to Bahrain.
Americans will welcome you if you want to go along to discuss cases
or to see their cases.    The Gynae is run by a woman and whether
a man would be allowed there I do not know.

    Saiq.  6500 ft.  Climate delightful.    Comfortable room to
yourself with bed provided.       XXXXXXXXXXXXXXXXXXXXXXXXXXXXXXXX.
XXXXXXXX    I will leave my camp kit, sheets, pillow etc.    (Camp
kit in case you want to spend nights away).    Pleasant mess with
only two other officers.    Bring necessaries such as soap, tooth
paste....no shops or other amenities.    Frozen food is flown
in sometimes and we eat well.    A company of soldiers provide
only a few cases and the real workis with civilians.    2000 live
in scattered villages, to which one goes on foot.    There is no
malaria and the people are reasonably healthy - much eye trouble.
They are friendly but feckless so that with language difficulties,
lack of diagnostic aids, their habit of not keeping appointments,
it is difficult tp have the kind of standard of Medicine one would
like.    Amount of work depends on how often one wishes to walk out
to villages to see what there is.    It is really too small a
population todeserve a doctor in the context of this country, but
we are here as part of the rehabilitation of the area, which was
badly bombed in the rebellion and are leant to the Foreign Office
for this scheme only.    One does a certain amount of real good
however, in that occasionally lives can be saved, of persons
```

The first day, I joined a convoy of the Northern Frontier Regiment, going out to Ibri, 80 miles to the west. Here, was an
encampment of SAS who had been involved in capturing the Jebel.
On the way, we came to a huge oasis, which at one time must have
formed a little feudal state on its own, Bahlah. The whole oasis was
surrounded by a massive wall, 14-15 feet high, six foot at the base.
At the top, was a walkway, four foot down from the top of the
wall. It went all the way round, like the Great Wall of China, round
the outside of the oasis, and where there was a large rocky hill,

who would otherwise have been left to die.   I have compromised
between saying 'If they want treatment they can come and tell me'
(they are too lazy for that to be honest) and going a continuous
round of all the villages (which would mean an awful lot of
walking for each case of the common cold!).   Personally I
have been very busy however for an awful lot goes on here in the
way of transforming a camp into a permanent station, training
a novice Force, exploring the country.   There are very few
oficers and yet everything needs close supervision.   The officers
also have to do a lot of ordinary mechanical jobs themselves (mending
lights, fridge etc) for the soldiery are so primitive.   I have
looked after the mess and done many other things connected with
the above matters.   HOWEVER there would be no need for any
locum to do anything at all.   He would be completely his own
master.   Personally I have found in an enlightening
experience working with these two contrasted backward people, the
Baluch soldiers and the local arabs.   There is no interpreter
hre at the moment but one should come soon.

Amongst reasons why I am glad to have this post is the fact
that the practical alternatives - BAF & Bahrain - usually
give no chance of any medical experience and are much less
pleasant and interesting in other ways.   I might get sent back
to Aden but between lack of a.c. in that climate and what I hear
about human relations there, I have no wish for that.   If the
authorities learnt that the medical work here is rather normal
General Practice than rehabilitation, that it is fairly limited
in scope and that I have been working a good deal for SAF in
other ways,   they might easily withdraw me.   It is 'policy'
to give no help to SAF beyond what has been officially laid down.
I therefore ask you to keep the above guff under your hat both now
and when you have finished here.

I look forward to seeing you before I go off and to hearing
about Somaliland and other things you have done.   You have certainly
seen the widest variety of country of us all.

I hope your wife is well.   And you will have been a father
for some time?

Yours

*BRING SPARE PAIR DESERT BOOTS FOR YOURSE[LF]
me goes through them fast here.*

The signature is Graeme Matthew's. The postscript: bring spare pair of desert boots for yourself, one goes through them fast here

almost mountain, between two parts of the oasis, the wall went
over the top of it. In the centre, a massive outcrop of rock, 50 foot
high, on top was thick walled citadel, also 50 foot high. Massive
towers on each corner, a complicated defence system at the main
gate, just as complex as any of Edward III's castles that he built in
Wales.

We passed a few small villages alongside oases, but there were a

Khubarah Village on the plain, Jebel Akhdar behind, 1960

number of deserted ones. In the past, when they had slaves, they dug watercourses, called phalages, deep ditches that were roofed over with masonry. These watercourses would go from the bottom of the mountains carrying the water, anything up to twenty miles or so, so that water was carried out to areas where there was fertile soil. Here small villages had grown up.

The reason there were deserted villages was because of the nasty British, who in the latter part of the nineteenth century, from about 1860 onwards, developed their empire in East Africa, and finished off the Arab slave trade. The Arabs had used their slaves to walk down these long, dark, watery phalages to maintain them. They hadn't been maintained for about 80 years or more. Now the phalages were falling in, blocking off the water supply, so the villages had ceased to exist.

The main town, Nizwa, had lots of close-planted palm trees with very lush vegetation underneath. There was plenty of feed for cows, sheep, camels and goats etc. Nizwa didn't have a surrounding wall. The houses and street blocks were close to each other. The housing was two storey, a street about 10-12 foot wide; thick heavy doors in the lower storey, no windows, only windows in the upper storey. On the outskirts were four or five storey towers, the size of English windmills, strong points to help defend the town.

A Street in Niswa

In the centre was a massive fort, a complex of buildings, which would have held over a thousand people. The most important part, a large, circular tower, was 50 feet or more high. I don't know whether there was anything under the tower, the lower 30 feet appeared to be solid. Above, the walls, which were about 8 or 9 feet thick, went up about a further 25 feet, to a walkway round the top with a series of ovals, 4 × 3 feet, which could contain a crouching rifleman. At the base, was a flat area, 30 feet; above the ground, every 12 foot, all round the circular tower, was an embrasure through which a cannon could have been fired. This central area dominated the whole town, a defensive and protective point. The fort was guarded by Baluchis, and there were some of the local Arabs, who we found making gunpowder.

I have a slide of these chaps, two men and a boy. The rifles are old Martini Henries, with the silver scroll work that the Arabs so delighted in. They were single shot, breech loaders, with a lever action to eject the fired bullet before reloading. They fired a heavy lead 0.45 slug. This was the same 'modern rifle' that allowed a company, under 120 men, of Welsh Fusiliers to fight off over 4,000 Zulus at the Battle of Rorke's Drift some eighty years earlier. The manufacturer is waving his mortar pestle in the air with one hand and his rifle in the other. Behind him, a teenager, (no beard) is wearing the big curved Arab dagger and scabbard, highly decorated

with silver. We were rather intrigued that they were making gunpowder.

It was just towards the end of Ramadan. In Nizwa, as in other Arab towns, when the sun went down at night a man would be watching, and as soon as the top rim went below the horizon a cannon would be fired. Everyone could then start to eat and drink. We watched him make his gunpowder, until one of his friends came to have a look. His pal lit a cigarette, we promptly disappeared!

The Sultan of Muscat's flag flew on the top of all his buildings and forts. This was red, so I can say quite definitely, at the height of the cold war between the USSR, NATO, America, etc., I was serving under the Red Flag!

Matthew had already left and gone to Bahrain. I was waiting until a plane became available. Convoys of donkeys went 3-4 times a week, carrying supplies. I suppose I could have walked, but I don't think I'd have arrived for a fortnight. I found altitude sickness can interfere with your ability to get about. I went up by what is known as a single pioneer - a single-engined aircraft.

While I was waiting for my single pioneer, I met a sergeant from the SAS. This chap had been on a job with the SAS, come home and been given three months leave. He was about thirty, a very fit and smart young unmarried man, he'd decided to visit his pals. He'd

The Great Fort at Niswa

Inside the Great Fort tower

scrounged a lift with the RAF from England to Germany, to Gibraltar, to Malta, to Libya, then to Uganda and Tanganyika, from there to the Oman and had been spending a few days with his other SAS sergeant pals in Ibri.

His leave was due to finish in two weeks time, he was now heading home. He'd got a lift to Bahrain. His intention was to go from Bahrain to Cyprus, Cyprus to Gibraltar and back to England. It had cost him hardly anything. He had hitchhiked on RAF planes to get this far and was now going home. Being a smart looking young man, he was welcome in every sergeant's mess that he had stopped at. He'd had a nice three months holiday, touring the world with little expense to himself. If you have chaps with that ability, it's no wonder the SAS can do so well.

The Jebel Akhdar is 40 or 50 miles long, 10 or 15 wide, extremely high, with numerous deep wadies, winding and twisting in all directions. Some wadi sides are five or six thousand feet high. You can understand why it had been so difficult to capture it. The rebel leader was called Sulieman bin something. He was like a feudal ruler of the place.

It was highly developed. Wherever there was any space, a little wadi, or water collecting point, phalages had been built over the centuries, collecting water at the head of each wadi. At each village, were collecting tanks and phalages carrying the water to the fields.

Twin Pioneer landing, Niswa airstrip

- 230 -

Single Pioneer

The fields were terraced. Sometimes, there'd be a small plateau that was terraced and cultivated. Other places, on the side of a not so steep wadi, there'd be a series of anything up to about 100 terraces, each had a wall - anything from 2 to 6 foot high - and a strip of land, which might vary from about 6 to 15 foot or more. Only about a third were cultivated. The rest belonged to the Sulieman chap who had been the feudal ruler.

The population paid rent for their own fields by labouring in the fields of the ruler. They may have looked poverty stricken to us, living in mud and stone huts with no proper sanitation, but from their point of view, they were quite a prosperous community. Each man would probably be 'gardening' - I'm not using the term 'farming' - about two acres of terrace, which in addition to growing crops, grew a lot of fruit, which was taken down to Nizwa to be sold. They didn't throw anything away. I remember visiting one house where we were sitting round having a drink of water then tea in tin cans which probably used to contain beans or pineapple chunks. When they were empty, the Arabs would get a little hammer and file, smooth off the inside of the top the tin to use a drinking receptacle.

I got involved with these people more and saw more of their family life than I saw of many other Arab areas that I went to. They didn't seem to have the nasty attitude to women that the Aden

South end, Jebel Akhdar

peasant had. Their relationships with their wives was very good. Their wives were a respected part of the community.

The problem was, whilst they had been fighting, our aircraft had been bombarding the Jebel. There was a lot of bomb and rocket damage, blown up houses that hadn't been repaired. The greatest problem, was damage to the phalages, which they had relied on to irrigate the crops. That is what Matthews had been doing. He organized the engineers. Using metal piping, they repaired the phalages so that the Arabs could irrigate the land.

The phalages were lined with some form of concrete, a home made concrete. They travelled for miles, often you'd see a phalage on a wadi side, a good 30 or 40 feet up, here and there a phalage viaduct would take the water supply over a tiny wadi.

The reason a doctor had been sent up there was because the British authorities were worried about the possibility of epidemics. They found a doctor who could be spared and he was sent to the top of the Jebel. His equipment was ancient in the extreme! Ten years previously we'd been in Syria, where there had been a MI room at station called Habanyana. The MI room, if you can call it that, was equipped with all the stuff that had been in Habanyana 10 years previously, together with various other odd bits and pieces that people had to spare.

There was no sending off a request for supplies every month, as there had been in Somaliland. Here, you had to use what you'd got! There were virtually no antibiotics, we did have plenty of Streptomycin, which was the second antibiotic ever to come out. Instead of it being a nice white powder that could be dissolved in sterile water, this was in an oily suspension. On its side, it said 'use by ...' the date was 8 years previously. There were plenty of sulphonamides to use instead of antibiotics, a certain amount of old local anaesthetic, and other odd things. There was massive supply of quinine tablets. Where on earth they got the quinine from, I don't know. Numerous tiny tubes of Aureomycin Eye Ointment. There must have been somebody, somewhere with a glut of this and it had been sent off to the top of the Jebel Akhdar. It was all rather primitive.

The tribesmen on the top of the Jebel Akhdar, traditional enemies of the Sultan, were not allowed any medical treatment at all. The only medical treatment they got was what I or Matthew could do for them. The Baluchi soldiers, and Omani Arabs, could be transferred down to the Nizwa hospital, or into Nizwa itself, where there was a dispensary run by a Pakistani doctor, Dr Rashid, a pleasant sort of chap, but he wasn't a surgeon; he was a physician, so the medical support service was limited. In Muscat, there was a mission hospital. I don't know which Christian society ran it. Arabs could be sent there for treatment. English folks could be sent back to Aden or to Bahrain, if they needed anything more they could be sent back to England.

I left Nizwa airstrip in a single pioneer that was taking some more urgent supplies, up to the Jebel top. By urgent supplies, I mean such things as a crate of twelve bottles of gin! I'd gone off smoking again. I stopped from the moment I left Aden until I got back, the only stuff you could get were vile Turkish things that tasted like camel dung. Saig itself had been a village, but was deserted. The water table on top of the Jebel had dropped by about 15 or 20 feet, so although there was a fair amount of water at certain times of the year, there wasn't enough to maintain a village. There was a small wadi, with a large flat area, which had been the village. It came right to the escarpment where the Sheraijah Wadi started.

Here the escarpment dropped for about 1,000 feet. I was quite intrigued (well, shit scared really), when the single pioneer approached the escarpment, the pilot turned the engine down a bit

Saig Fort, Men's Lines
The hospital was to the right of this picture. There is a patient in my waiting
room, sitting on a branch under the shade of a bush, the waiting room

and we seemed to be sinking as though we'd crash into the escarpment. Just as we got to the face, coming up the wall was a big
draught of hot air that had been heated up in the bottom of the
wadi, rushing up the escarpment face. This caught the plane, lifted
it up, and dropped it on the end of the runway, and we were able
to taxi in to Saig. Saig wadi was about 500 yards long; at the head
of it was a group of storage tanks. The upper half was terraced. The
wadi wall on the right hand side as you landed was 50 foot high.
On top, a little modern white painted administrative fort, two
storeys high with a four-storey tower at one end and a three-storey
tower at the other and flying away on top of the four-storey tower,
was the Sultan of Oman's red flag!

At the bottom, on the fort side of the wadi, was a series of
substantial flat terraces on which the company camp was based,
and where the living quarters of the three European officers were
built. These were known as barousties. Mine was a flat roof, mud
and stone, square little house, 12 foot square with a door and

window, about 9 foot high; the walls were made of mud and stone, and plastered with mud, inside and out, then allowed to dry in the hot weather. The roof was a series of thick tree or bush branches over which was put a lot of straw, with mud poured on top of that, then more straw and mud, more straw and mud, finally the whole lot was smoothed down, leading down into one corner where a little wooden gutter stretched out to take the water off the top.

The inside of the roof had been smoothed off with mud and dried, and the whole lot was whitewashed inside. The walls were about 2 foot thick, so my living area was about 10 foot square. The window had been taken out of an aeroplane that had crashed on top of the Jebel. At the back was my bed and alongside, a curtained off area with rough shelves and a rough wooden thing to hang clothes on. There was also, against one wall, a stone and mud built thing that was supposed to be a desk. Just inside the door, another plinth made out of mud and stone on which I kept my washing bowl, with a mirror over it. Alongside, a series of rough shelves, on which you kept your shaving gear etc.

One morning I was just about to put the flannel to my face when I noticed, right in the middle, a little black scorpion, about two inches long, which I am rather glad I did not apply to my face. Scorpions like dark, smelly places, such as shoes and boots. We all had to develop the habit of checking our boots, turning them upside down, banging them on the floor at the heel, in case a scorpion was lurking in the depths. I never came across any in my boots, but I got into such a habit, that it continued for about 3 or 4 years after I'd got back to England, intriguing my Professor of Obstetrics, Professor W. I. C. Morris, when I was Resident Obstetric Surgeon at St Mary's Hospital, Manchester. I always assisted him with Caesarean sections. I was still subconsciously, when getting dressed after assisting, knocking my shoes on the floor. This gave rise to the Professor asking me 'Goldthorp, I've been wondering, why is it, before you put your shoes on, you always turn them upside down and bang them on the floor?' He was somewhat amazed when I answered 'Scorpions, Sir'.

My hot and cold running water supply consisted of two jerry cans of cold water. I became a dab hand at shaving myself with cold water. We did have the usual compliment of sweepers and dobhimen to keep the place tidy and do your laundry. I had what all ex-soldiers know as a 'housewife' - I had to start repairing tears in my trousers, shorts and shirts, and sew my own buttons on, which I might add, 43 years later, I am still doing. I also had a

My Baroustie

portable canvas bath, into which I'd pour a couple of buckets of water, stand in and soap myself all over.

You can see the gold cross in the picture above that Margaret gave me the day I left Crowle for the second trip to Portsmouth when we knew she would not be joining me. For over 16 years I never took that cross and chain off. I slept, bathed, swam and played sport wearing it. Unfortunately there is psoriasis in my family and the constant irritation caused a tiny patch to appear on my neck. I removed it and it is now a treasured possession of my elder daughter.

It was to ward off demons, especially the ones with long hair, sparkling eyes and nice figures. I cannot claim my behaviour as a married man away from home was exemplary and that I avoided all temptation. I cannot say that I avoided all temptation for the simple reason that there was no temptation. Perhaps I should thank God that I was sent to Aden. I heard what happened to those that went to Singapore where there were many unattached European ladies and extremely friendly local ones.

Even at night time, although we were 8,000 feet up, it was still pretty warm in that part of Arabia. The flat wadi where Saig village had been was about 60 or 70 yards across. There was another small escarpment of 20 feet on the other side, at the bottom of which

Sheireijah Village, bomb damage

Sgt Major, Darvish patients and audience, Ead 1960

was the kitchen for the officers and on top was a whitewashed officers' mess. I say officers, there were only three of us - a major, whose name I cannot remember, and a captain called Mike W—. The Baluchi soldiers would follow him anywhere, he led patrols looking for the bad guys and dissidents, they would follow him but only when he was sober!

At the base of the escarpment, on that side, was the hospital. It consisted of two rooms. You went in through the door, into the first room, which was extremely well lit, because the roof had fallen in! That's where we stored things that wouldn't get damaged by being wet. The actual room, or hospital, was a little bit dingy. It was lit by another window inserted from a crashed aircraft! My examination couch was built alongside the wall, opposite the window, 3 feet from the ground, mud and stone, with sun dried bricks on top to make it smooth. In here, in various corners, piled in various places, on numerous rough shelves, were the bits of equipment that I have described previously.

The escarpment was at the head of the Sheraijah Wadi. There was Sheraijah village and a terraced area in a low bowl with a reasonable amount of water, the Sheraijah Bowl. The Bowl came to an end, then a steep slope went down a long way, about 100 terraces deep. Beyond was another little village, away from cultivated areas and water, extremely dry, called Solut. This wadi joined a major wadi

Askari, Head Coolie Talib, Headman Halfan, Darvish, Sgt Major

Monsur Bin Nasser and family

and eventually wound its way out onto the plain. That wadi, the major Maidan Wadi, must have had sides that were about 6,000 feet high.

These villages were situated at various heights. We were above the mosquito level. The Anopheles mosquito, which carries malaria, is said not to go above 5,000 feet. We were in the cooler area, instead of having mosquitoes, we had body lice instead. Typhus is spread by body lice, and one of the reasons it spreads so rapidly is that body lice don't like the body temperature when it goes up with fever, say from a normal 98.4 F to 104 F. Then they all clear off, onto someone with a normal temperature. The body lice on the Jebel Akhdar had moved upward, because it was too hot down in the bottom parts of the wadies and on the plain. They'd moved up about 7 or 8, 000 feet where it was a bit cooler - where I was! It took me about a month to work out why I kept having these big red itchy blotches round my waist, just under where I wore my belt.

Ramadan had just ended, and it was the Eid holiday. On the second day I went with one of the Omani Officers Darvish on a visit to Sheraijah. The villagers were very pleased to see us and we spent a pleasant afternoon in their company. They themselves had not been involved in the rebellion, but they had suffered because of it, as you can see from the bomb damage.

To the west of us, 4 or 500 yards away, was another wadi, the Wadi Habib, and Habib village. This village was about 50 feet below our level, where the water table was still high enough; it was still a prosperous little village.

We had a mess servant - a little Arab lad of about 12. I had my own medical orderly and interpreter, Salah. Instead of wearing the same type of uniform as the ordinary Baluchi soldier, his was slightly different. He had a green beret, which was the medical orderly's beret. The Baluchi headgear was the same as the Trucial Oman Scouts, the Shamag and Aggle.

The Shamag is the square Arab head scarf worn all over Arabia, pinky red splotches on a white background, with tasselled edges, worn on the head, but wrapped round the nose and mouth during a mild sand storm, and over the head and face during a serious one, lying alongside your camel, keeping the sand out of your lungs and eyes. The aggle, two bands of rope round your head, keep the shamag in place. The two bands were made out of one piece of rope, it was used to hobble the front legs of your camel, while you slept at night. The camel could search for fodder but not stray far.

Salah was intelligent and a good interpreter; he could speak

Arabic, Baluchi and Urdu, unfortunately, he couldn't speak English! I couldn't speak any of them, but I had a slight smattering of Arabic. I don't know how we managed it, but Salah and I could conduct quite complicated conversations. He could interpret people giving medical histories in Arabic, to me. With facial grimaces, hand waving, rude Arabic and English words, we managed quite well. Salah was quite an asset.

There wasn't an awful lot of work to do, medically speaking, but I did have a home visit on the first afternoon I got there. The visit was a mile and a half away, on the flat Saig plateau, to another little village. It must have taken me two hours to get there and two hours to get back. We were up at 8,000 feet, which I wasn't used too, every 5 or 6 minutes, I had to sit down and rest for two or three minutes. It took me about a fortnight to get over mountain sickness.

Coffee Custom

If we'd been walking for some time, Salah and I, when we approached a village, would take our water bottles out and have a drink. We knew it would be quite some time before you actually got a drink of water. On arrival, you met the headman and all the

Monsur the Teacher, as a good Arab host he is preparing our coffee

Coffee and Chai ceremony

senior men. You went round shaking hands going 'Salaam Alicum, Alicum As Sallam' etc.

We'd then go to sit in the meeting house, where our introductory coffee would be prepared. A brazier would be brought, filled with charcoal, lit and fanned until it got red hot. A large cast iron spoon would be produced several handfuls of coffee beans poured onto it, which were then roasted. The beans were then put into a large mortar made out of solid silver and, using an equally large solid silver pestle, they would be ground up. During this time, another solid silver, highly decorated bulbous coffee pot would be placed on the brazier, filled full of water and boiled. When the water boiled, the ground coffee beans would be thrown in; a couple of handfuls of sugar, often various locally grown herbs, such as mint.

When it was finally ready, they started with the senior guest, which was me, second senior guest, Salah, and if I had another soldier with me, third guest. Otherwise, the third man down would be headman of the village; there would be a whole row of fellows down to the little lad of 6 years old at the bottom end. The coffee pourer would now produce three porcelain, highly decorated cups, about the size of an egg cup and from the height of about 2 feet or more, pour two teaspoonfuls of coffee into the coffee cup, hand it to you, which you drank. The next cup would go to Salah, and so on. It was considered polite to take three cups of coffee, after which you turned your hand upside down, holding the coffee cup upside down, and wiggled it, which meant 'no thank you'. Whereupon the coffee pourer would take it, fill it up and hand it to the fourth man down the line. They went on until they got to the little boy at the end. When this rigmarole was over, you would then be asked if you would like a drink of water.

Then chai (tea) would be prepared. Goat's milk and water would be poured in a saucepan, brought to the boil, several handfuls of tea leaves were thrown in, along with sugar, mint and other herbs. It was boiled for a certain length of time, then bringing round the drinking receptacles, you'd have a mug full, including the tea leaves!

After that rigmarole, which lasted about an hour, you were allowed to see your patient. When you'd seen the patient, and probably two or three other patients who had taken advantage of your being there, and were getting ready to go home, you had to start all over again. This time, it was tea, water and then coffee.

Fuddles

A fuddle is an Arab feast. I'd been one or two fuddles in Dahla, but those were more official affairs organized by the Arab officers. The fuddles I'm going to describe now were in the houses of the local Arabs. They had, like the old English system, dinnertime (fuddles) at 12.00 noon.

Another important point in Arabia - you had a clean hand, which you ate with, and a dirty hand, which you wiped the nether end with. If they went to the loo, a piddle for example, an Arab selected a long, narrow stone which he held in his left hand, and when he's finished, he hits the appropriate member to knock off the remaining drops. Similarly, if he wants to go for a 'poo', he selects a nice, round stone which, when he's finished, he uses the stone in his left hand to wipe himself with.

I had to make sure I didn't use my left hand to eat with. If you're gnawing at a bone, you're allowed to use your right hand and the fingernails to pull off the bits of meat, and you can hold the base of the bone in your left hand. Since we didn't have tables or chairs, or anything like that, I always sat in such a way that my left buttock was on my left hand, so I wouldn't accidentally use it and insult anybody!

When asked to a fuddle, after going through the coffee rigmarole, you went into the dining area. The wives would be preparing the meal during this time. Three or four men would then bring in a large, solid silver dish that must have been half an inch thick and a metre across, it would be piled high with rice, on top of which would be a boiled goat or sheep, which we ate without knives, forks or spoons, ripping bits off.

What you usually did was pull a bit of meat off, put it on one side, get a handful of rice, bounce it around in the middle of your right hand until you had it in a ball, poke a hole in the middle with your finger and stick the meat inside and eat it. I well remember sitting next to the head man of one village, and he had a nice thick sturdy right thumb nail. It was about half an inch long beyond the end of his thumb. As most thumb nails are when they get that long, it was somewhat black in appearance. During the course of the meal, we got fairly close to the bone in the thigh, he used his long sturdy thumb nail to scoop out a nice, tasty bit of meat from quite close to the bone. He then made a ball of rice, put the meat inside and handed it to me! Now, what do you do now! You're the honoured guest, mate, you're not going to insult him! I ate it!

What I did like about the Jebel Akhdar Arabs is that they did look after the ladies. What usually happened at one these fuddles, when the rice and meat had gone cold and the men had finished, it was taken next door and the women had a go. On several occasions, I noticed the dining area in the Jebel Akhdar houses was divided into two by a curtain. As soon as the meal got going, some of the men would quite surreptitiously, hoping I wouldn't notice, divide the rice into two portions, put a substantial chunk of the sheep on it, and hand it to the ladies. At one time, I looked up when this was going on, there was a gasp of embarrassment all round, because I gather this wasn't supposed to happen. I was quite pleased at seeing that, so I gave a big smile and gave the universal sign of approval thumbs up! There were big smiles all round, big smiles from the ladies in the room next door. The ladies could have their meal while the rice and meat was still hot, and we continued with ours.

When the meal was over, they'd bring round various Arabic preparations for sweet. These, in my mind, were a bit over sticky, too sweet and left a lot to be desired. There was one sort of jelly affair made out of mint and other things, but I didn't want to upset anybody, so I ate them. Not all of them, you could refuse second helpings. After that, a water bowl went round so we could all wash our hands and settle down to talk. (Arabs washed their hands after a meal not before). How we managed I have no idea, but with Salah's occasional help, we had quite animated discussions. Then would come the scents - roses and other Arabic perfumes, which the fellows would rub on their faces, in their hair, beards and armpits.

I followed suit. I hope you'll forgive this comment, but I must have come out of those Arab fuddles smelling like a brothel! I remember one occasion, when there was a little confab in one corner, between two or three of the senior men. They obviously had got something very, very special, which they thought I would enjoy spraying on myself. They suddenly came up and produced this bottle of Old Spice, which of course, I recognized. They proceeded to scatter Old Spice all over themselves and me.

Smelling like a brothel

'Oh, aye. How does he know? How many times has he been in a brothel?'

Well twice to be exact.

Once at the age of 22, to deliver a baby. Once at the age of 67, when my wife bought two tickets at the Kalgourlie Tourist Office, in Western Australia for the 'Brothel Tour' which included an English cream tea, with scones, clotted cream and strawberry jam. Langtrees, named after the Jersey Lily, one of Edward VII's bits on the side. It had just undergone a three million dollar refurbishment. Although prostitution is illegal in Western Australia, Langtrees can be found on the same street alongside The Central Police Station and Central Criminal Court.

When WOG got fleas in a brothel

The young innocent, age 22.

St Mary's Manchester is 250 years old, starting as a charity hospital. In its early days it could not afford to run a proper hospital. It was a home delivery service. In 1955, 50% of its deliveries were at home. Its district delivery area was Moss Side, not the newly built, gangster drug capital it is now, but numerous tiny streets of two up and two down terraced houses, occupied by relatively poor working class Irish Catholic families, who often required our services.

We did three months training in midwifery. A GP was supposed to be able to take care of his own home deliveries. A month at Withington learning the basics, and two months at St Mary's Whitworth Street, Central Manchester. What a glorious base. The Mecca Dance Hall behind the hospital, a News Theatre across the road, the Shakespeare pub just beyond that. The Palace Theatre directly opposite, with its bar, the best Worthington in town. A strip club underneath at the front, you could hear the Bongo Drums playing beneath the labour ward as you did a delivery. The senior midwives approved of the strip club; it guaranteed work in nine months time.

A large Gaumont and Odeon cinema 150 yards away on either side of the road. The Gaumont Long Bar, the haunt of all the older Manchester puffs. That's were we went in groups of 5 or 6 holding hands, with knuckledusters in our pockets, just in case. The older gentlemen of that persuasion would demonstrate their generosity and try to impress us by buying the beer. But we always cleared off after a couple of pints, to be on the safe side.

Our first month was to observe the abnormal deliveries, when we drove the resident doctors to distraction, by refusing to get up at night, to watch this 'fantastic breech presentation'.

The second month was accompanying the District Midwives to home confinements. We had to do a minimum of twenty. There was no problem of getting up at night to accompany the district midwives. Unlike the resident doctors they had no difficulty at all.

District midwives are tough, vicious frightening creatures, quite capable of barging into your room at night, accompanied by a highly nubile student midwife of 22 or 23, dragging you out of bed, ripping your pyjamas off, and ordering you, standing there shivering, buck naked, in full view of the highly nubile one, 'Get your B—y clothes on, you're coming with me'.

That had only happened once - the rest of us, living in terror of it happening again, were out of bed like a shot as soon as the phone rang.

My midwife, that night, a lady in her thirties, picked me up about midnight, and she drove to a substantial terrace in Moss Side. Not knowing whether our patient was in labour we were sitting alongside. The room a massive back room, contained several other young ladies and an older one who appeared to be in charge.

Central heating, not then being the fashion, and smokeless zones still to come, a large coal fire was roaring up the chimney. This was always a necessity, a. to keep the room warm and b. to throw the afterbirth on when delivery was complete. It was September, the room hot, I was dozing half asleep.

Midwife, 'You know where you are don't you?'

Me, 'What?'

Midwife, more forcefully,' You know where you are don't you?'

Me, 'Yes, Moss Side.'

Midwife, eyes rolling upwards, thinking God give me strength. 'I don't mean that. Do you know what sort of house this is?'

Somewhat puzzled. 'A big terraced house.'

Midwife irritated, 'We're in a brothel. The old lady cleans and tidies up. The others are the tarts.'

Me, 'Good God. Brothels actually do exist then?'

Midwife, with tears of frustration in her eyes. 'Oh God. You great lummox, of course they exist. You can't be that innocent!'

Me, 'I just thought folk were exaggerating.'

Midwife, 'Where did you grow up, the world's not a bed of roses you know.'

Me, 'Crowle, it's village in Lincolnshire, the fellows don't go short there, there's plenty of enthusiastic amateurs.'

Midwife, 'I'll bet they don't.'

Me, 'Besides how was I to know. I've never been in one. I never realised they would be scruffy as this.'

Midwife, 'This is only where they live. They're all curious. It's a weekday, not very busy. This woman has a Jamaican pimp and a Chinese boy friend, they want to know what colour the baby will be.'

An hour late it became obvious that our patient was in labour.

Midwife, 'I'd better get her ready, enema and shave that sort of thing. I don't think you ought to be around for that.'

Midwife to older woman, 'I'm going to give her an enema and a shave, that's personal. I don't think my young doctor should stay for that. Can he go anywhere?'

Older woman, 'There's our front reception room he can go there.'

Women having babies should thank their lucky stars that they are having them now. Nowadays a small disposable enema, about 4 ounces, then two pints of hot soapy water. High, hot and a hell of a lot.

In some areas midwives did a midwives' trim, with a pair of scissors. We were a teaching hospital; it had to be done properly, a complete shave. It was said to be done for aseptic purposes, to prevent infection. We thought it was more likely done for contraceptive purposes. Hubby having a three or four month attack of celibacy, rather than subject his tender bits to a female hedgehog.

I went out into the expensively carpeted and wallpapered hall, that I had been too sleepy and bog-eyed to notice when I arrived. Then the reception room, massive, expensive carpets, curtains and wallpaper. Numerous large cosy easy chairs, and a modern radiogram. Daily papers for all tastes from the *Daily Mirror* to the *Manchester Guardian* as it was then.

I settled quietly on a settee in a corner and started reading the *Manchester Evening News*. A few minutes later an altercation was heard coming through the front door. A resident and her minder had just returned, in a gruff woman's voice, Anglo Saxon virtuosity that would have put my father to shame.

The room door opened and in came an alien from outer space, or it could have been the monster from the black lagoon. It may have started off in life in the feminine gender. God knows what it was now. It was 5ft 10 inches tall with four-inch high heels. It wore a tight black leather dress, with a tight white lacy top; you know the sort of thing, full of holes in patterns. This was tightly applied to the upper torso, with high uplifted, what should we call them, 'Tits'; breasts would be far too flattering and normal.

The whole apparition was surmounted by a bouffant hairstyle of highly curled peroxide blonde hair. It looked taller than a Guardsman in a Busby. A hatchet face so wrinkled after smoking 60 fags a day for 20 years, that it looked 150 years old. Where one normally expected a mouth was a deep red crimson gash. This creature from the black lagoon took one look at me and must have thought:

'Oh! Goody, goody, a little boy to play with, I'm going to enjoy this one.'

Being full of gin it took what it thought were mincing steps toward me. It put on what it thought was a seductive voice, which in view of the 60 fags a day for 20 years, sounded like a bag of gravel.

'Hello. Ducky, darling, what are you doing here?'

With a wiggle of its hips that was certainly not provocative. I, surreptitiously inching away toward the corner, said hopefully, 'I'm with the midwife, I'm a medical student.'

It approaching closer said ' Oooh, a young doctor. Mmmh, oooh, ooh, I do like young doctors.'

My immediate thought was 'Boiled, roasted or fried?'

It produced what it thought was a smile, revealing a set of badly fitting false teeth. It leaned over me and I nearly suffocated from the blast of gin and tobacco fumes that hit my face. I inched further into the corner.

Then it pointed to the dip between the upper protuberances, and said, 'I've got a little lump on this rib. What do you think it is?' Leaning even further forward.

Inching further away, I made my right hand into a ball with my middle finger straight out. Making absolutely sure that I touched neither protuberance, I touched the supposed lump and blurted out the first thing that came into my head.

'Osteochondritis.'

'Oooh, ooh, mmm, mmm, what a big word for such a little boy.'

I was now rammed in the corner, I could not inch any further when it said.

'How do you like my legs? Do you think I have nice legs?'

It put out a leg on its four-inch high heel, and slowly started to lift up its black leather skirt. That leg seemed to go on forever, it was the vilest leg I had ever seen. There must have been something wrong with its circulation, that never ending leg was covered in red and blue patches. It also had the biggest, longest, knobbliest saphenous varicose vein I had ever come across.

Cringing into the corner, trying to become invisible, I began to feel absolute despair, when suddenly the Seventh Cavalry arrived. The door opened and the midwife said without looking in.

'It's OK now, I've finished, you can come back in.'

'Yes, Sister,' I croaked.

Realizing that was not my normal voice, my benign midwifery sister, whilst wiping her hands on a towel, looked round the door with a friendly smile on her face. The smile froze and then turned into the expression of a she-wolf whose cubs are about to be slaughtered.

Towel doubled, turned into a club. Six long strides, she was over the room belabouring my assailant about the head.

'Get your B—y hands of him, you filthy old cow. *He belongs to me!*

It turned to face the onslaught. Towel transferred to left hand, my rescuer let fly with a right uppercut, such as I had never seen. That uppercut was filled with all the venom and hate that generations of respectable practitioners of women's second oldest profession have felt for the practitioners of women's oldest profession. It collapsed, pole-axed.

Mother midwife, shaking her sore right hand, placed her right arm over my shoulders and with the care usually reserved for a new born lamb, led me from the room.

'Now lad, it's all right, you'll be safe with me.'

Feeling a little morale boosting was necessary, she added:

'Nice healthy lads like you, shouldn't have to pay for that sort of thing. How old are you?'

'Twenty two sister.'

'Have you got a girlfriend?'

'Well I have a favourite girl.'

'What does she do?'

'Well, she's just past her finals. She's been made a staff nurse.'

'A nurse, I knew you were a good lad. We've got to keep you young lads fit and healthy for our girls. We don't want trash like that messing you about.'

The patient delivered about 6.30 in the morning, I can't remember the sex or whether it was half Jamaican or half Chinese. But they always say, that if you go into a brothel you catch something. I did. The room was hot, jacket off, sleeves rolled up; I saw them, three fleas investigating the hairs on my left forearm.

Back to base at 7.30, the row I made woke my pals. Into a bath, strip, shake your clothes, more fleas, throw clothes in laundry bin, fill bath with water, and drown the b—rs. Fill another bath; lie in it for ten minutes, only nostrils and lips showing. Drown the b—rs.

Go to breakfast, pals require detailed description. The rest arrive including our two ladies, the two Joyces. The story has to be repeated. Lunch-time a summons to the doctors' mess at lunchtime from god himself, the ROS, the act repeated. Ten years later I was to become the ROS. My beloved wife with three babies under her belt, feeling I was now totally committed, rapidly brought me down to size. She told me that ROS did not stand for Resident Obstetric Surgeon, but Rotten Old Sod.

Whenever I went on one of these fuddles, I always insisted that I look at the children. I mentioned the large amount of Aureomycin Eye Ointment that I'd got; trachoma, a viral infection of the eyes and can cause blindness, was rampant on the Jebel Akhdar. I went through all the kids, pulled the lower eyelid down, and put a good thick layer of Aureomycin cream on it.

Below 5,000 feet I also had a tummy tickling session. I felt for the spleen which in children if they have malaria, is usually enlarged and tender. I hadn't any modern treatment for malaria, but I had buckets full of quinine tablets. All the children with enlarged spleens, were given a week's supply of quinine. Whether it did any good, I don't know. Whether the Aureomycin did any good, I don't know about that either. It made me feel better and it probably did our British relationships good – how to win friends and influence people. I never felt scared on top of the Jebel. I never carried a gun. Salah and I would wander for miles going from village to village. We were always welcomed. I got the feeling that the villagers were glad to get rid of the old boss Sulieman.

Medical Work

There wasn't an awful lot. I was called out occasionally and I would wander round and do my best. Did a bit of dental work. Some mornings, there'd be a couple of soldiers and maybe two or three villagers. Some mornings, there'd be about 10-12, but never more than that. I often left in the morning, after breakfast, with Salah, taking our gear with us, and visiting the villages. Once I got used to the altitude, we went all over the place. We'd leave in the morning, with our water bottles, a chapatti rolled up and stuck in your pocket to act as lunch. Going ten miles away, down deep wadies 3 or 4,000 feet and then up again. I was always able to get back at night time. There's only one occasion I didn't, and I'll speak about that later. It wouldn't have mattered if I hadn't because these were traditional Arabs. A traveller, even if the traveller is your sworn enemy, arriving in your village at night time, you are duty bound to feed him, give him drink, let him sleep safely overnight and you cannot follow him for three days afterwards. I always reckoned that if I'd upset somebody that badly, in three days I could be back in England!

I was on the Jebel for 10 weeks and by the time I finished I was as fit as I'd ever been. There was hardly any spare fat on me. When I left Somaliland, I had gone a bit chubby, about 12 and half stones. Now, I'd probably be about 11. I was still pretty hefty, but it was all muscle. My thighs were like tree trunks and calf muscles like balloons. Average speed three miles an hour on the flat, we didn't really slow down much going up the wadi side. If we were going up a 4000-foot wadi, Salah and I would sit at the bottom for a few minutes, have a drink and a little rest. Then we'd start and didn't stop until we reached the top, when we'd have another sit down. As we walked along, we'd be chatting to each other in our funny language.

I did a bit of surgery, mainly lumps and bumps that the locals wanted me to remove. I wouldn't do anything major. I was asked to repair a few hernias and I am sure I could have done under local anaesthetic, but I didn't think it was a particularly good idea! I do remember seeing one hernia - the fellow showed me and the rest of the village, who were highly entertained, because it was huge. It was so big it virtually occluded his genitals, which was why the other chaps in the village were so amused by it. It almost went halfway down his thigh. It was easy to reduce, but he could have easily got into trouble. I told them that he ought to get down to the hospital in Nizwa and have it seen to.

In the same village, I saw a hydrocele the size of a grapefruit. That was, of course, causing problems. A hydrocele is a cyst full of fluid that you find in the scrotum near the testes. I confirmed that diagnosis because when you shine a light through it from behind it looks translucent. Under a bit of local anaesthetic, I aspirated it, removing 200 ccs of fluid. I had to warn him it would come back and he ought to get down to Nizwa and have it operated on.

The young Arab lad also had a problem; he was about 12. He'd broken one of his front teeth and developed a root abscess, it was bulging in his gum - what we call a gumboil. I did offer to remove the tooth, but he refused. He was prepared to put up with the pain, because as he said, he'd never have another tooth! Eventually, it became so painful I decided to try and incise it. I wondered what to anaesthetize it with. For abscesses then, we used Ethyl chloride spray. This would freeze the abscess ready for incision. I thought of spraying it on the gum, not thinking, of course, about the vapour. One time, Ethyl chloride had started off as an anaesthetic, so the lad suddenly started looking a bit vacant, and I realized I was anaesthetizing him. The problem with Ethyl chloride, it stopped being used as an anaesthetic because it caused cardiac arrest. When I remembered that, it nearly caused my cardiac arrest! I stopped and the poor lad had to put up with his root abscess.

Leprosy was supposed to be common out there. I'd never seen a case. I don't think I saw any leprosy, but to be honest would not have known if I had.

Whilst visiting Wadi Habib, I found a new method of selling a goat. I'd been asked to see one of the people in the village. When I got there, the meetinghouse was full of men, and in one corner was a live goat tied up, and chaps gradually get drifting in and out. I realized that the owner of the goat was selling bits of it! If an Arab Muslim kills an animal, it has to be eaten the day that it is killed. This man had notified all the villages around, that he was going to kill a goat, and all the men were coming up buying the various bits as they came. He wouldn't kill it until he had sold all the bits! I didn't wait to see what happened, because I had to move on to another village.

Round Ups

We had round-ups. All the platoons went out patrolling the area; they brought in all the convoys of donkeys they found. At times, we'd have two to three hundred donkeys in the camp. They could be fully investigated to make sure that they weren't carrying any contraband, but more important, arms, ammunition, land mines and such like.

I've mentioned Mike the Captain. He was a good man; hard

working and a good soldier. Prior to working in Arabia, he'd spent several years in the traumatic jungle warfare against the Communists in the Malayan Jungle. Unfortunately, he was beginning to get a bit fond of the gin bottle. When sober, he was fine. I went on one or two walks with him; he took me to Sulieman's Caves. This was a cave complex that the RAF had tried to blow up on numerous occasions. The wadi around it was absolutely devoid of vegetation, because they'd bombed it so many times. Whilst I was there, we had a major disposal effort; they'd found lots of mortar bombs and other ammunition. Mike was busy blowing them up.

Occasionally, the Major would have an arrangement with one of the Baluchi sergeants, and gave him a couple of half bottles of gin. Send Captain Mike off on a patrol that would last for about 10 days, the sergeant having enough gin to get Mike 48 hours away, when he had to get on with the patrol. There was no chance of him getting any more booze. Eventually, the drink situation got so bad, because the Major didn't mind a drop or two, although he was in no way addicted, the number of crates of gin that were being flown up on the single pioneer was excessive. No wonder, later on, I was questioned about it.

On one occasion, Mike got pie-eyed as usual; the Major was a bit over the edge, and I was cheesed off to the back teeth. I looked at the gin supply; there were three full bottles of gin left, which I took. I walked for 500 yards, to a wadi about 5 - 600 feet deep, and threw three full bottles of gin down it. Next day was a problem when Mike came round. We had a few cans of Mackesons, which he drank. I had been experimenting with Jebel dates - little sweet things about the size of currants. I had three one-gallon carboys. I made water traps with bits of glass, which I'd heated and bent. I tried to make wine from Jebel dates. It was a vile tasting mixture, and there was Mike, drinking it!

Living with a couple of blokes so closely, and they're the only other Europeans, one gets very close to them. That was when I made another mistake. It was when I was flying to Bahrain. We dropped in at Muscat staying for a couple of hours, the local Lieutenant Colonel RAMC came to see me. He started questioning me. Obviously, the amount of gin that was being flown up to the top of the Jebel had been noted. He must have noticed the evasive action I took, but I couldn't at that time 'shop' Mike. It was just beyond me.

It was a silly thing to do, a bad mistake. When we took off and I thought about it, I realized that Mike should be taken off the Jebel and sent back to England to be dried out. When I eventually got to the Trucial Oman Scouts, the day I landed, I spoke to the adjutant. A week later, I got the message, Matthews had been tipped off by the Lieutenant Colonel at Muscat. As soon as he got there, he put Mike on the next plane to Muscat. I never knew what happened to Mike. I have mentioned his name - I hope he's fit and well, and retired by now. If he is, I hope he doesn't resent me mentioning him. I can't mention the Major's name, because I can't remember it.

Wandering around the Jebel, we found two or three places where a plane had crashed. Whether because the pilot had made a mistake, or whether it had been shot down, we didn't know. There was one pilot's grave there, I've got a slide of it marked 'a little corner of a foreign field'. Soldiers were buried where they fell. There were a few Arab soldiers that had been fighting for Sulieman buried about the place.

Waste disposal I certainly remember how that was organized, because in one of the double-roomed houses, they had an Elsan, and there were problems with it. The Elsan got full and something had to be done about it. Neither the Major nor Mike would help; though they still liked to have a SH*T. The sweeper wouldn't help either. Eventually, I had to do something. I persuaded one of the Arab officers to threaten to kick the living daylights out of the sweeper, so that he would help me. The sweeper and I dug a great big hole, carried the Elsan out, slopped it down the hole, and cleaned out the Elsan. What a horrible thing to have to do, but it wasn't the first time ...

1946, massive heavy snow falls in Lincolnshire. The snow was four or five foot deep, we couldn't get to school, which delighted us. Unfortunately, the snow was so thick that the Crawshaws, the night soil merchants, couldn't get round. They came round with Tilley lamps at night with a big horse drawn 'can', emptying the cans that could be described as 'out back'. My dad had a large, modern house. Built in 1932 with all the mod cons. It had electricity, which the farm didn't have. When it was first built, we had hot and cold water. Rainwater from the roof went into a big cistern at the back of the house. One of my jobs as a kid was pumping water from the cistern into a massive tank in the roof. Water for drinking was from a well in the back garden, that was shared by the people next door. It had to be put through one of those tall brown water filters before it could be drunk. In 1936 we had water attached to the house from the mains.

The County Authorities had promised that in 1935, they would put main drains in. When my dad's house was built; there was a bathroom and a separate, proper flush toilet. Only it didn't have any water, and if you flushed it, it didn't have anywhere to go. We had a big tin can in a little brick hut, 10 yards from the back door, which was emptied by the Crawshaws once a week.

In 1946, the Crawshaws couldn't get round and the can got over-full. Now, a 43-year-old fellow that works on the farm and in the steelworks, a tough guy, who has a leather belt, 2 inches wide, and a 13 year old son, doesn't see why he should have to empty the tin can. I won't tell you, but just guess who had to go down into the orchard, dig a great big hole, come back, drag the can down to the orchard, pour the contents into the hole, on his own, without any help, and then fill the hole in.

We weren't the only place like this; there were the posh folks – the Ramsdens – up at Tetley Hall. They were quite well off; they had a three-holer – two holes for adults and one for children. In 1948 we became modernized and unionized. The Crawshaws were sacked and replaced by a modern lorry, looking like a petrol tanker. It was of course improper for union members to work at night so the whole town stank to high heaven one day a week. Main drainage finally arrived in 1975.

Gradually, from the late forties onwards, people started to put in septic tanks, but you couldn't get my dad to spend his money on things like that. Then, in 1955, having known Margaret for about nine months, she came to visit the family for a few days. There we were, a nice, respectably brought up city girl, with gazundas in the bedrooms, and an outback. I don't think she went for a week. She must have impressed my dad. When I went home for the summer holidays, he had actually spent some money and put a septic tank in. Now, we had two flush toilets, one next door to the bathroom and one replacing the out back.

The Sultan's Representative

We had the Arab equivalent of our political officer. A tough, firm, Arab, who came periodically with his rifle and went wandering around the Jebel, visiting the headmen, telling them what to do and what the Sultan of Oman expected of them. We got the message that some chap had got his Martini Henry rifle, with a 45 lead slug in it, taken a pot shot, and actually hit him. We had to go fetch him. The bullet had gone in under the axilla, a flesh wound, it went through under the left scapula and out through his back, leaving a big hole. It hadn't bled much and it wouldn't cause him a lot of trouble in the long run. We went out with two platoons and a stretcher to fetch him. This was the only time I went right to the top of the Jebel at 10,000 feet. It took us half a day to get there. We carried him on the stretcher, eventually to the escarpment, that went from top of the Jebel, down onto the Saig plateau, 1500 feet below. How we were going to carry him down. We hadn't been all that good at carrying him so far, nearly dropping him. The man himself was convinced he was going to be dropped. He decided to walk down with two men on either side, acting as his supports. I got him back to the 'hospital', started Sulphonamide tablets, cleaned and dressed his wounds and arranged a Casivac aircraft to fetch him. Physically, he was all right, but I must admit from the tough political officer he had been, he was a bit shattered. His bottle had gone.

Khalil Bin Thabet

Khalil bin Thabet was about 17 years old. He had been trying to catch a goat on the wadi side, slipped and straddled a rock. He'd badly damaged himself, he'd ruptured his urethra and stopped passing urine. He'd been left to recover and gradually become comatose. The village he lived in was 6,000 feet down, in the Maidan wadi. About 2 o'clock one afternoon, Thabet and his brother managed to get to the top of the escarpment and bring the unconscious boy to the 'hospital'. Khalil bin Thabet belonged to a tribe that was personae non-grata to the Sultan; there was no way he could get treatment. He should really have been flown to somewhere like Bahrain or Aden; even to have flown him to the mission hospital that was at Muscat probably would not have been good enough. It needed extra special surgical skills, and I was landed with it. Number one, we didn't have any catheters - I put in an urgent request for catheters and some did arrive about 4–5 weeks later, after Khalil had gone home. They were thick, red things that must have been made in about 1940. Totally unsuitable, they would have been all right to catheterize a stallion.

It would not surprise me, if a modern-day British politician or a modern Omani Arab politician would deny that this policy was ever adopted. Young Goldthorp was a fool, he should never have attempted to treat Khalil, he should have got him transferred. The last thing I wanted to do was treat Khalil's ruptured urethra. I sent several requests asking for him to be transferred to the mission hospital at Muscat, even the Major who was not the most sympathetic of men

Thabet, Khalil and Salah, three weeks after treatment
(my house is behind Salah)

Salah and guide on a donkey track. Taken from the top of the escarpment.
Khalil's village is along the wadi on the left

At the bottom, still two miles to go but on the flat. Thabet and his brother carried Khalil up this wadi. Halfway up is the hidden village that we spent the night. Not your average NHS home visit.

tried, each time the answer was no. 'Deal with it yourself.' That was the message from the Lieutenant- Colonel RAMC at Muscat. I was even denied permission to get Khalil flown down to the RAF hospital at Nizwa. There was the donkey supply convoy, would Khalil still have been alive two days later when the convoy got back to base? How do you balance an unconscious full-grown male on a donkey? What about a sling between two donkeys, good idea on the flat, not so good on a narrow rocky ledge above a 200 foot drop, when the rough track slopes downward at 1 in 2.

I examined Khalil carefully. I'd never seen a case of rupture of the bulb of the urethra. The areas where the urine had gone, the areas where the body had swollen, with certain ligaments restricting the spread of the fluid, so that only certain parts swell, was exactly as had been described in Bailey & Love's *Short Practice of Surgery.* I felt pretty sure what I was dealing with it. How was I to deal with it? He'd been unconscious for 2-3 days, so he would be dehydrated, there'd be some infection and bruising. But how the hell could I get him to empty his bladder again? We had plastic giving sets, and various types of bottles of fluid, some Saline, some sugar and water, some of what's called 'Hartman's' solution and various other solutions. Any old conglomeration had been sent up the Jebel just in case! I got a knife and some sandpaper, cut the end of a giving set, made a nice catheter end and sandpapered it down. I passed that. I managed to get it into his bladder, because he started to drain urine, and also started draining some of the old urine from the rest of the body. As regards the dehydration, once I got him draining urine, I put up a drip and gave him any old stuff, whatever I had, just to get the fluid in. As regards antibiotics, I've mentioned the ancient Streptomycin. I knew that there was a danger of it causing deafness, but I worked on the principal that it was better to be deaf and alive, than be able to hear and dead! I injected one bottle every 12 hours until it was used up in six days.

We started off, no change for two days.

After a couple of days, his dad came rushing to see me, in a great state of agitation and pleasure, something had happened! I went to see Khalil; he was still unconscious, but he'd opened his bowels. There was mess all over the place, but the fact that he'd done it, had given his dad and uncle a lot of hope. The following day, he started to come round, gradually improved and I was able to start feeding him. We eventually moved him; there was a spare room in the house where we had the Elsan. I made a bed for him, and put him, his father and uncle there.

This caused me to have a row with the Major and Mike, because that's where they went to do their whatsits. When I suggested that they should get hold of Khalil and chuck him down the wadi side they decided to cooperate. We kept Khalil over three weeks, when he was passing urine all right, eating and drinking satisfactorily. Eventually his uncle and his dad took him home. I said I'd see him the following week.

The following week, they sent a boy about 14, to fetch us. Salah and I headed off that morning to see Khalil. We walked to the edge of the Saig plateau where the escarpment was, whereupon the young Arab lad disappeared over the edge. I looked over, it seemed like a sheer drop - he was walking down with his heels on little ledges about 3 inches wide, taking the short cut, the one that humans use, to get to his village. I said to Salah, or I communicated to Salah, that there was no flippin' way I'd go down there. I found that there was a specially built donkey track. My opinion was that in that part of the Jebel Akhdar, donkeys were a damn sight more sensible than Arabs!

Salah and I reached Khalil's village and were met by his father and the headmen. We went through all the rigmarole of coffee,

Khalil in hospital

meetings and greetings and, finally, I was able to examine Khalil. At that time, he seemed to be doing pretty well. There was one thing I was disappointed about, with myself more than anything. Not being a nurse, it hadn't occurred to me - but, Khalil had been nursed on his back, all the time before he was brought to me. I'd tried to turn him a bit in my so-called 'hospital', but he'd still been on his back most of the time. I examined his sacral area; there was an area about the size of a plate, where the skin had gone dead. The edges were eroding and new skin was forming.

I felt bad, because it had never occurred to me. A simple nursing procedure that the average student nurse would have known. I should have been moving him from side to side. After seeing Khalil, his father wanted to show his thanks, and had organized a glorious fuddle.

I asked a photographer friend to have a go at printing the Khalil in Hospital slide. I am pleased with result although I had to increase the highlights and mid-tones on the scan (above).

The drip set can be seen. Khalil's pillow is filled with straw. His uncle is holding his head and his father's concerned face is looking at that of his son. It does not matter if you are black, white, brown or yellow, a father's face would always look like that. Underneath we are all the same.

Salah and I went back to camp, promising to go to see Khalil again. The week I left the Jebel, I decided to go and see him. A 21-year-old Lance Corporal had arrived. He was the head of a survey party, that was going to map the Jebel. He'd come along to set up the camp for the survey party. I told the Major that I was going to see Khalil the following day and he said 'That young Corporal has nothing to do, take him with you'. That night, I told the Corporal he would be coming with us. Salah and I set off the following morning and went to pick the Corporal up. There he was, covered with packs with a sten-gun and God knows how many clips of ammunition to go with it. I said, 'What on earth are you carrying that lot of clobber for?'

'I've been told the Jebel is a dangerous place and I must always travel in full kit, fully armed'. We couldn't persuade him otherwise, so we set off. We were all right going downhill; he carried all his gear and everything went fine. It would be about 6,000 foot or more that wadi.

I saw Khalil, this time I wasn't happy. I had that instinctive feeling that he wasn't going to make it after all. Lay people may not think so but coloured people can look pale. Khalil was still passing urine, eating and drinking, but there was something about him. I thought he was anaemic (thin blood) and may be some uraemia (kidneys not working properly) His back wasn't much better either. Coloured people can glow with health, or just look ill; living among them it had become instinctive. Something that I have never lost. Coloured people can suffer from sunburn, just like Europeans. A few weeks later in Sharjah, I and several British sergeants, together with some Arab medical orderlies went on a Sunday morning breakfast picnic, on the shore of the Arabian Gulf. All wearing swimming trunks, we went swimming and playing volleyball in the sun. The British were already sun-tanned, The Arabs more used to being fully clothed; Monday I was treating the Arabs for sunburn!

The problem started when we started back up the wadi side, with our accompanying heavily armed corporal. Three days on the Jebel, he had not adapted to the height. A fit young man at ground level now became an annoying liability. Salah and my usual march up the wadi slowed down to a crawl. Gradually I was carrying his Sten gun, Salah some of his packs, then his gun and all the ammunition, Salah had all his packs. Eventually Salah supporting on one side, I on the other, two minutes slow walk followed by two minutes rest.

We started at 1400 hrs, it would have taken Salah and me one to two hours, 1730 hrs we had barely got half way. There is no twilight in the tropics; in 45 minutes it would be jet black, no moon only starlight. I spotted a small village down a side wadi, turned of the track and got there with about five minutes of light to spare. As travellers we were taken to the meetinghouse, supplied with fresh water and some chapattis to stay for the night. No sheets no blankets, a doctor's bag plus sten gun and ammunition for a pillow.

We did have torches for light. As Salah and I settled down on the rough mud and stone floor for the night our Corporal started grumbling. He grumbled even more vociferously 10 minutes later. Always well prepared I took out my can of AL65, scattering powder over the place I intended to sleep, made a large oval round the area with powder, shook the powder up my shorts, front and back of my neck, undid my belt and shook the powder round my waist. I handed the AL65 to Salah, he did the same. Our corporal watched in fascination. 'What are you doing that for?'

I said nothing but pointed to the floor beyond the circles of powder. A large army of body lice was marching towards us. Up in a flash, the corporal. 'I'm OK now Sir, let's go. I'll be no trouble, I can keep going, we can't stay here.'

'Do as you like corporal, keep to the path if you can. Salah and I are staying here until it's light. Only an idiot would try walking on that path. You can't see it if the moon's full, which it isn't, never mind by starlight.'

Our very unhappy corporal stayed but he hadn't a clue what to do with the AL65, Salah and I had to do it for him. AL65, army issue anti louse powder, number 65.

The floor was not comfortable, a rather restless night, we dosed on and off. Crack of dawn we were off, same procedure as before. It took us over six hours to get the corporal up the rest of the wadi side. We reached Saig camp after 1300, accompanied the corporal to his tent put his kit and weapons inside. He collapsed on top of his camp bed and slept until the following morning. Me, I was ravenous, in a foul mood, I had hardly eaten since breakfast the previous day. Lunch was over, the cooks were having a siesta, and there was no cold food, chapattis, nothing. I had to wait for the evening meal; if Mike and the Major had not got there in time I'd have eaten the lot.

Two weeks later that young corporal would be running up and down those wadi sides like a gazelle.

Three or four days later Captain Matthew arrived, I handed over to him. There was not much to hand over, but I went into great detail about Khalil bin Thabet, asked him to do the best he could for him. I have never met or heard of Captain Matthew since so I do not know what happened to Khalil. I hope and pray that my instinct was wrong.

I collected my kit, said goodbye to the Major and Mike. The Single Pioneer took me back to the Niswa airstrip where I had to wait for a couple of days for a plane to Bahrain. Next stop the Trucial Oman Scouts.

Since writing the above I received the following letter from Graeme Matthew.

19th November 2002

Dear Bill,

You must think me very rude not to have responded to your letter of 28th August and the script of your book. In fact I eagerly read the book straightaway but we went on holiday and I am afraid that it lay in the pile of things to do, waiting for me to write, a pile which does not seem to be less than it ever was despite retirement!

Your pictures and descriptions brought back the Jebel and the life out there most vividly; I became positively nostalgic and am most grateful for the chance to read your account. The steep climbs out of the wadis, the intricacies of good manners at a fuddle, some of the characters and many other details came vividly to mind.

I do not have a clear memory of Khalil bin Thabet. I do remember trekking to see someone off my usual routes, just after I got back, and finding them not there. I do not recall the name or what I was told of them. Sorry!

Comments on a few points may help. Firstly, the national service doctors were sent to the Oman following deaths from heat exhaustion of (I think) two British soldiers (not SAS) at the time of the fighting. The order had been given that a doctor had to be attached to all British units serving there. That meant only the engineers who rebuilt the falajes on the jebel and visiting battalions on exercise. It was curious to send a doctor without appropriate drugs or equipment but it was probably not understood that SAF's own provision was rudimentary. Obviously one could in practice also look after the officers and NCOs seconded to SAF (and, indeed the contract officers) but that was not why we were there. The engineers did their work independently but officially under the command of the Governor of the Jebel Akhdar, first Colin Maxwell, then Eric Roe, both contract officers. After the engineers left it was arranged that I should stay on as Civilian Relief Medical Officer answerable to the British Consul General in Muscat and responsible for offering care to the Jebel people except when British units came on exercise, when I came off the mountain to accompany them. Money had been provided by the Government on the Foreign Office vote for the civil relief operation, in practice in reparation for the harm done to the Jebel people, who had not been rebels, but who were caught up in the conflict when the rebels took refuge there.

' The major part of the vote was used as grants to people to rebuild their bomb damaged houses. Since the houses were built largely from local materials, this was really a financial injection into the local economy and/or, more cynically, a way of ensuring that indolence did not stop the evidence of the military unjustified bombing by the RAF being removed. The grants were administered by the Governor but, when Eric Roe left, I was asked to take that over; it was difficult to do it fairly because of subterfuges, understandably, to get hold of some of the money and my dependence on interpretation!

When I got to Saiq, there was little by way of drugs and equipment and that was antique, as you describe. I asked the Consul for supplies and the service authorities in Aden sent various drugs which were about to run out of date. I remember there was, e.g. a useful amount of antibiotics which allowed me to treat cases of pneumonia etc.

The eye infections leading to blindness was the most apparent health problem and I realized that this was trachoma. My father got the RSM library to send me out some articles about its treatment and the tubes of ointment were sent to me by Lederie after I had written to them describing the problem and asking for help. Because sustained treatment is necessary I showed the teachers in the Koranic schools how to administer the drops daily, with each child having its own bottle. Two of them did it effectively and there was and there was a marked improvement amongst the children of those villages. Otherwise I dished it out more casually to anyone with an inflamed eye, rather as you describe. But that didn't deal with the problem of irritation due to the scarred in-turned eye lids, which caused the blindness. On this Dr Thoms of the American Mission Hospital got permission to come to the Jebel on two occasions and taught me to perform the operation of partial tarsectomy and eversion of the lashes. That worked well and there were many people relieved of the gross discomfort of inturned lashes and, in the early cases, improvement of their sight. Thoms supplied the sutures and local anaesthetic with which to do this. That was the most worthwhile things I was able to do for the Jebel people. I can't remember when that happened; perhaps been after your time.

Thoms also taught me to use a penile ring block local anaesthetic and circumcise a generation of boys who had been denied this religious necessity because the travelling 'wise woman' who had previously done the job had never come after the fighting. One used soluble stitches using their ends to tie on the dressing, so that the dressing dropped off without the boys having to come back; this was also very popular!

In general, I didn't feel that I did all that much good; there were sporadic cases where I could make a diagnosis and had a treatment available but all to often I found it difficult to decided what was wrong. I remember trying to examine women who had to remain fully covered, and those with presumably cancerous lumps beyond my help; and many frustrations. I did manage to send a few patients to Dr Thoms; the SOAF plots flew them down to Bait al Falaj and we carefully told no one and asked no permission.

By the way, I am virtually sure that there was no RAF hospital at Nizwa. Dr Abdur Rashid was the SAF (Sultan's Armed Force) doctor there, with reasonable accommodation at the SAF camp but poor supplies as I remember; I think he used to go into Nizwa itself to treat people as well as seeing civilians in the camp. He was a Pathan, recently trained at Peshawar and a good man, fluent in English, who later trained as a surgeon and emigrated to the USA and married an American girl. Indeed there were no RAF units stationed in the country at all, unless down in the South at Salalah. There was a substantial RAF hospital in Bahrain, which was an RAF command.

The officers at Ibri were seconded British regulars with SAF but no SAS men. Indeed the SAS had left before I got there, although there may have been SAS men in the country on the quiet. That is as well as your ingenious holidaymaker!

All the very best to you!

Yours Sincerely,

Graeme Matthew

Chapter Thirteen

Sharjah, the Trucial Oman

I spent 5 days in Bahrain, just killing time. I remember very little, the mess was air-conditioned but almost empty, no one to advise what to do and what to see. The climate miserable, hot, humid and sticky. Oil was already being produced in quantity, a lot of modernization was going on. Previously the economy had been fishing and pearl diving. A lot of the fish was sun dried. God did those areas stink. When the fish was dry like cardboard it was packed into bales, shipped to the mainland where it could at times travel by camel train for a year until it was soaked in water cooked and eaten. I had tried to eat some, on the top of the Jebel Akhdar; it must have taken two years to get there. Dried fish was a product of all the sea-coast of the Gulf; I believe it was produced in many other areas as well. A good source of protein, but not for me.

Finally an RAF plane flew me to the airport at Sharjah. Although the RAF ran it, it was also the International Airport of the Trucial States, all the civilian aircraft landed there. Transport was waiting and took me to my new medical home, the Medical Section at Sharjah. This consisted of examination rooms, offices, a dispensary and a ward of approximately 16 beds, a male ward only. Minor surgery could be done there. I also had a separate MI room nearby.

My own personal transport, was Major Hind's landrover. Mechanically sound but it looked as if it had roved a bit. Best of all, no driver, I drove it. It roved a lot more while I was there. It contained two Jerry cans of water, one of petrol, Tilley lamps, blankets, cooking stove, kerosene and tins of food of all descriptions, not army issue rations but proper stuff. I could have lasted a week in the desert with what was there. Though I never risked it, we always travelled in a minimum group of three vehicles. The local guardroom always knew where we were going and we always made contact by radio when we arrived.

The officers' mess was a modern two storey air-conditioned building on the seafront at Sharjah. All mod cons, proper showers, bathrooms, washbasins and, glory be; flush toilets. Hot and cold running water, the water was drinkable, lit up with electricity like a cruise liner, the usual bar, beer lager and spirits, and the monthly mess bill. There was a bar at the airport, that was supposed to be for Europeans only, Arabs were supposed to be teetotal, but nobody had told the Trucial Arabs. Those unable to arrange admission to the airport lounge, made other arrangements. You would think I was a right booze artist, with two bottles of whisky a week on my mess bill. I continued Major Hinds' welfare organization, similar to all the other officers. That was to keep two local Arab officials supplied with a bottle of whisky each week. It wasn't charity either, the recipients paid their share.

Modern Sharjah, unlike other states in the United Emirates, is now totally dry. Sharjah was unlucky; the only state not to find oil. Expecting large oil revenues it borrowed billions of pounds to start building a modern state. Unable to pay the interest let alone repay the capital, they were in a mess, until Saudi Arabia came to their rescue, on condition they became strict Moslems. Dubai has special shops where Europeans can buy over-taxed alcoholic drinks, not Sharjah. It is illegal to take alcohol into Sharjah, not even drive through with a bottle of wine in your boot.

What I disliked about the officers' mess in Sharjah was the £3 per day ration allowance, the bastards wanted the lot. You couldn't make anything on the side unless you could arrange to disappear into the desert for a few days. The food wasn't all that brilliant either.

That whole area no longer exists, it has totally disappeared under a large modern city. Shops, large stores, multi-storey hotels, ultra-modern hospitals, office blocks, large banks etc, have replaced it. Sharjah and nearby Dubai exist because of creeks. That of Sharjah is not really a creek, 100 yards off shore is a large sandbank several hundred yards long, acting as a huge breakwater making it safe for the smaller dhows of the time to anchor there. There were no wharves, cargoes and passengers had to be ferried out by boat.

Along the high water mark ran a road of hard packed sand. Then a row of buildings of which the officers' mess was one. Next a street, the soukh or market, small shops on either side, part of the street covered with sheets of cotton to hide the glare of the sun and keep the area cool. I went shopping there a few times, and had some Arab silver jewelry made to take home for Margaret. I hated it, I did not like that soukh, the small one at Dubai was all right but Sharjah gave me the creeps. As I walked along I could always feel that little one-inch diameter area below my left scapula where the assassin's

Sharjah Creek, Dubai on spur of land on the horizon

stiletto would go. When one considers all the out of the way places I had been to and felt perfectly safe, that feeling was unusual. In actual fact, the average Englishman was as safe in Sharjah at that time as anywhere.

There was another row of buildings on the landward side of the soukh. Then a wide-open area, an unpaved main road. Then, spread about, the suburbs. The locals' houses were made out of palm fronds, the walls of the courtyard of palm fronds, the house walls of palm fronds, over the sleeping quarters of each house was a tower of palm fronds. Each tower consisted of four Vs. The point of the V at the centre, the wider open neck of the V at the outside of the tower. The four Vs faced the four points of the compass, so that from whatever the point of the compass that a wind or breeze was blowing it would be directed down onto the sleeping area. An Arab form of air conditioning, keeping cool at night. Europeans may have thought that the Arabs were very primitive, but I think that within their own limited resources they were very sophisticated indeed. The main street passed two very old palaces, the Sheikh's Palace and the Women's Palace. I have slides of those.

Dubai creek was more impressive than that of Sharjah, you could understand why a town had grown up there. The creek was wide, deep and went inland a long way. Why it was there I could not fathom, was it the mouth of a river that had dried up thousands

Sharjah Soukh

Main road Sharjah, air-conditioning towers made out of palm fronds

of years before? Dubai, when I visited it a few years ago, is totally unrecognizable. They have decided to keep a little tiny area of the original town, with the two storey houses and narrow streets. The creek where I waited for a small dhow acting as a ferry to carry me across is now crossed by a six-lane motorway.

I carried out primitive dental procedures on British, Arab soldiers and British civilians, feeling embarrassed because they wanted me to do it, whereas I had been to dinner at the only dentist in Dubai's house, a very personable young man from Pakistan. I visited the only hospital, a mission hospital, run by a very nice boozy Irishman, a bachelor who had been there since before the Second World War. We had dinner at his home where he had the most fantastic collection of what then was the latest thing, long playing records. His doctors were from Pakistan, mostly the equivalent to LAHs, Licentiates of the Apothecaries Hall, an old English qualification, such medical schools are not recognized by the General Medical Council in the United Kingdom.

When I visited Dubai a few years ago the creek was lined with dhows twenty or more times the size of the dhows that I saw in 1960. The other thing to notice as we walked along were the hundreds of fridges, TV sets, cookers, etc put on the wharf without supervision. In England they would have all disappeared within 24 hours. It reminded me of the Comet loads of gold in wooden boxes that you would see on Sharjah airport, with two or three old Arabs armed with Martini Henri rifles asleep on the top. No one worried about theft, if anyone pinched it and you caught him, a quick bullet. If you could not catch him, then get it back from his relatives. The more stolen, the wider the band of relatives. If, because of your cousin fifteen times removed, someone comes takes all your goats and camels, you are not pleased. The chap whose gold has been pinched doesn't have to worry about retribution. The cousin fifteen times removed does it.

Why were we there? Piracy and slavery; at one time the Trucial Coast was known as the Pirate Coast. The Omanis who respected one thing only, power, had been subjected to our sea power. The treaties involved foreign policy only, though the British ran and paid for most of the army. Internal power and politics were an Omani affair only; we were not supposed to influence them in any way. Now their income was derived from fishing, trading. pearl fishing and subsistence agriculture. To this Dubai added gold smuggling into India and Pakistan, where there was an insatiable demand. Their government's refusal to allow valuable foreign exchange to be wasted on gold made matters worse.

Dubai Creek, political officer's jetty

Oil had just been found in Abu Dhabi, the elderly sheikh had received his first million pound payment in gold. He was said to have put it under his bed and slept on it. Shortly afterwards there was a palace revolution, his son took over and started to develop the place. At that time they were exploring for oil in the rest of the Trucial States. State borders had not been agreed on between the Oman, the Trucial States and Saudi Arabia. There was argument as to which state owned which village the Oasis of Buraimi, where it could be said that Britain and the United States were at war, BP supporting Saudi dissidents living in the Trucial States and American Oil Companies supporting dissidents from the Trucial States living in Saudi.

The local political officer described an experience which confirmed the Arab of that time's attitude to a killing. At dinner in the officers' mess he said that he now knew who had laid a landmine in an attempt to kill him. He had been away from his headquarters, when early in the morning a lorry containing an Arab contractor and several workmen had driven into his compound to do some repairs. Shortly afterwards a dissident laid a landmine on the side-track leading to his headquarters. The political officer's landrover had a narrower wheelbase than a truck. The PO drove his landrover up the track and missed the landmine. At the end of the day's work, the contractor and his workmen got in the truck to drive home, the truck hit the landmine and three local Arabs were killed. The PO had spent months trying to work out who the culprit was. Now he knew, the culprit was living in Saudi Arabia, his uncle, brother and cousin had been found shot dead.

At the time the Saudi authorities were prepared to supply a landmine and pay 40 Maria Theresa dollars to any Arab who was prepared to lay it in the region of Buraimi Oasis, whether the Omanis reciprocated I never found out. They had hit upon a brilliant idea, they paid 40 Maria Theresa dollars for every landmine handed in. A crafty Arab could do himself a bit of good by collecting a land mine and 40 dollars in Saudi, then bringing it to Buraimi and collecting another 40 dollars by handing it in.

Medical Work

This was pretty routine, mainly Trucial Oman soldiers and their families; I did not see many non-army local people. There were British soldiers, together with British civilians, in actual fact there was not much illness in either group. The Arabs went to the Medical Centre, while most of the British came to my MI room. I often worked there alone. At the Medical Centre there were about 15 Arab orderlies and half a dozen British sergeants.

Arab medical staff

Author in Trucial Oman Scout's uniform

The Medical Centre was mainly GP work with a fair bit of tropical medicine thrown in. Mostly guesswork, I had no pathology back up. I have a slide of a slim Arab who had tuberculosis and amoebic hepatitis. A thin man with his liver marked in pink coloured material. His liver went down below his belly button. Diagnosis was guessing what the disease was, treating it, if he got better, that was the diagnosis, if not try again.

There was casualty work. The main road between Sharjah and Dubai was the flat sandy seashore packed solid by numerous trucks and lorries. A hundred yards wide, everyone travelled with the accelerator flat on the floor, as fast as was possible. Head-on crashes occurred. A three-ton truck came to the Medical Centre with the contents of two landrovers that had crashed head on. Severe British and Trucial Oman Scout casualties went to Bahrain, local Omanis to the hospital in Dubai, broken arms and legs we sorted out ourselves, but there were two Arabs of unknown origin, unconscious with severe head injuries, and we did not know what to do with them. They were still there unconscious when I left two weeks later.

British civilians came to the MI room, where I met two young bankers, young men in their late twenties with responsibilities that they would not have been allowed in England until they were 50. There was one of these branches of a British bank in all the major towns in that part of the Arabian Gulf. They did two tours of three

Sergeant Bracken, RAMC, TOS; Orderly Abbas and Abbas' little boy

years with a year at home in between, the first tour as the junior and the second as the senior manager. Good tax free salaries, modern living quarters on top of the bank, sweepers, cooks, bearers and dhobi men paid for, ration allowance and landrover transport provided. The older chap was engaged; both reckoned that at the end of two tours they would have paid off the mortgage on their house in the London suburbs. London house prices were just as exorbitant then as they are now. They also had an entertainment allowance; presumably they entertained some Arab clients, but mainly they entertained me, members of the officer's mess and any other young European they came across. They were very splendiferous affairs in the flat's dining room, WITH WINE, something we soldiers could never get hold of. The officers' mess reciprocated, they were honorary members. I presume the bank paid for their medical care but they preferred the current MO.

The airport was reasonably busy with commercial planes but fog was often a hazard. One foggy night we heard a plane come fairly low over the officers' mess. Next day we heard that it had missed the airfield, continued southeast in the direction of the mountains and disappeared. Search parties were sent out, they were still looking for it five weeks later when I left Sharjah. It was not the first time it had happened, several planes had disappeared in the Omani mountains. Presumably now that area is a well-developed modern country they have been found.

The RAF occasionally assisted the troops in their peacekeeping efforts. They had strafed a village, but when they attacked the dissidents had moved on and the normal occupants had returned. They strafed three women. We got word three days later; I had to fetch them. We went in the usual three-tonner, driver, mate and self with two Arab orderlies bouncing about, being tossed from side to side, covered in bruises in the back. We drove over a rough wadi bottom full of large boulders that the truck had to negotiate. This was the first time, probably only time I saw Laudable Pus. When you read the ancient surgical texts, laudable pus is a sign that in three months time all will be well. After chopping off the leg, tying a ligature with dirty old thread round the femoral artery, then cauterizing the wound with a red hot iron, one waits until laudable pus appears. Laudable pus is from what I could make out shiny yellow, glistening drops oozing from the wound. When this happens the femoral artery has sealed off, the end gone rotten and you can now safely pull on the ligature, which has been left long and remove it, without pulling the end of the artery and your patient dying from a torrential haemorrhage.

At operation your patient had a 60% chance of dying now it is only 10%.

All the ladies had bullet wounds in their legs. Fortunately the bones had been missed, all were flesh wounds. Four days on they were severely inflamed, temperatures of 102 to 103 Fahrenheit. with shiny glistening drops of yellow pus oozing regularly from the bullet holes. Tiny little ones at the entry point massive ones at the exit where most of the pus was coming from. I cleaned and tidied the wounds up, could not see any evidence of cloth or other foreign body in the holes, and gave each one an injection of a million units of soluble penicillin. This is absorbed and excreted rapidly so I repeated the dose after six hours on the way back.

Two male relatives came with us, we returned along the rough wadi with the injured women. Our driver extremely carefully drove slowly, it took twelve hours to do the journey that had taken us three to get there. What a change when we finally took the women into the medical centre. The bug would be staphylococcus aureus, in England now resistant to nearly every antibiotic, you will have heard of MRSA (Methillin Resistant Staphylococcus), this strain had never been near penicillin, and it had not even heard rumours. When I dressed those wounds twelve hours after the first injection the inflammation had gone, there was no pus, the bullet holes were dry. Temperature down, the women were smiling, drinking water and complaining about being hungry. We had a problem, we were a men's hospital, where could we put them? An urgent message to the Irish doctor at the mission hospital, could he take them off us? No problem, they were transferred. What happened, as usual I never heard anything further. I suspect that in a couple of day's time they would have been ready to go home. Good old penicillin.

On one occasion I was discussing the problems of neglected labours with the old Irish doctor. We got on to treating ruptured uteri. Wombs that tear during labour so that the baby is expelled into the abdomen, usually with tremendous internal bleeding.

'I have a 100% survival rate,' he said.

I said 'That's marvellous, and without blood transfusions too!'

'No it isn't,' he said. 'They come to me on the back of a camel. Taking three or four days, 95% are dead before they get here. If they are still alive when they get here it's a miracle, I can't lose.'

The Schizophrenic

This was a serious political problem for our commanding colonel, and an ethical one for me. One of the battalions consisted of Adenis, recruited from the Aden protectorate. In addition to British sergeants and officers they also had Omani sergeants and officers. British officers did not have much to do with the day to day running of the battalion. No one had noticed that the behaviour of any soldier was unusual. An Adeni soldier walked across the parade ground where a Trucial Omani Company Sergeant Major was conducting a parade, he had his rifle with him, which was not unusual. He walked up to the Sergeant Major and shot him through the head, killing him instantly. When his fellow soldiers arrested him he offered no resistance. This had occurred several months before I got there.

I had to look at him every week but strict instructions. 'Under no circumstances, Doc, are you to give him anything without the Colonel's prior agreement.'

My knowledge of psychiatry was minimal to the extreme. Everyone, including me, thought he had some form of schizophrenia. I vaguely remembered something about severe cases going into a catatonic state where they just sit and don't move. I thought that the Adeni was almost in one. He was kept in a cell in the army prison. Whenever I saw him he was just squatting there, not moving, didn't look at anyone, did not appear to notice when I entered. He just squatted there; chain smoking, lighting one cigarette from the butt of the previous one averaging over 60 a day. He was clean, he wasn't dirty. There were no complaints about him defecating and urinating in the wrong place. He and the cell did not smell. Water was always present in the cell and he never looked dehydrated. He was given his meals, sometimes when I visited him the meals were uneaten. There were no attempts to feed him, yet I thought he was eating enough because he never lost weight or appeared to deteriorate in the 8 to 10 weeks I was there. The army's principle, do nothing, look after him, give him food and drink, it is up to him to eat or drink, let him smoke like a chimney, and with a bit of luck and careful neglect he will get pneumonia and die. Then we can give his body to the Sergeant Major's relatives.

'And we do not want a snotty nosed young National Service Medical Officer, full of bloody daft ideas about medical ethics, buggering it all up.'

The problem was that the army, Britain, had offered substantial monetary compensation, or the livestock equivalent. The Sergeant Major's family was top drawer Omani Arabs already wealthy, money did not matter, and only the perpetrator's body was acceptable.

'Of course it does not really matter if you British, with your stupid principles and absolutely barmy ideas of letting a murderer off, can't let us have him. There is a whole battalion of Adenis, we'll shoot one of those instead.'

Knowing that the locals had threatened to shoot one of them, the Adeni soldiers were on the verge of mutiny. The atmosphere was so tense no one dare empty the armoury where the Adenees were based. The Trucial Oman Scouts was run according to British Army law. The Colonel dare not order a Court Martial because the defendant would be unable to plead because of insanity, there would be no place to confine him or treat him, he would have had to taken to England for treatment. To local Arab eyes we would be protecting a killer, they would however be able to satisfy family honour by shooting an Adeni soldier.

When I grumbled about this in the officer's mess, I was firmly put in my place. They were of the opinion that to stick to my medical ethics in this situation was paramount to mutiny, and should I disobey the Colonel's orders in any way, then I should be court martialled myself and all the other officers would vote guilty. Fortunately the decision never had to be made. All the time the unfortunate Adeni had been in prison, negotiations were going on with the dead man's family to try and find another acceptable way to resolve the matter. As usual I have no idea what happened.

The political scenario

The dead man's family gets fed up with waiting and shoot an Adeni soldier. The Adeni battalion mutiny. The British should have prevented it; the duty British officers and sergeants are the first to be shot. The Adenees shoot an Omani Arab. The Omanees retaliate, the British are responsible for controlling the Adenees so the British duty officers get shot then the Omanees shoot an Adeni soldier. The Adenees are expecting this reprisal so all hell lets loose and a blood bath starts. Possibly no European in the area is safe, they will be blamed for starting it all by not handing the schizophrenic over in the first place. The Adenees are highly trained soldiers, there is no love lost between both sides, there would be a killing spree. Then there would be the International Consequences, America and the USSR becoming involved.

Pneumonia seemed a brilliant idea to the officers at the time, however if push came to shove and he did develop pneumonia, I don't believe either the colonel or any of his officers would have taken the decision. It would have been avoided with the usual 'Do what you think best Doc!'

The commander in chief of the Trucial Oman Scouts was an important position, especially from the political side. It was held by a Full Colonel, a staff officer, who had done several three-year postings there. A staid bachelor in his late forties, on his last leave he had surprised all his officers by marrying for the first time to a lady twenty years his junior. His new wife joined him in his sparsely furnished bungalow. A rather extensive amount of renovation was required. This and the appearance of the young lady caused comment among the local Arab big wigs. The adjutant was delighted to report a conversation with them in the officers' mess.

'It was so nice that the Colonel who was getting older and would soon be retiring had got a new young wife to look after him.'

Then came the punch line:

'Does his first wife like her?!!!'

It was summer time in the gulf, awful weather, hot and humid, at least 90 degrees Fahrenheit and 95% humidity. Air conditioning was alright but it felt worse as soon as you went outside, in Aden you got used to it and did not notice the difference. Social life was minimal, playing cards in the officers' mess, and that was it. There were no more close relationships with the Arabs, no more fuddles. The British medical orderly sergeants organized breakfast picnics on the shores of nearby small gulfs on Sunday mornings, where we could also go swimming. These were all medical affairs, no other

Breakfast picnics

- 279 -

officers were invited. I belonged to those senior sergeants and was taken under their wing. They were very enjoyable affairs, up at 0530 so we could be off at the crack of dawn before it got too hot.

There was one problem - football. Football is not one of my favourite games. I have lived in the Manchester area since 1950 and still have not been to football match. I was lousy at it at school, my fellow pupils tried me in goal to start with, but I was useless, the ball always went in between my knees. I was finally allocated to left back, with the instructions, don't try to kick anything, just get into the other side's way: 'Remember Bill, the other side's way, not ours.'

In the sixth form I did accompany our school football team on Saturday mornings to away matches with other schools. I played second board down to Phlip-phlop Pearce, Captain of the Chess Team.

The English Sergeants started an argument with the Arab orderlies as to who could play football better, Arabs or English. Naturally it ended in a challenge to a series of football matches. There were about 15 orderlies, they could field a team. There were only six sergeants, four sergeants from other units were coerced, threatened or blackmailed to join the team, but the sergeants were still one man down. No guesses are allowed as to who became the eleventh man. Have you ever tried playing football, at 90 degrees Fahrenheit and 95% humidity? What a daft idea, the Arabs orderlies had been playing football in those conditions since they were little lads; they scored ten goals to one of ours. No matter what I said, that series had to be completed, with me as eleventh man, pouring sweat, exhausted, shattered, over-heated trying to get within kicking distance of a ball that flew from Arab to Arab like a comet. The sergeants just would not give up.

'It's OK Sir, we'll beat 'em next time, we're just getting the hang of it. We've arranged the next game for Saturday, Sir, don't forget'.

How could I, Sergeant Bracken had organized the mess orderlies to make sure I was up on time.

Buraimi oasis

I felt so sad when I visited Buraimi a few years ago, an oasis no longer, just a big hot modern city of 800,000 people. They have kept a small piece of the old oasis and small mud and stone ex-mosque for tourists to visit. The oasis was large consisting of 8 or 9 villages, Dubai, Oman and Saudi still arguing about which village

Water Point, Buraimi Oasis

belonged to which country. There was a very ample water supply, brought by underground phalages from the mountains. There were open areas; water points where camels and other stock could be watered and women collect water for use in their houses.

I may be sad that the oasis I knew has gone but I am not sad the women get their water from a tap like we do. Some of the water points were large and deep; you went down steps to reach it. At the end of the day we went swimming. There was the strange feeling of being nibbled by tiny three-inch long fish that lived in the phalages; they were removing flakes of dead skin. Buraimi was visited once a month. I stayed there a couple of nights on each occasions. The second occasion my hosts were short of rations. I showed them Major Hinds' collection of tinned stuff. That night he acted as host, unknown to himself as we all had a slap up feed. The way he subsequently threw me out of Sharjah made me never regret that meal we had at his expense.

Buraimi was about 100 miles away. The days were hot and sticky, so we made the journey by night. There was no road just a track over stony desert, wadi bottoms and sand. Usually we went in groups of three landrovers, or two rovers and a truck, leaving just before dusk 1730 hours, we drove until 2000 hours, stopped, made tea and ate some chapattis. Dug up some sand to make it soft, put a blanket down, wrapped another blanket round you and went to

Coffee shop, Buraimi road

Halt for repairs, Buraimi road

sleep. We tried to wake about 0500 hours, threw our blankets into the landrover and were off, hoping to reach Buraimi by about 0900 hours. When we arrived we would get washed, showered, shaved and have breakfast.

The headquarters of the army was a fort, Jalali fort, its appearance would have been a boon for Hollywood; it would have done Beau Geste proud. White painted, a thick high 12 feet high wall all the way round. The officers' mess in one corner. A round building, with smaller round buildings on top going up three storeys, green door, green window shutters for windows with no glass, loop holed in the upper stories, an old mussel-loading field gun on one side of the main gate.

Similar quarters in other corners, one a REME section the other a medical section. That had a staff of five, a British staff sergeant and two corporals plus two Arab orderlies. During a mutiny a few years before, an RAF National Service Medical Officer had been shot and killed in the fort. There was no running water, it all had to be brought in from the phalages. Cold water was available for drinking. There were large earthenware, non-glazed porous pots four feet tall, they were kept full of water. Water seeped through pots, evaporating on the outside keeping the contents cool. It was summer time, the temperature extremely hot, over body temperature, anything from 105 to 115 degrees Fahrenheit. Everything you touched was warmer or hotter than you were. If you sat down the chair was hot, if you picked up a spoon to drink the cool soup at lunchtime, the spoon was hot. After midday one tried not to move. At night we

Jalali Fort

slept in tents, as the night wore on you would put more on your bed to keep warm, by 2 or 3 in the morning you would be under a couple of blankets and would need them until dawn. At dawn it would be freezing, but as soon as the first rim of the sun showed over the horizon, you started to warm up, by the time it was fully above the horizon you would have thrown your blankets off, it was too hot.

Evenings after dinner would be spent outside the tent, talking, gossiping. with the usual lagers that had been kept cool in a kerosene run fridge. Lighting would be by Tilley lamp, two or three would be hung from the higher guy ropes of the tent. They attracted myriads of insects, which perished in the heat. It was too dry; there was no open water, mosquitoes did not bother us. There were none breeding in the phalages. The tiny fish ate the larvae. The light attracted camel spiders, massive with bodies the size of your hand. They scurried across the area lit up by the Tilley lamps. Now was the time for target practice. All present, three to five officers opened up with their revolvers as the camel spiders scurried past, lots of fun and noise but not much harm to the spiders.

During one of our drives we passed a large three-storey mansion, the women's palace, luxury prison would be more apt. All the close female relatives of the Sultan who were of marriageable age lived there. That is his sisters, daughters and nieces. The problem, if these young ladies got married, although neither they nor their husbands could claim the throne, their sons could. In the past the sultans had had enough trouble with sons, brothers and nephews claiming the throne, leading to war. The sultans did not want to make matters worse by having their female relatives' sons to contend with. Some of the ladies would marry when the sultan wanted a political alliance or to a very wealthy high status man in a country far enough away, where the Omanis would not consider a son to be a true Omani.

Toward the end of August Major Hinds returned. Two months leave in the fleshpots of Aden, no wonder I found him such a miserable rude word beginning with b and ending with r, for the few hours I knew him.

'Captain Goldthorp, I want you on the plane I have just come in on, when it goes back to Aden.'

Me, aghast. 'What! Can't I go in a day or two? I've got friends here I would like to say goodbye to.'

'Colonel Matheson says you're a good bloke. You don't mind where he sends you, you're no problem while you're there, but he can never get you to come back. You are not going to con me, you'll be on that plane this afternoon. Now go and get your kit.'

'But what about my mess bill Sir? It's dishonourable not to pay your mess bill.'

'By Christ that's a brilliant one, Colonel Matheson said you'd dream up every excuse under the sun. Bugger your mess bill, you're getting on that plane regardless, I'll send the mess bill on to you.'

God knows what happened to that mess bill, I never got it, so never paid it. I got up as usual that morning went to work as usual, no one had warned of Hinds arrival, that night I was on a plane back to Aden. Well what could I expect, the poor sod had just spent two months leave in Aden in the hot season, no wonder he was such a miserable! A regular, surely he could have wangled something better. I had two weeks leave due, no way was I going to spend them in Aden, a little bit of organization would be required.

I landed at Khormaksar, no one was expecting me, and I scrounged a lift into Steamer Point and was dropped of in the Crescent. I was not expected, the Arab manager promptly assumed he would be able to double his profits for the year. He was absolutely full up but might be able to put me up for an exorbitant price. Matters became overheated, I was about to duff him up; he was about to call the police, when Colonel Matheson appeared out of the dining room.

'Hello Bill, I wasn't expecting you so soon. What's all the shouting about?'

'This bloody idiot's trying to overcharge me for a room.'

'What' s this?' said the colonel. 'The place is half empty, if the army uses another hotel this place would have to close.'

It was now Yes Sir No Sir. Kiss your arse Sir, no problem. I was accommodated in less than fifteen minutes. The following day was spent locating my trunk, the day after I was called to see Colonel Matheson.

The colonel's office two days later, in spite of the fact that I had enjoyed the previous 5 to 6 months, one thing was definite: as far as the colonel was concerned, I had not. It had been very hard rough and difficult, I was so glad to be back in civilization.

'Well Bill, how did you get on?'

'A bit rough, Sir.'

'Oh! I had not realized it was that bad, tell me about it.'

'Well the Jebel wasn't too bad, Sir, but nobody had warned me about altitude sickness, it took me a few weeks to get over that.'

'Well no one has mentioned that before, Bill.'

'It wasn't only me Sir, there was a young corporal from a survey party, he had it pretty bad. There were only three of us Sir, me, a major and a captain, I've never seen two chaps drink so much gin.'

'I had heard that might be a problem, what about you?'

'Don't like the stuff Sir.'

'What about the work?'

'Not much to do, to be honest, but I don't like the arrangement where the local people can't get treatment.' I then told him about Khalil bin Thabet, and the poor supply of drugs and equipment. You could say I laid it on a bit thick.

'What about Sharjah?'

'God you think it's hot and sticky in Aden, it's not a patch on the Gulf. It's miserable. And Buraimi Oasis, I never realized it could be so hot. More than body temperature, everything you touched was hotter than you were.'

'Well Bill, you haven't got much longer, I'd like you to take over the Royal Dragoons for the rest of your time. I'd like you to start as soon as possible.'

Thinks, 'NOW's the time, let's go for it.'

'I've still got two weeks leave due Sir.'

'I would like you to get them over with, I don't want your time with the Dragoons interrupted.'

'It's still the hot season in Aden Sir, it would be miserable.' I was now planning to take my leave at the most inconvenient time possible if my request was turned down.

'My cousin Beth has got married since I have been away, she is with her husband in Kenya. I've never met him. He runs an experimental farm near Embu. I know it's not allowed Sir, for National Service officers to go on leave to Kenya, but do you think you could arrange it?'

Now it was out, hand played as best I could, given the impression that the last six months had been very rough, done my best under difficult circumstances. Had I been able to impress the old boy?

'Hmmm. Leave it with me Bill. I'll have to think about that.'

Good old Donald Matheson, he came up trumps. A message next day, there will be a seat for you on the next Thursday plane to Mombasa, he expects you back two weeks later, as soon as you land you are to go to Little Aden and take over as MO to the Royal Dragoons.

I have often wondered, Colonel Donald Matheson was very astute. Did he see through my various ploys?

Chapter Fourteen

Kenya

Cousin Beth was one of my favourite cousins, an attractive fair-haired young lady, two years my senior. We sometimes went out together in a group to the Olde Tyme Dances held in the village halls around Crowle and Epworth. In addition to being a good dancer Beth also caught the interest of other young gentlemen, who would be escorting their pretty younger sisters, and a discreet swap for the evening could be arranged. Beth was a star attraction at my twenty-first birthday party. She would be very intrigued to know that she was mentioned recently when I attended W. B.'s fortieth wedding anniversary. An old student friend of both W. B. and myself came up to me and said.

'Hey Wog, what happened to that good looking cousin of yours? You know, the one we met at your twenty-first. Beth, something or other she was called.'

How's that, a young lady remembered 48 years on.

My twenty-first party held in the town hall in Crowle market place, now in danger of falling down. Held by a prominent local Methodist family, the refreshments were of the softer variety. The profits of the Cross Keys also in Crowle market place must have soared that night once my medical school pals located it. They all still say 'And ye dad was as pissed as a newt.' Something which I have never seen. Myself, stone cold sober, never touched a drop. SCOUT'S HONOUR, IT'S TRUE!

I caught the leave plane to Mombasa, landed early in the morning and spent the day wandering round Mombasa. I remember Kalindini Road a long dual carriageway with arches made of large imitation elephants tusks. Traders were selling numerous types of woodcarvings, I bought quite a few, to find the same carvings marketed in England at exorbitant prices a few years later. Five p. m., I caught the night train to Nairobi. Three classes, third the cheapest, absolutely crowded with Africans, the second where I was, not so

many, British and European, soldiers and civilians, colonial administrators and such like. The first class full of obviously wealthy
Indian families. It was during that journey that it was explained to
me that while the British ruled Kenya, the Indians owned Kenya.

The passenger coaches were all corridor coaches; my carriage
contained two leather seats, about seven feet long, intended for four
passengers. The back of the seat swung upwards to form an upper
bunk. A berth attendant brought blankets, sheets and pillows at
2100 hours; you had to make your own bed. As far as I can remember
there were four toilets on the coach, where you could also wash
shave and have a shower.

There was a first and second-class dining room, none for the third
class where facilities appeared to be minimal in the extreme. Mombasa had tended to be hot and sticky, there was no air conditioning
in second class, I don't know about the first class. I spent the first
hour until night fell enjoying the view as the train crossed the
coastal plane, passing through interesting though primitive African
villages. Once it became dark I went to the bathroom, got washed,
changed and went to the dining room. I have no recollection of
the meal. Once my bedclothes arrived I made my bed and slept
until dawn. Then washed, shaved, went to breakfast and watched
the scenery until we reached Nairobi. Whether we were passing
through a game reserve I don't know, but it seemed like it,
numerous animals of all types with scattered infrequent villages.

I had only heard of one place to stay, the poshest and the most
expensive, The Norfolk Hotel. It always had been, and for all I know
still is, its reputation is like that of Raffles in Singapore. I had no
difficulty in getting a room, but the 24-hour charge horrified me,
a week's stay would have bankrupted me. I had to get out as quick
as possible. The priority was to contact Beth and Terry; I had their
address and had notified them that I would try to get leave to visit
them. With the assistance of a friendly young African telephone
operator, who thought that anyone who had survived over a year
in Aden was blessed by the Gods and deserved his deepest sympathy, I found their telephone number and made contact. Terry
was unable to get away until the weekend. Could I survive in
Nairobi until then? By now it was lunchtime, I went into the dining
room for the buffet lunch. I have NEVER EVER seen a buffet lunch
of such luxury since. I could hardly believe my eyes, every sort of
food imaginable, every luxury imaginable. I have been in luxury
hotels all over the world, medical conferences where several billion
dollar pharmaceutical companies have been trying to impress doctors with their generosity. I have attended luxury buffet lunches

galore, but not one that came anywhere near that one at the Norfolk Hotel. On that occasion I had actually paid to be there, I made a right pig of myself, I could hardly move when I had finished. I could not avoid wondering however what the average Kikuyu had had for lunch that day.

Another thing I learned at the Norfolk Hotel was the Kikuyu art of fishing. There were notices all over the place. It was not sufficient in Nairobi to lock your doors and windows; you had to put everything away in drawers where they couldn't be seen. Kikuyu look through every window, every crack between curtains, they carry fishing rods under their coats. They were very skilled with these rods, they could be pushed through small apertures and the hook and line used to remove anything of value in the room.

Instead of a siesta after lunch I went out immediately, found the nearest army barracks, got the address of the Nairobi RAMC Headquarters and headed there. The officers' mess located, the mess president found, situation explained, I became a member of that officers' mess for the rest of the week. Cost, the local daily ration allowance and pay your mess bill the night before you go. I remember very little about it, most of the officers were married, there were no more than three or four officers in the mess, that had the capacity for 30. On two occasions I hired a taxi for half a day and the driver took me round what was then known as the King George VI Game Reserve. The amount and variety of game I was shown was phenomenal, I must have used up seven or eight rolls of film on those trips. Otherwise I roamed around Nairobi, kept out of the shops and saw a couple of recently released films at the cinema. Terry drove down from Embu on the Saturday, joined me for lunch in the mess and we returned to Embu in the afternoon.

Terry, a graduate in agriculture, ran an experimental and research farm in the Mount Kenya area. I found that very interesting, they were trying to improve the quality of stock animals, and were having remarkable success with the local sheep. He looked after some high quality prize winning rams. He was also experimenting with various strains of the local crops, growing them in small plots with differing soil and climatic conditions. The aim to discover which crop did better in particular conditions, in order to improve the yield and benefit the subsistence farmers. Terry was in his second three-year tour at the farm, as far as I can remember he remained there until Kenya became independent.

It was pleasant to see Beth again and I was delighted to notice a little bump, which became their elder daughter a few months later. Terry and Beth had a very nice modern bungalow and British life

Beth and Terry

style. I could not help noticing however that they were not living as high of the hog as I had become used to over the past 18 months, in spite of the out of the way places that I had been. Whilst Terry like all Europeans had a good salary, the Kenyan Authorities thought they ought to feel at home as much as possible, for instance, Kenyan Income Tax. They also had other problems that I had forgotten about, water rates, sewage rates, electricity and telephone bills. On the way back to Embu Terry had drawn into a garage and had actually paid for petrol. I had driven thousands of miles in Somaliland and various parts of Southern Arabia without paying for a teaspoon of it.

The centre of Embu was full of Indian owned shops, cinemas etc. Most of the Africans shopped in the market, an exotic, crowded, noisy cheerful place. Terry took me shopping for vegetables and fruit there, where he had a marvellous time, arguing and bartering in a mixture of Swahili and English with the mammy traders. From the shrieks and types of laughter, I gathered that some of the mammies' comments must have been a bit 'near the knuckle'.

The most memorable visit was to Ron Randle's rhino catching camp. The local rhinoceros population was in danger of extermination from poachers, powdered rhino horn being highly prized in Chinese medicine as an aphrodisiac. Ken Randle was trapping as

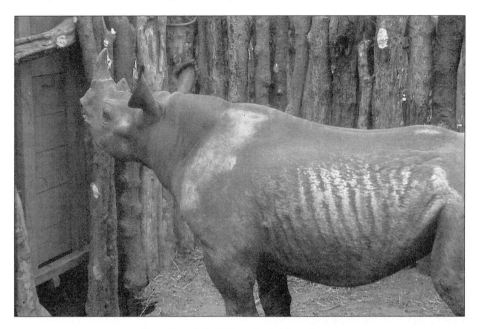

Ron Randle's Rhino Catching Camp

many as possible; they were then drugged and transported to reserves as far as possible from the native population. His camp consisted of holding pens made of foot thick tree trunks dug about four foot into the ground so that an angry rhino could not shove them over. There were about 10 rhino there when I visited it, mostly half to almost full grown, only one full grown, as naturally they were difficult to catch. His staff and wardens were all Kikuyu who were just as keen as he was to preserve the rhinos. What is particularly tragic is that as anyone with a bit of intelligence knows powdered rhino horn is useless as an aphrodisiac, unfortunately the uneducated people who use it do not know that. You cannot expect an African labourer with a family to feed to be all that sympathetic when those Far Eastern people offer such high prices.

The rest of my leave passed all too quickly. Terry took me back to Nairobi; I got the train back to Mombasa, and then the plane back to Aden. The three previous times I had returned to Aden it had been back to civilization, water from taps, flush toilets, street lights etc. This time it was back to the god-awful dump. Just me, my pals the two Brians and all the rest had gone home. There was a star on the horizon, in less than three months I would be leaving Aden for good - I hoped.

Chapter Fifteen

The First, the Royal Dragoons

The last ten weeks were a bit of an anti-climax; I almost became a proper soldier again. I became the Regimental Medical Officer to a right posh lot 'The First, The Royal Dragoons.' The oldest cavalry regiment in the British Army. I may have started off a bit critical, but in actual fact they were a grand bunch. The officers accepted the fact that they had been landed with a right crackpot of an MO with equanimity.

The Royal Dragoons were raised when Charles II got married to a Spanish princess. Part of her dowry was the Port of Tangiers. The Dragoons were raised to protect the port. Therefore the Royal Dragoons are far posher, far more ancient and far more superior than all the jumped up new Guards cavalry regiments lumped together. We were based in Little Aden, very important because BP had an oil refinery there. As my pals had gone home, and it was a good 25-mile drive to Aden, I did not go there very often.

Dr Blair in *Conscript Doctors* describes life in a senior cavalry regiment, everyone on first name terms regardless of rank. The colonel in command was more like a paterfamilias than a Commanding Officer. It was a pleasant way to spend my last few weeks but if I had had to spend the whole of my two years as their medical officer it would have driven me mad. Wartime with a fighting regiment would have been OK but peacetime - boring, boring.

They did have a medical hero often discussed by the older officers who had been subalterns in the war. Their MO, a regular, joined them in 1937. He stayed with them throughout the whole war and was present at every battle and campaign they were on. He became the lynchpin, the constant presence, the one who could always be relied upon to be there. Until at the end of 1944, when the war was virtually won, he was killed by a sporadic artillery shell that the depleted German Artillery occasionally fired.

I now started a chuff chart. A chuff chart is a calendar, the last day you were in Aden and in the army marked in multi coloured crayons so they stand out. Every day is crossed off with a massive highly coloured cross, the closer to the final date you get the more chuffed you become.

Social life revolved round the officers' mess. No sports or games were organized. The mess was full of mentally competitive games, chess, cards, bridge, backgammon etc. There was a certain amount of gambling, poker playing and such like. It did not take me long to realize that the poker experts, in spite of the very low stakes, would have soon cleaned me out. Occasionally I joined in a game of poker, but only if they played by my rules, which were instead of money, we played for matches. My attitude and experience of gambling is that the weight of my bet guarantees that any horse will loose. I do not know if it was indulgence or relieve but my fellow officers let me join in, with alacrity.

One unfortunate Captain was said to belong to the family that brewed Mackeson's stout; it was said that his family got one old penny for every bottle or can the officers' mess used. Therefore none of the other officers would drink it. Nobody would play poker or any other gambling game with him either. A mess bill which would have bankrupted the average chap would have been peanuts to him. He seemed a very pleasant sort of chap, but to the skilled gamblers in that place he was a menace. When he made a big bet at poker they just could not work out whether he had a good hand or was using his excessive wealth to bluff them. I was told he had once raised the stakes at poker by £200 at a time. Amounts the expert cardsharps just could not afford to lose.

There were no official mess dinners, but the colonel and his lady entertained all the officers before lunch on Sundays. Lunch was at 1300; the colonel arrived at 1100. There was a small open air but covered garden to the rear of the officers' mess, where we all gathered, and the beverage Black Velvet, Guinness and Champagne, very pleasant in hot weather. A copious amount was disposed of; even at NAAFI prices it must have cost the colonel a packet. At one we entered the mess for lunch, the most awfully hot curry I have had the misfortune to taste. The colonel and the other officers thought it was great. The first afternoon I had severe indigestion, the amount of curry I'd had minimal.

The second week, the Colonel's lady noticed that I was just eating rice flavoured with mango chutney.

'Don't you like the curry, Doctor?'

'No Ma'am, last week I had indigestion all afternoon, it's far too hot for my palate.'

'I'm pleased you have noticed that Doctor, in fact it is far too hot

for my liking as well, although I have always put some on my plate
I don't eat it.'

'You've never complained before,' said the Colonel.

'I know dear, but you all appear to enjoy it, I did not want to
upset anyone. But the Doctor doesn't enjoy his lunch either.'

Thank God for the colonel's lady - after that there were two
curries. The usual hot one that the addicts ate, and a milder one,
supposedly for me and Mrs Colonel, although I could not help
noticing that some of the curry addicts seemed to prefer the milder
version. Even the mild version was as hot as I could stomach.

There was a little discussion with the adjutant about uniform,
because what I wore bore no resemblance to what the Royal Dragoons were wearing. There was no animosity on either side. 'What
do you want me to wear? I've only two months to go, I've been an
Aden Levy, a Somaliland Scout etc. etc. I've spent at least twice my
tropical kit allowance on uniform.'

'OK, Doc, forget about it.'

The only other memory I have of the Royal Dragoons is the visit
of some brass hats, those they call Staff Officers, the ones with red
bands round their hats. I was unaware of the intended visit and was
slouching back from the MI Room to the officers' mess with my
hands in my pockets, most unsoldierly. I reached the circle in the
centre of the camp and was leaning against a lamp post watching
a staff car approaching. It contained the Colonel, his driver and
three fellows in the back. The Colonel had a look of abject horror
on his face, the three blokes in the back massive scowls. Suddenly
when the car was four yards away I noticed the red bands. Up
straight and the best salute I could manage, four extremely smart
salutes returned, the Colonel's with a look of immense relief, and
the three at the back with brilliant smiles. Later the adjutant, 'You
nearly gave the Colonel a heart attack today. He said won't it be
nice when the Doc goes home! Though he was bragging to the staff
officers about all the places you've been to.'

The First, The Royal Dragoons, were used to having proper Medical Officers they did not normally have to put up with National
Service doctors. I was considered different, the old Arabian hand.
You would have thought I had been out there 10 years not barely
two. Discussions and questions were delayed until the Doc gets here.

'Doc's a funny bugger, he's not a proper MO.'

'He's only killing time with us until he finishes.'

'He seems bored to death with our lot.'

Third voice, ' He's been around a bit though, seems to have been
everywhere and met everybody.'

First voice. 'We've only got him because he'll be going home soon. If he had six months or more to do, they'd have sent him to the back of beyond again.'

Second. 'They say he's OK and gets on with the locals a treat.'

Third. 'Bit of an idiot from what I've heard, goes anywhere and won't carry a weapon.'

Second. 'It's funny though when he gets excited during an argument.'

'Yeah.' Said the third. 'Starts talking in pidgin English and waving his arms around, in sign language, as though we are a gang of Arabs.'

Cough; make a lot of noise, so they shut up before you enter the mess lounge. You would have thought I was 47 not 27.

Of social life there was very little, there was a unit cinema, a different show each week, I can't remember much, but knowing my luck I probably watched *What Lola wants Lola gets* again. Afternoons were not too hot, it was the winter season again, and I spent it wandering around the hills, cliffs and seashore of Little Aden.

One officer found a source of oysters, which he and some friends proceeded to eat. Bloody idiot, I was beginning to wonder what vile, virulent intestinal bug I would have to treat. Surprise, nothing happened, they got away with it.

Later on 'You want to try some Doc, they're great.'

They had found some more.

'Stupid bastards, not bloody likely, you got away with it the last time. You'll get the shits for sure and expect me to deal with it. I hope you're up all night with belly ache as well.'

Their luck was in, not a gripe, a groan or a twinge.

We did have a swimming area; BP had enclosed a large area with massive rocks dumped into the sea to form breakwaters, and an obstruction to sharks, the tide coming in and out through holes between the rocks.

Mid October 1960, came a message would I go and see Colonel Matheson. A word with the adjutant and a lift in one of the unit's trucks got me to Steamer Point. Knock on the Colonel's door.

'Come in Bill, take a seat. How you getting on at Little Aden?'

'OK Sir. Nice bunch of blokes, routine MO work.'

'Bill, Colonel MacWilliam has been in Aden. He came to see me, three days ago. They're worried all the doctors are leaving. At the moment it looks as if Somaliland will become independent without any doctors. There are six at university in England at the moment but none of them will be ready for three or four years. We were wondering, you will be finishing soon, how would you like to take over and run the Somaliland medical service for three years.'

- 295 -

Little Aden, Autumn 1960

'Pardon me Sir?'

'Yes, Bill, I know you don't think much of administrators, but you are a natural administrator. When you are not being your usual obstreperous self, you can lead as well. I've watched you turn on the charm time and time again.' (I did not at that time realize that I had that ability. It was only after I became a consultant that I did it deliberately and cynically to get my own way. It never worked with midwives, who saw straight through me. 'Dr Goldthorp! Just what do you want?') 'You got on well with the Somalis. You might not realize but whatever job you do, administration will take up at least a third of your time.'

'I was thinking about Obstetrics and Gynae. at home Sir, besides I can't do it on my own Sir.'

'Think about it Bill. There's a new ministry replacing the Colonial Service, if you are interested Colonel MacWilliam, the Governor and I will back you and get you a contract for three years. We are thinking about advertizing in Pakistan, you know for graduates from Medical Schools not recognized in England.'

'Well it's very kind of you to think about me Sir. But even if I did take it on there's Margaret to consider as well.'

'Who?'

'My wife, Sir, and the little boy.'

'Oh Dear, I'm afraid we had forgotten about them. But the offer still stands, only if you accept we will have to make arrangements for your family.'

'I'll think about it Sir. I'll give you my answer in week, if it's yes it will only be provisional, depends on what my wife says.'

'Thank you Bill, drop me a line with your decision.'

If I had been single I think I would have taken the offer, I would have disappeared into the third world, British Medicine would have seen the last of me. Pity, I bet some folks are saying. The cons far out matched the pros. Administration, general medicine, obstetrics, the simple inhalation anaesthesia I could cope with. It was the surgery that worried me. I needed at least a year in one of the extremely busy general surgical units with attached casualty miles from a teaching hospital, where an overstretched general surgeon would be only too happy to hand cases on to a keen junior to give me the confidence to work from a textbook.

I give one example - my driver Mohamed's little girl, about five years old, broke her upper arm, the humerus. I set it and plastered it. Next day Mohamed brought her back, her hand had swollen. Now what do I do? Round to see Dr Deering. I then had a good hour's instruction on fractures in children. Take it off immediately, otherwise pressure of the swelling will affect the nerve and the arm will be paralysed. Swelling after fracture is common in children, you should never put a full plaster on, only a back slab, bandage the arm against the back slab. When the arm swells the bandage can be readjusted, when the swelling goes down then you can think about a proper plaster. I have never done orthopaedics, so I do not know if that was correct but it seemed logical to me. It was simple things like that, that worried me. I also thought that as senior man the Somali leaders would expect me to do some major surgery, which I would incompetent at.

When I had been in Somaliland the wives had a small British society to belong to. How would Margaret cope on her own, without any other European ladies around? Who would look after her if she became pregnant, then there was William, what if he became ill? Three years older before I started training in Obstetrics, the competition was hard enough as it was. Would I be able to go back to Senior House Officer level after being top dog for three years? Would I and Margaret be able to put up with an SHO salary after being on a good salary for three years?

I was very flattered to have been asked, but I decided against accepting the offer. Indeed it was not a proper offer, the Ministry of Overseas Development may have thought me unsuitable. I understood how doctors had been bitten by the Africa bug in the past. There were quite a few who were suffering because of it. Their careers ending in their mid forties as the Colonial Service ended. It was right that African doctors should take over the care of their own people, but I couldn't help feeling sorry for them, although if they had been prepared to accept the lower salaries paid to the African doctors they could have continued working there. The African bug bite had been accompanied by a European life style.

Second week of November 1960, I got my metal trunk out, packed as much as possible. I kept my only set of English civilian winter clothes, a minimal amount of tropical kit, both battledresses, boots and all my winter army kit. Took the trunk to Steamer Point and arranged for it to be returned to my parents address in Crowle. The battledresses, boots etc had to be returned when I was finally discharged.

Home

Finally mid November I went to see Colonel Matheson to say goodbye, there were no friends left in Aden. I said cheerio to my recent short-term pals in the Dragoons, and went and caught an RAF comet at Khormaksar to fly home. The day I left Aden, a BOAC comet leaving Aden for London crash-landed in the Sudan. The news was all over the English papers and the TV Margaret began to think she was a widow before her marriage had really got started.

We stopped over for a few hours at Libya, where I changed into battledress, landed in the south of England, and as far as I can remember ended up at Crookham. The following day three of us nearly gave the quartermaster sergeant a heart attack by taking our webbing, battledresses and boots to hand them in as we were supposed to. One battledress and one pair of boots I had never even put on, the other and the boots had been worn for less than six weeks. I'd been a captain for a year but both still had lieutenant's pips on them. The poor sergeant nearly had a fit.

'What can I do with those, nobody has brought anything back before.'

'We don't want them.'

'Take them home Sir. Please. They'll ruin my books, it will take ages to get everything sorted out again.'

We got the impression that no matter what the army said nobody took anything back. The boots came in useful for hillwalking, one battledress I wore while spending a fortnight's holiday painting the house and for gardening, the other when I last looked was in my old metal trunk in the garage loft. It would be wonderful if I could still get into it.

Winter tourism was still not heard of in 1960, we attracted a lot of confused stares on the November trains, a group of heavily suntanned blokes, who sounded like Englishmen but looked like Indians. We all travelled to Waterloo Station together, I have already described our admiring thousands of busy office girls rushing to catch their trains home. We parted, shook hands, said 'Might see you again sometime,' but never did.

I took the train to Doncaster, where I was met by my dad, Margaret and a fourteen-month-old tough guy who glared at this brown faced man, whom his mother had hugged and kissed, and then had the temerity to sit with, in the back of grandpa's car, holding hands. The glares from the kiddy seat, next to grandpa, continued all the way home. William did not seem to relish the fact that he now had competition for his mother's attentions.

Aftermath

My wife was very pleased to see me, so the most important aftermath was my oldest daughter, Suzanne Clare, born on my mother's birthday, 25 September 1961. With William on 28 September 1959, I began to think we should have called them Goodbye and Hello.

It was not easy being a Senior House Officer for two years with a wife and two small children, without National Service I would have been a much better paid registrar by then.

Did I miss it, I certainly did, if I had not been married and a free agent, I would have disappeared into the backwoods of Africa, Arabia, New Guinea somewhere remote and backward, where there was only exotic diseases, exotic people and me. Every week I looked at the last pages of jobs available in the British Medical Journal, Seychelles, Mauritius, St Helena, Fiji, New Guinea, and various parts of Africa with the Ministry of Overseas Development. Australia and Canada also advertized but I never read those. Even now after being retired nearly five years I still read those adverts, the posts are much more sophisticated now, but I still read them and wonder.

For the last half of my disembarkation leave I was on two salaries. Within three weeks I had found, been interviewed and appointed to a SHO post in Gynaecology. I started work about two weeks before Christmas. That time of year being very quiet, one night on duty I attended the hospital Christmas party. There was a lovely legs competition. I took off my trousers and in underpants joined the end of a line of young and not so young ladies with skirts hitched high. My legs were still muscular and deeply sun-tanned. By unanimous acclamation I was awarded first prize, three pairs of ladies' nylon stockings!

The ration allowances had accumulated nicely to just over £500 we visited Kendal's in Manchester and bought a whole load of stuff well over £200 worth. I was still terribly naive in many respects.

Salesman. 'Would you be paying cash Sir, or ...?'

Me 'What I'm not that stupid. I don't carry that amount of money on me. Won't a cheque do?'

An embarrassed Margaret, led me quietly away and explained that most young couples would have bought the items on what was known as the never-never principle.

A year later, Margaret's father, a headmaster, was retiring; wanting a quick sale for his house he let us have it for what he had paid for it several years before, £2,400. My mother who had just sold her third share of the family farm gave us £500, I added £100 from the ration allowances and borrowed £1,800 from Manchester Corporation at 6%. The just over £6 a month still creased my limited resources. How I cursed. The rest went in examination fees and associated costs. The National Health Service now pays junior doctor's costs for their first attempt. You could not claim it back from the Income Tax either; it was an investment in yourself, like buying shares. Fortunately the house was ideally situated on a very extensive bus route, so that I could get to all the major hospitals in Manchester. The Health Service did not start paying for the costs of moving house when you changed jobs until after I became a consultant.

The officer's white overcoat did sterling service for just over two years until it started to drop to bits. The unused officer's khaki shirts, bought on my first day in National Service, were now worn nearly every day.

Envy

When I was a registrar I met an old student friend. He was one of the most intelligent of our group of forty. Top marks in everything all the time. He fancied being a neurologist, specialist in the brain, a very demanding specialty; without doubt he would have been a top notch one. He had married an attractive girl outside the profession. He had signed on for a three-year short service commission, and lived the officer's high life in Germany. On return, he had started as a Senior House Officer in Medicine. Before six months were up, he faced the ultimatum, money now, go into General Practice, or say goodbye to me and the kids.

We greeted each other with pleasure; I could not avoid noticing his natty new suit as he showed me his brand new saloon car. Fortunately the hospital doctor's white coat covered my frayed cuffs and collar and my old baggy grey flannels. I used the bus, not a car. I was able to tell my friend that I had just received notification

William and the Aftermaths

that I had passed the examination for Membership of the Royal College of Obstetricians and Gynaecologists.

It was not me that was envious. I had married into the profession. I had a wife who understood, who was prepared to put up with the hardships and difficulties, who backed me all the way.

I HAD MY ROCK AND MY ANCHOR.

There were two more aftermaths:

Jennifer Margaret 7 August 1963

Richard Andrew Jonathan 29 June 1968.

Epilogue

The author became a consultant in May 1968, retiring 30 years later in July 1998.

A Fond Farewell to a not so Retiring sort of Chap

Good ladies of Tameside
Oh how will you fare?
When our Dr Goldthorp no longer is there.

For years now he's diagnosed, prescribed and treated,
Now and then becoming a bit overheated.
He's cared for all ladies whatever their state,
And actively contributed to Tameside's birth rate.

Though a time must arrive in a young man's life,
To lay down his scripts, his gloves and his knife.
To travel the world, relaxed and contented,
Hopefully not driving his good wife demented.

But here in the Theatre I'll make no bones,
We'll miss him most for those loud ringing tones,
That shook the walls and made the paint blister,
No longer to hear
BLOODY HELL SISTER

Ms Heather Diamond, Theatre Sister

As mentioned Chantyboy and W. B. became highly respected GPs.

Piss Head P—ce returned to England and became a GP.

David F—, a retired gynaecologist, still has his young female House Surgeon looking after him, he has eleven grandchildren.

Graeme Matthew MBE, his administrative abilities stayed with him, he became a Principal Medical Officer with the Department of Health.

Iain Stewart has still to be located, *Conscript Doctors* records him becoming a Consultant Pathologist in Essex.

All the MOs who remained in Aden for the full two years, did like Tony Thorne make life-long friendships. I with all my various postings just passed through like a ship in the night.